The Years Ahead Report: A Review of the Implementation of its Recommendations

By

Helen Ruddle, Freda Donoghue and Ray Mulvihill

NATIONAL COUNCIL ON AGEING AND OLDER PEOPLE

REPORT NO. 48

This Report has been prepared by Dr. Helen Ruddle, Dr. Freda Donoghue and Mr. Ray Mulvihill of the Policy Research Centre, National College of Industrial Relations

for

THE NATIONAL COUNCIL ON AGEING AND OLDER PEOPLE
22 CLANWILLIAM SQUARE
GRAND CANAL QUAY
DUBLIN 2

ISBN 1 900 378 06 X

Price £10.00

Table of Contents

List of Tables and Figures

Tables

Figures

Foreword

As part of its terms of reference, the National Council for Elderly (now the National Council on Ageing and Older People) was requested to advise the Minister for Health on the implementation of the recommendations of the report *The Years Ahead - A Policy for the Elderly*. *The Years Ahead* report was published in 1988 and now, nine years on, the Council in fulfilment of its brief publishes this substantial review of the report. The review was a major undertaking and required contact at many administrative and front-line levels with Government Departments, the eight health boards, a large sample of the local authorities and many other organisations.

There are two main messages contained in the review. First it is clear that *The Years Ahead* report, while influential and based on sound principles, is no longer an adequate blueprint for the development of services for older people. It has been superseded in many respects by national and regional policy developments. It also paid inadequate attention to the role of older people and their carers in the decision-making process. The Council therefore supports the recommendation contained in the review that a new strategy on health and social care services for older people be developed. This strategy would focus on the principles governing service delivery, rather than the detail of day-to-day care.

The second message from this review is the slow rate of development in many areas of service provision since 1988. The Council is particularly concerned that many excellent recommendations on the extent and nature of home and community care have not been implemented. It now believes that the only way to ensure certain core services are provided to the level required is to create a legislative framework to govern their delivery. Again this legislation would not prescribe the detail of day-to-day care, but would provide a firm basis for the funding and development of core services.

On behalf of the Council I would like to thank the authors of the review, Dr. Helen Ruddle, Dr. Freda Donoghue and Mr. Ray Mulvihill of the Policy Research Centre at the National College of Industrial Relations. I would like to thank Professor Joyce O'Connor of the Policy Research Centre for overseeing the review, Ms.

Geraldine Hennessy and Ms. Mary Healy for providing administrative support to the researchers and Ms. Barbara Crowley for overseeing the fieldwork.

I would also like to thank the members of the Consultative Committee, which I was honoured to Chair, for their advice to the researchers at a number of meetings and through correspondence, and for their assistance to the Council in formulating its views on the review. The members of the Committee were Mr. John Brady, Ms. Mary Courtney, Ms. Una Doherty, Ms. Margaret Dorney, Mr. Frank Goodwin, Mr. Bernard Haddigan, Mr. Jack Killane, Mr. Joe Larragy, Mr. Eddie Matthews, Dr. Patricia McCormack, Mr. Brian Murnane, Mr. Donal Murphy, Mr. Matt O'Connor, Dr. Sheelagh Prosser, Mr. Bernard Thompson and Dr. Margo Wrigley.

Finally, I would like to thank our Director, Bob Carroll, and our Research Officer, John Browne, for overseeing the project on the Council's behalf. I would also like to thank our Resources Officer, Catherine Mulvenna, for her work in preparing the report for publication and Céline Kinsella, Fionnghuala Ní Néill and Carol Waters for their secretarial support throughout the course of the project.

Michael White
Chairman
September 1997

National Council on Ageing and Older People Comments and Recommendations

Introduction

1.   In 1988 the report of the Working Party on Services for the Elderly, *The Years Ahead...A Policy for the Elderly* was published. The four main principles of the report were as follows:

- To maintain older people in dignity and independence at home in accordance with the wishes of older people as expressed in many research studies.
- To restore to independence at home those older people who become ill or dependent.
- To encourage and support the care of older people in their own community by family, neighbours and voluntary bodies in every way possible.
- To provide a high quality of hospital and residential care for older people when they can no longer be maintained in dignity and independence at home.

The report also stated that services for older people should be comprehensive, equitable, accessible, responsive, flexible, co-ordinated, planned and cost effective (p. 39). *The Years Ahead* report had more than 120 main recommendations relating to health and social care services for older people at home, in the community, in hospitals and in long-term care. It was adopted as official policy by the Department of Health, and, according to the 1994 health strategy document *Shaping a Healthier Future* (p.66-67), remains the guiding influence on the development of services for older people.

2.   The National Council for the Elderly (now the National Council on Ageing and Older People) was established in January 1990 in succession to the National Council for the Aged which began in June 1981. The Council was asked, as a part of its new terms of reference to advise the Minister for Health on the implementation of the recommendations of *The Years Ahead* report. Accordingly, the Council commissioned the Policy Research Centre of the National College of

Industrial Relations to carry out a review of the implementation of the report. The Council now wishes to comment on the findings of the review.

Difficulties with *The Years Ahead* report

3.   Taking the report as a whole, it is obvious that *The Years Ahead* is no longer an adequate blueprint for the development of older people's health and social services. The review posed four main questions. First, have recommendations been universally implemented in the manner envisaged by the Working Party? The answer here is almost always no.   Second, is it likely that the recommendations will, in the near future, be fully implemented in the manner envisaged? Again the answer is almost always no.   Third, are there regional variations in the implementation status of recommendations? Where relevant, the answer is almost always yes.   Fourth, are the implementing bodies satisfied with the recommendations of the report? Here the study findings are mixed, but real questions have been raised about the value of certain recommendations.

4.   The Council does not wish to question the fundamental value of the report, which was based on excellent principles, and which contained many useful recommendations.   There is also no doubt that the report had, and continues to have a major influence on the thinking of service providers.   The essential difficulty is the non-statutory status report.   Despite its adoption by the Department of Health, the report did not compel the authorities named (mostly the health boards and local authorities) to implement recommendations in the manner envisaged. The report recommended that a legislative framework be put in place for the development of older peoples services. The main providers to be included in this framework were as follows:

- An obligation on health boards and local authorities to promote the well-being of older people in their areas of responsibility, especially those on low income or vulnerable for medical and social reasons, and to plan, in consultation with each other and voluntary bodies, to meet these needs;
- An obligation on health boards to provide services to support dependant elderly people and their carers in the home;
- An obligation on local authorities to provide for the repair and adaptation of the dwellings of older people, particularly those on low income;
- An obligation on health boards to appoint Co-ordinators of Services for the Elderly and Advisory Committees on the Elderly. (p. 184)

This legislative framework has not been created, and in general services for older people are still provided on a discretionary basis. This would not have been an insurmountable problem if a lead agency had taken responsibility for encouraging the co-ordinated implementation of recommendations, from 1988 onwards. Unfortunately this did not happen, with the result that older people and their carers remain reliant on the goodwill of the health boards and other service providing agencies to provide the essential services they require. It has also allowed regional variations in service provision to continue in a fashion not envisaged by the Working Party. The lack of a unified approach is exemplified by the finding that some of the agencies contacted were not aware of recommendations they were to have implemented.

5.   Policy developments in the period 1988-1997 have also affected the implementation of *The Years Ahead* report. Most important in this regard is the 1994 health strategy *Shaping a Healthier Future* published by the Department of Health. Although this document endorsed *The Years Ahead* report, new principles for service provision were introduced which in some ways were at variance with the approach taken by the 1988 report. *The Years Ahead* report was strong on detail with numerous recommendations on staff levels, bed numbers, and organisational structures. The 1994 document, by contrast, focuses more on the principles behind service delivery. Crucially, services cannot be assumed to have an inherent value (an assumption usually made by *The Years Ahead* report) but must demonstrate the health and social gain they produce.

6.   *Shaping a Healthier Future* also stressed the importance of consumer participation in the planning of services and the accountability of service providers, principles largely ignored by *The Years Ahead* report. Given the number of changes that were recommended by the report, it is remarkable that no thought was given to asking older people about their value or to informing them about the changes proposed.

7.   The 1994 health strategy proposed that important decisions about regional services should in future be taken at a regional level and that the Minister and Department (of Health) should not be involved in the detailed management of the health services (*Shaping a Healthier Future*, p.30). This was confirmed in the Department's 1997 *Statement of Strategy*. Following the proposals of the *Report of the Commission on Health Funding* (1989). *Shaping a Healthier Future* also contained a firm commitment to replace the existing health boards with regional health authorities who are to be given greater autonomy. This process makes it likely that regional variations in models of service delivery will become the norm. This is contrary to the spirit of *The Years Ahead* report, which implicitly advocated common organisational structures and service delivery models across the country.

8.   The 1990 *Health (Nursing Homes) Act* has also created conditions not envisaged by the Working Party which considered the community hospital sector to be the most appropriate source of long-stay care. Since the 1990 Act the private nursing home sector has enjoyed a period of rapid growth with close to 7,000 beds available in 1994 compared to 5,552 beds in 1988 (Keogh and Roche 1996). Some

of this growth is undoubtedly due to the incentives provided by the subvention scheme introduced in 1990. While there was undoubtedly a need for more long-stay care beds in some parts of the country, it is noteworthy that the only significant legislation on services for older people since 1988, has lead to a growth in institutional rather than community based care.

9. A further difficulty with *The Years Ahead* report was its significant underestimation of the growth in the size of the older population. Projections prepared for the Working Party estimated that 394,700 people would be 65 years or more in 1996. In fact the preliminary census report indicates there were 415,000 older people in Ireland in 1996. Recent projections prepared for the Council predict that there will be more than 520,000 older people in Ireland by 2011 (Fahey 1995). This compares to a figure of 437,400 used by *The Years Ahead* report. The unforeseen increase in the older population has obvious implications for the service levels originally recommended.

10. These figures need not necessarily imply a pessimistic outlook for the resources available to older people. A recent report indicates that Ireland can look forward to an unprecedentedly low dependency ratio in coming years with a middle-heavy (i.e., economically active) population (Joint Oireachtas Committee on the Family 1997). The report projects a fall in the overall dependency ratio to 50 per cent by 2006 from a high of 73 per cent in 1966. The Council agrees with the recommendation in the report that:

'the opportunity presented ... should be used to improve the quality of care for those older people who require it' (p.15)

There is little evidence, however, that population ageing in Ireland will lead to an increase in resources directed towards older people. *The Years Ahead* report recommended that the government should, in the light of the changing demographic trends, adopt a conscious long-term policy of redeploying resources to services for older people (p. 32). It is clear now that the Irish health care system in its present guise has great difficulty in redeploying resources from one sector to another, whether for demographic reasons or not (Fahey 1995). Although exact figures are difficult to obtain, there has been a large expansion in spending on child care in recent years following the 1991 *Child Care Act*. There is little evidence of a corresponding growth in services for older people despite the demographic shift. Even within services for older people, there seems to have been little change in the proportion of resources devoted to community versus institutional care, despite an emphatic commitment to the former in many official policy documents.

11. *The Years Ahead* report, while addressing many important issues relating to health promotion, had a relatively narrow vision of the role of older people in the

maintenance of their own health. The emphasis was on the delivery of health education by formal service providers such as Public Health Nurses. Since 1988 there has been a growing acceptance of the importance of self-help and voluntary groups in the development of a healthy ageing culture.

12. The current review also raises doubts over the inherent value of some of the recommendations made by *The Years Ahead* report. This is difficult to ascertain because we have had to rely on the experience of the implementing authorities. Naturally, these authorities wished to defend the manner in which they interpreted the report. This may have lead to a defence of those recommendations that were implemented and criticism of the value of those that were not. The Council must accept, however, that certain recommendations gave rise to serious misgivings and need to be re-examined. There seems to be particular difficulties with the relative emphasis placed on ongoing care versus therapeutic treatment services for older people. The *Years Ahead* report placed relatively little emphasis on the treatment of acute illness in general hospitals, and this contrasts unfavourably with the emphasis placed on continuing care services. The implicit message seems to be that illness in older people should normally be considered a chronic problem rather than a treatable episode.

13. Finally, it is obvious that funding for many developments, particularly in the 'cutback' years immediately following the report's publication, was not made available. Particularly effected were community care services such as day care, day hospitals, community hospitals, psychiatric services, paramedical services and panels of Registered General Nurses. This contrasts unfavourably with the £65m spent on implementing the *Health (Nursing Homes) Act* over the period 1990-1997. As noted in the review, the low level of resources given to community care raises serious questions about the financial commitment to maintaining and supporting older people in their own homes.

14. In summary, although *The Years Ahead* report was a progressive force in the development of services for older people, its style, content and status render it an inadequate guide for future developments. The Council believes that a new blueprint is required, building on the ideas of *The Years Ahead* report but in tune with current policy initiatives.

A future strategy
15. The Council recommends that a strategy for the development of health and social care services for older people be developed under the guidance of the Department of Health. This strategy would contain an explicit statement of the principles that should underly the delivery of services to older people, incorporating the values of equity, quality of service and accountability espoused by *Shaping a Healthier Future* and the guiding values of *The Years Ahead* report

described above. The Council is particularly concerned that any new strategy has a firm commitment to the principle of consumer orientation, with older people and carers involved in the planning and evaluation of services at all stages. There is much evidence that older people and carers are a thoughtful source of feedback on the services they receive and can provide an expert insight into quality in community care practices (Evason and Whittington 1993).

16. The strategy should provide guidance on the future development of the co-ordination posts and structures outlined in *The Years Ahead* report. It is now clear that the health boards in particular do not consider the model proposed an appropriate blueprint for their local needs, although some aspects of the 1988 model have been adopted. The strategy should therefore provide guidance to the health boards on the principles governing co-ordination at different levels rather than the detail of particular posts and structures.

17. The strategy should specify the desired balance between community and long-stay care for older people. The Council endorses the target set in *Shaping a Healthier Future* that 90% of people over 75 years should reside in their own homes in the community (p. 67). This target is useless, however, without a plan for ensuring it is met. The Council recommends that national guidelines for the placement of older patients in long-term care be outlined in the strategy. The strategy should specify the desired mix between traditional long-stay accommodation and alternative community accommodation such as sheltered housing, and outline how sectors identified as inadequate are to be developed. There should also be a target for the proportion of funding provided in health budgets for home and community care services designed to support older people at home.

18. A model for the planning and funding system to be used with services for older people should be outlined in the proposed strategy. The Council has previously recommended that a transparent formal mechanism for distributing health and social care resources in an equitable and flexible manner on the basis of need be developed (National Council for the Elderly 1996). This mechanism should be based on information collected across local areas feeding directly into the decision making process. The assessment process should have a strong consumer focus, with older people asked to define need from their own perspective. Social as well as health need should be addressed.

19. The strategy should provide guidelines on the ongoing measurement of health and social gain following interventions with older people. It is imperative that outcomes following health and social care interventions are in some way assessed and inform a scientific resource allocation system. Again the assessments should be directed at the individual and what they perceive to be

important. The strategy should also take account of the principles, targets and action plans to be set out in the Council's forthcoming Health Promotion Strategy for older people.

Legislation

20. The Council believes that a legislative framework governing the provision of essential services to older people is also required. In the current climate of devolved decision-making the Council considers it essential that certain services are provided as entitlements rather than on a discretionary basis. The Council wishes to state at the outset that it believes the home help service, Meals-on-Wheels, day care, respite care both inside and outside the home, paramedical services and sheltered housing are essential and should be designated as core services. These services have a proven record of providing social gain and should be available to older people whenever required, throughout the country.

21. These services should be designated as core services underpinned by legislation and appropriate statutory funding. Core services may be defined as 'support services which are essential for older persons to maintain a quality of life and a level of functional autonomy which enables them to live independently in the community and, consequently, to avoid unnecessary hospitalisation or admission to long-stay institutions' (Mulvihill 1993). Core services should be differentiated from other important community support services provided by voluntary bodies (e.g. social outings, clubs) for the purpose of planning and funding. The home help service in particular should become a statutory entitlement.

22. The development of core services has enormous potential for (i) the improvement of the quality of life of older people, (ii) the creation of jobs through the provision of useful and necessary social services, and (iii) the development of a community dynamic which would support its dependent and frail population. The 1994 Programme for Competitiveness and Work advocated the 'development of social services which secure greater social equity and protect the position of those who are most vulnerable in our society'. The Commission of the European Communities (1993) has also pointed to 'home help for the elderly and handicapped, health care, meal preparation and housework' services as a potential source of new employment. The core services concept offers an ideal opportunity to make these aspirations a reality.

23. National guidelines on eligibility criteria and charges for health and social care services should be outlined in the legislation, where these guidelines do not currently exist. A commitment to providing such guidelines was given in *Shaping a Healthier Future.* Three years later they are overdue.

24. The legislative framework should also cover the involvement of voluntary service providers. The framework would ensure that the same quality and level of service is provided in areas with and without a well developed voluntary sector. It would also standardise procedures for the funding of voluntary services and for the provision of other assistance by statutory bodies where required.

25. The Council believes that legislation safeguarding the rights of carers is required. At present carers are forced to work in conditions that would be clearly illegal in the formal workplace, in order to qualify for the Carer's Allowance. The regulations mean that carers are forced to forego their right to training and asked to work at home for 168 hours per week. These conditions are highly unfair given the regulations governing working hours in formal employment. The working conditions of those judged ineligible for the Allowance are also extremely difficult because of the low level of health and social services (e.g., respite care) available from the statutory sector.

26. In addition to the legislation and strategy outlined above, the Council would like to comment on a number of specific domains. The following comments and recommendations should be used to inform the proposed strategy and legislation, and be incorporated where relevant.

Co-ordination
27. All health boards have made organisational changes to encourage co-ordination but the degree to which these changes reflect the thinking of the Working Party is variable. The district organisation of services around populations of 25,000-30,000 people has only occurred in three health boards (Mid-Western, North Western and Southern), with the rest indicating that an alternative form of organisation is preferable. In the Southern Health Board, the health and psychiatric districts are not co-terminus. There may be difficulties at local level with the implementation of district structures, due to a perception that some areas may gain and others lose out.

28. Without a district organisation of services, it has not been possible to appoint District Liaison Nurses in the manner outlined by *The Years Ahead* report. Even in health boards with a district structure, the recommendation has not been completely implemented. In the North Western Health Board, the post is held by Matrons of community hospitals and not Senior Public Health Nurses as envisaged. In the Mid-Western Health Board the role is carried out by Senior Public Health Nurses, but the amount of time dedicated to the organisation of services for older people is only 50-60 per cent. In some boards, District Liaison Nurses have been appointed at higher organisational levels (usually community care level). A further variation occurs in the North Eastern Health Board, where the liaison role centres on acute hospitals.

29.   District teams for the elderly have not been created as envisaged. In general, health board managers feel that the creation of a team at district level whose only purpose is co-ordination would be wasteful and time consuming. The district is the smallest unit of organisation for services, and there seems to be a view that any team at this level should directly provide services as a team. The community ward teams in the Eastern Health Board are an example of this approach.

30.   Co-ordinators of Services for the Elderly have been appointed in all but the Midland Health Board. In half the boards they operate at community care level as envisaged and in the rest they operate at board level. In some boards, the Co-ordinator is not a community physician as was envisaged. Advisory committees on older people's issues have been appointed in only two boards.

31.   The slow implementation of the proposed co-ordination structures by the health boards may in part reflect problems with overall management plans. Some health boards are currently in a state of flux because of the transfer of responsibilities between of the special hospital, general hospital and community care programmes. Further problems include the introduction of Public Health Medicine posts, the phasing out of Director of Community Care posts, and in some boards, the high turnover at Programme Manager and Chief Executive Officer levels.

32.   Despite the problems in co-ordination on health and housing issues reported by regional authorities, the Departments of Health, Social Welfare and the Environment report satisfaction with their current co-ordination mechanisms.

Recommendations
33.   The Council recommends that the post of District Liaison Nurse as outlined in *The Years Ahead* report be reviewed by the Department of Health. The Council is increasingly concerned about the need to develop an approach to co-ordination at the individual level and believes that the organisation of services for individual older people at a local level should be a full-time post carried out by a professional with specific training. Here we have in mind the provision of a package of services to those older people identified as being on the margins of institutional care but who might benefit from case management. We believe that this concept has much to offer and should be further explored through research and piloting as a possible basis for co-ordinated care in the community. Such an approach would not only contribute to overcoming the fragmentation of community services but also to improving community-hospital-institutional care linkages.

34.   The need for an identified key person to draw together the disparate elements of the caring network and to supervise the implementation of agreed packages of care for an individual and their families has come to be widely accepted in recent years (Browne 1992). This key person has been variously referred to as a case

manager, a liaison worker and a care co-ordinator. The task of such a worker should be to design, manage and monitor a package of care utilising all existing resources, statutory, family, neighbourhood and voluntary, to support an older person at home. In organising packages of care the case manager has of course to bear in mind that some dependent older people do not like the idea of a number of different people calling to their home or caring for them.

35. It is likely that the availability of such key workers would contribute much to the quality and consistency of care for individual older people. It would ensure appropriate use of statutory services and support the spontaneous caring network of family and neighbours. Case managers would also help to forge stronger links between the community and institutional-based services and more meaningful co-operation between statutory and informal care providers. They would also have a central role to play in the context of a more dynamic and vibrant voluntary sector and in providing voluntary-statutory partnership. In Ireland the role of the case manager would have to be introduced in consultation with existing health board personnel with appropriate training being provided. Existing roles and responsibilities would have to be examined and new organisational mechanisms put in place.

36. District teams as described in *The Years Ahead* report should also be reviewed. These teams have not been popular with the health boards and have not proved successful in practice. The review should place particular emphasis on ways of ensuring that the efforts of General Practitioners are co-ordinated with others service providers. The most important aspect of co-ordination is the link between the General Practitioner and Public Health Nurse. This becomes particularly important when the older person has been discharged from hospital. An alternative to the district team which could support this type of co-ordination might be an integrated information system, capable of recording contact at community and hospital levels. The review should also examine alternative ways of involving the voluntary sector in the planning of local services.

37. The Council believes that the post of Co-ordinators of Services for the Elderly has proven successful when created. As a model of good practice the Council advises that this post should be created for all community care areas in the country. The Council also recommends the appointment of full time Co-ordinators of Services for the Elderly at health board level. This post is particularly important for the encouragement of voluntary service provision at a local level, for the co-ordination of statutory and voluntary efforts and for the development of board-wide information systems. The Council would advise against the current system in some health boards whereby overall responsibility for older people's services is carried out at Programme Manager level. This is an essential post which can not be undertaken on a part-time basis.

38. The Council recommends that the Departments of the Environment and Health investigate ways of increasing the co-ordination of their activities. There is evidence that co-ordination between health boards and local authorities is poor and without policy guidance from the relevant government departments this is unlikely to change. The Council believes there is an urgent need for a inter-departmental strategic policy committee with executive powers to oversee social housing for those with health needs. At a local level the planning committees of local authorities should have a representative of the health boards.

Health promotion
39. The Council has begun the development of work on healthy ageing through a three strand programme (a healthy promotion strategy, development of a healthy ageing network and assisting research on interventions designed to improve the health and quality of life of older people). This programme is designed to assist the development of a healthy ageing ethos in Ireland.

40. At local level, health education with older people is usually carried out by Public Health Nurses and tends to operate on an opportunistic basis, usually once contact has been made with the health services. This means that health education with healthy older people is rarely carried out and the best opportunity for illness prevention is lost. A major difficulty is the lack of guidance on the content of health education services. Standard materials are not available, and the Public Health Nurses generally rely on their own knowledge and experience. Public Health Nurses also provide health education services to carers, again usually on an opportunistic basis and in an unstructured manner.

41. Some progress in encouraging more positive attitudes to ageing and older people, and a greater awareness of ageing issues has been observed. The work of Age and Opportunity has been particularly valuable in this area. The Irish Congress of Trade Unions and the Retirement Planning Council of Ireland have produced some literature on retirement planning, but little has been done by other agencies.

Recommendations
42. The Council urges the health boards to further develop dedicated programmes for promoting older people's health and to introduce and evaluate initiatives and interventions likely to produce significant health and/or social gain for older people.

43. At a national level, the Council reiterates its recent recommendation that a cross sectoral committee be established under the Department of Health to provide guidelines on the content and operation of a training system for formal social care workers and informal carers (O'Donovan, Hodgins, McKenna and Kelleher 1997).

44. The Council wishes to reiterate its recommendation that a comprehensive public education programme on the nature of mental disorders in old age be undertaken by the health boards in conjunction with the Department of Health and other relevant agencies such as AWARE, the Alzheimer Society of Ireland and the Mental Health Association of Ireland (Keogh and Roche 1996). An equivalent programme for care professionals should also be undertaken. The professionals to be targeted should include general practitioners, public health nurses, social workers, psychiatric nurses, occupational therapists, physiotherapists and nursing home staff. Again the health boards should be the lead agencies, in conjunction with relevant professional bodies.

Housing

45. The housing situation of older people has been subject to a number of influences in recent years. Older people continue to have high rates of home ownership: according to the 1991 Census 79.8% of older Irish people in the community lived in owner occupied dwellings. Many of these homes have benefited from repair and adaptation initiatives, so that their overall condition has improved. Continued vigilance is required, however, as older people live in the oldest houses. In 1991, 33.0% of older people lived in houses built before 1919. This was high given that only 20.5% of all the private dwellings in Ireland were built before 1919. Only 26.1% of older people lived in houses built since 1961, which was very low given that 52% of the total Irish housing stock was built since 1961. While it would be a gross simplification to say that the poorest quality dwellings are the oldest, it is fair to say that the oldest dwellings tend to need the most attention to ensure they meet minimum standards.

46. Public spending on social housing is becoming increasingly diversified, with a greater emphasis on the non-profit/voluntary sector. Local authorities have scaled back their building programmes in the past decade and this has effected housing for older and disabled people. Over the period 1988-1995 an average of only 236 units were completed or acquired each year compared to an average of 736 over the period 1972-1987. However, a significant public housing stock for older people still exists, with 26,223 older persons (7.3%) living in houses rented from local authorities in 1991 and a further 26,150 older people (7.3%) acquiring houses from their local authority. Other than the fact that they are bungalows designed for one to two people, local authority older person's dwellings often do not take into account the problems caused by mobility impairments in old age. Local authorities also manage some group schemes of self-contained dwellings in terraces or apartments, but the support services available in these schemes have been scaled back in recent years.

47. To compensate for the slowdown in new local authority housing, the non-profit/voluntary housing sector as a whole is expanding, and now comprises over

9,000 dwellings. Over the period 1988-1995 much of this new housing was designated for older people but in future it is expected that an increasing proportion will be designed for other groups in need (e.g., the homeless).

48. There is much heterogeneity in the level of support services provided to residents of voluntary housing schemes. In some of the larger sheltered housing developments in Dublin and Cork there are on-site wardens, alarm systems, communal areas and visiting care services such as home help and paramedical care. At the other extreme are two to three unit developments in rural areas which provide little or no visiting support or communal facilities. Between these extremes are small group schemes which have some of the care supports outlined above but which have had to scale back other services in recent years (e.g., on-site wardens).

49. Visiting home care and on-site services are not always provided by the health boards to voluntary housing residents and funding is not available from the local authorities to enable voluntary organisations to directly provide the services. The lack of a co-ordinated approach to voluntary housing is highlighted by the recent Department of the Environment policy document *Social Housing - The Way Ahead* (1995) which contains no reference to *The Years Ahead* report. The Department of the Environment is not involved in the ongoing support of voluntary housing schemes because of a lack of resources.

50. As well as care and surveillance services, *The Years Ahead* report recommended that the Department of the Environment should consider ways in which voluntary housing organisations could be assisted with the ongoing costs associated with caretaking, essential repairs and insurance. At the moment the Department does not contribute towards these costs which places considerable strain on voluntary organisations, and may dissuade some organisations from initiating new schemes. The level of capital assistance given to voluntary housing organisations may also need to be significantly increased in the near future if it is to keep pace with increasing building costs.

Recommendations
51. Given that most older people live in quite old, privately owned houses in the community, the most important housing issue continues to be the standard of their homes. The Council recommends that a co-ordinated approach to repairs and adaptations and the provision of ongoing domiciliary health and social services be developed. The Council believes that the various schemes for adaptations and repairs to older people's homes run by the health boards and local authorities should be streamlined and operated by one local agency to simplify the application process for older people. The schemes should operate as part of a larger package of care, to ensure ongoing health and social services are provided if needed: this

will require health board and local authority co-ordination. National guidelines on eligibility and charges should also be developed to eliminate the regional inequities that currently exist.

52. To ensure that the quality of older people's homes is maintained in the long-term, the Council recommends that planning permission for new private housing developments be granted only when a proportion of the development is suited, or can be easily adapted to the needs of older people. Most new housing is not suited to people with mobility problems and will pose problems for the occupants as they age.

53. A national plan on social housing for older people should be developed by the Department of the Environment. Policy in this area is currently driven by non-specific aspirations but clearer targets are required to ensure that need is met. The strategy should specify the role of different types of social housing in meeting both welfare and health needs and outline national criteria to be used when allocating units. It should also outline a legislative framework to govern the role that local authorities play in directly meeting housing need and in supporting the voluntary sector.

54. A central principle underlying the plan should be that high quality sheltered housing be available to those older people who choose it. Sheltered housing should be an option for all older people before institutional care is considered. The Council notes that that the recent interim report of the Joint Oireachtas Committee on the Family on the needs of older people also advocates a renewed focus on community based accommodation for older people (p.19-20). To ensure this is possible, there must be a large increase in the number of sheltered housing units available for older people. It is clear from the current review that the number of sheltered housing units currently available is inadequate. A 1989 report for the Council estimated that between 25 and 50 units per 1,000 older people were required (O'Connor, Ruddle and O'Gallagher 1989). In 1996 terms this would translate to between 10,375 and 20,750 units dedicated to older people. However, the current review reveals that there were less than 10,000 sheltered housing units provided for all age groups in 1996. Many of these units do not provide the full range of support services required by the residents. The Council believes that the non-profit/voluntary sector, because of the expertise it has developed in this area, should be the primary providers of additional sheltered housing schemes. To do this they should receive increased support from local authorities through the Department of the Environment.

55. A further principle should be an obligation on health boards and local authorities to provide visiting and on-site supports to all residents of grouped social housing schemes, when voluntary organisations cannot do so. Home

nursing and home help services, paramedical services and on-site wardens should be made available to all residents by the health boards. Where this is not feasible, financial support for the direct provision of services by the voluntary sector should be provided by the local authority. The health boards should liaise with voluntary organisations in the provision of day centres where the size of the development makes such centres feasible. Local authorities should be obliged to provide support to the voluntary sector for the ongoing maintenance and repair of non-profit/voluntary housing units. The Council acknowledges that the resources available to the Departments of Health and the Environment, and to the health boards and local authorities in turn, will have to be significantly increased if the above recommendations are to be implemented.

56. The ceiling on capital assistance given to voluntary housing organisations should be significantly increased in the near future if it is to keep pace with increasing land and building costs, and the burden of paying 12.5% VAT on construction costs and 21% VAT on professional technical services. The current limit of £27,000 for 1-2 person units requires particular attention. There is also a need to simplify the capital financing arrangements for voluntary organisations, which often involve a significant administrative burden.

Care at home
57. The anticipatory care structures envisaged by *The Years Ahead* report (case finding and preventive care by general practitioners and at-risk registers maintained by Public Health Nurses) are described as impractical in the review, because of time and resource constraints, the poor screening tools available, and the slow development of technology for maintaining up-to-date information. Anticipatory care by general practitioners is of particular concern, with a suggestion that many types of anticipatory care may not give adequate health gain.

58. The plan to provide a comprehensive system of domiciliary physiotherapy, speech therapy, chiropody and social work services as outlined in *The Years Ahead* report has not been implemented. Where these services are provided, they are located in regional centres such as day hospitals and day centres. It is becoming increasingly apparent that the health authorities do not see the home as an appropriate setting for these services and will only provide such care in rare circumstances. This may be due to a lack of resources but it has also been suggested that staff are not available or perhaps willing to work in the clients home. It has also been suggested that providing care at home may reinforce isolation. However, this ignores the valuable role that domiciliary services have in helping some housebound people, particularly those who have just been discharged from hospital, to recover and consequently end their isolation. In addition, for some older people, long-term home care is the only alternative to institutional care.

59. The Public Health Nursing and home help services have shown some growth over the last eight years. It is now clear that the size of the home help service envisaged by the Working Party was inadequate and the norms used have been substantially exceeded. Panels of registered general nurses have been established in most boards and four boards have also introduced care assistants to supplement the work of Home Helps.

60. Despite this growth, there remains considerable uncertainty over the future course of the home nursing and home help services. The status of Care Assistants and Registered General Nurses in the community seems unclear in relation to the development of a fully skilled home help service. The role of Public Health Nurses and Home Helps may also change significantly in the future following reviews presently being carried out by the Department of Health.

Recommendations
61. The Office for Health Gain, in conjunction with the Irish College of General Practitioners should carry out a review of the value of case finding and preventive care by General Practitioners as outlined in *The Years Ahead* report. The review should suggest alternative ways of ensuring the early detection and treatment of illness in older people, if the current methods are found to be inefficient or ineffective.

62. The Council anticipates that the forthcoming review of the Public Health Nursing service will address the difficulties associated with at-risk registers. The introduction of computerised information systems should be pursued with urgency as a possible solution to this problem. The Council also recommends that all older people over 75 years be comprehensively screened by the Public Health Nurse at regular intervals (e.g., every two years) to ensure that health problems are detected as early as possible. Older people who live alone, live in hazardous accommodation and/or have poor self-maintenance skills may require more frequent assessments.

63. In the current climate of uncertainty surrounding the role and structure of the home help service the Council is particularly anxious to ensure the future of this vital service is safeguarded. As indicated above, the Council recommends that the legislative basis for the home help service be amended to make it the mandatory responsibility of the health boards to provide or have this service provided to designated categories of older person. The home help service clearly provides both health and social benefits to recipients (Lundström and McKeown 1994) and should therefore be designated as a core service in legislation to ensure its future.

64. Despite growth in recent years, the home help service still requires expansion in both size and scope. In three health board regions there is no emergency service

and in four regions no out-of-hours service, weekend service or relief service for carers. The Council wishes to reiterate its recommendation that the home help service be seen as complementary to the efforts of carers rather than a substitute. The home help service should be available to older people whether an informal carer is available or not, and the Home Help should be available to work in tandem with the carer (e.g. in the provision of personal care tasks such as lifting or bathing) and not just as a relief service.

65. The Council also wishes to reiterate that the home help service is the most appropriate source of regular formal personal care at home for older people. While Home Care Attendants have a role in the provision of intensive care at home (e.g. following discharge from acute care) over short periods, the Council believes that the home help service should be able to provide routine personal care over longer periods. The recommendation of *The Years Ahead* report that the home help service should be comprehensive enough to assist older people with all the tasks of daily living, both domestic and personal, should be implemented across the country.

66. The distribution of Public Health Nurses across the country is inequitable and should be standardised. The Council recommends that all health boards should have a ratio of at least one Public Health Nurse (excluding the Senior and Superintendent grades) to 2,500 persons of all ages. This should not require a large increase in resources as some health boards already exceed this ratio. A broader nursing skill mix within the Community Nursing Service should also be developed. Certain services might often be more appropriately provided by professional and skilled carers other than the already overstretched PHNs. In general, the most cost-effective care option should be chosen to maximise the resources of the community services. The Council recommends a significant increase in the number of Registered General Nurses working with older people in the community to fulfil this recommendation.

67. The need for a seven day, 24-hour Community Nursing Service should also be examined. Many problems experienced by older people and their carers require the immediate and specific attention of a nurse. A 24-hour service, with 'on-call' nurses available at all times' would allow for an immediate response to such problems outside normal working hours. Such a service will place a burden on resources, but some developments are required to meet an outstanding need. Immediate priority should be given to the development of an 'on-call' system operating from 8.00am to midnight, seven days a week.

68. On the grounds of equity and quality the Council is concerned that many older people who require paramedical care at home are denied such services. The Council believes that such care is essential if ill and dependant older

people are to continue living in the community and recommends that the health boards reconsider their opposition to the principle of domiciliary paramedical services.

69. The Council is particularly concerned at the absence of a social work service for older people in Ireland. The Council recommends that social work services for older people be developed within health board community care programmes (as has been done in Donegal). The service should have responsibility for the following areas of social need:

- Protecting the rights of individual older people against exploitation or abuse (including financial, physical, sexual and psychological abuse). The community care social worker (in conjunction with other key staff, particularly the Public Health Nurse) should have responsibility for the identification of cases and the co-ordination of interventions to remove older people from abusive situations.

- Providing support and advice to carers for older people with dementia. The social and psychological strains on dementia carers are well established and would benefit from the particular skills of social workers.

- Developing boarding out services whereby older people who cannot remain in their own homes are placed with families who are recruited, trained and supported to care for them.

- Advising older people on their entitlements for social welfare, housing and health and social care services.

70. The Council welcomes the package of measures designed to combat crime against older people announced in 1996 by the then Minister for Social Welfare following the report of the Task Force on Security for the Elderly. In addition to these measures it would be worthwhile to take a strategic view of the issue. There is a coincidence of interest between measures designed to make older people more secure on the one hand, and, on the other, measures designed to ensure appropriate surveillance of frail dependent older people living in the community, particularly those living alone with significant medical problems. We therefore strongly urge that initiatives designed jointly to provide security and to alert medical service providers to an emergency be considered by any security schemes for older people.

71. Psychological counselling services for older people should be developed by the health boards. There are many psychological problems arising from the changes associated with late life (e.g., bereavement, retirement, ill-health, cognitive disorders and abusive family situations) which would benefit from some form of counselling. At present there are little or no psychological services available to older people, and few psychologists trained to deal with the problems

of old age. The post-graduate courses in clinical and counselling psychology should incorporate modules on old age to ensure trained professionals are available in future.

Care in the community

72. Given that domiciliary paramedical services are normally not available it would seem vital that these services be made available in the community. Yet there are significant problems here also. Transport to and from health centres, day care and hospitals remains poor, especially in rural areas. Despite a widespread agreement that this is a serious problem, there seems to be no urgency among health board programme managers and government departments. As with most issues relating to older people, responsibility seems to have devolved to the Departments of Health and Social Welfare and not to the Department of Transport. Thus an infrastructural facility which should underpin the provision of health and social care services has to be provided from the same budget and therefore compete with those services for funding.

73. Day care is probably the most neglected part of the community care sector. Day care centres seem to be low on the priority list of health authorities and are provided on a discretionary basis. The number of places and range of services provided varies significantly across the country. Overall, the number of places is well below what is needed and relies heavily on the efforts of the voluntary sector. Some support for the voluntary sector is given but an active involvement by the health boards in, for example, the training of day care staff is not evident.

74. The recommendations on dental health, aural and ophthalmic services have generally been met or have been superseded by recent policy initiatives. Some problems with sight testing still exist however.

Recommendations
75. The Department of Public Enterprise, as the Government Department responsible for transport, should re-examine the possibility of using existing public service vehicles in use in rural areas in more creative ways. The use of postal vehicles seems particularly promising. In many European countries, post is delivered between post offices using mini-buses, which double-up as public transport vehicles. Support should also be available for the permanent establishment of local initiatives such as the North West Connemara Rural Project.

76. There is an obvious need for additional health board day care places in areas without a well developed voluntary sector. In health boards with a strong voluntary sector there is a need for greater support from the health boards in, for example, the training of staff and the development of facilities. As already mentioned, the Council recommends that health boards be obliged in legislation to

provide day care services of a specified quality, and with a comprehensive range of services, to older people who require them.

77.   The Council believes there is a particular need for special day care units for older people with dementia. Most people with dementia live at home and are looked after by their families, often constituting a heavy burden for them. The day care units would play an important role in giving respite to the carer. Specially trained staff would be required for these patients where services such as chiropody, haircare, bathing and most importantly occupational therapy would be available.

Care in general hospitals
78.   Compared to community care, the hospital sector has fared quite well since 1988, albeit with marked regional variations. Thirteen and one-half new consultant geriatrician posts and ten new Departments of Medicine for the Elderly have been created in four health boards. Despite this progress, many geriatrician posts continue to be part-time, and the number of beds in geriatric units is still below the norm advocated by the Working Party.

79.   Between 1985 and 1996 the average length of stay for people aged 65 years or more fell from 15.3 days to 10.5 days (Hospital In-Patient Enquiry, unpublished communication). This has exacerbated problems for the interface between hospitals and the community. Adequate step-down facilities are lacking in most hospitals, leading to premature discharges. There is also a sense that many hospital admissions could be prevented by an enlarged community health care system.

80.   Hospitals normally have liaison personnel, responsible for informing General Practitioners and Public Health Nurses about patient discharges but follow up procedures are not as strong. Notifications to Public Health Nurses and General Practitioners are usually posted or are given to the patient: as a consequence they are often delayed or do not reach their intended recipient.

81.   The development of day hospitals in general hospitals has been very slow, often because these are seen as the responsibility of community care programmes. In rural health boards, it is perceived that day hospitals might serve the wider community better if attached to community hospitals or other community facilities.

Recommendations
82.   The Council recommends that all acute general hospitals should have a properly resourced Department of Medicine for the Elderly, lead by a consultant in geriatric medicine, and with access to the investigative and therapeutic facilities available in the rest of the hospital where necessary. The Council disagrees with

the view expressed by one health board that specialist geriatric departments are not appropriate for County general hospitals. The benefits of specialist departments include a greater expertise in medicine for older people and greater access to specialist assessment and rehabilitation facilities.

83. In the light of the review findings the Council feels that the norms for assessment and rehabilitation beds in geriatric medicine advocated by *The Years Ahead* report are both feasible and adequate. Meeting these norms will require a significant increase in resources, given current provision and the projected increase in the older population. The Council places particular emphasis on the development of rehabilitation facilities, which are essential if older people with health problems are to be returned to the community, capable of independent living. The recent focus on reducing length of stay in hospitals has increased the importance of good step down facilities on the hospital campus.

84. Consultant geriatricians are not just physicians to older people, but also have a significant role in planning services and in advocating their development. Older people are entitled to have full-time consultant representatives, with no conflicting responsibilities or loyalties. The Council believes that all consultant geriatricians in the larger urban hospitals should be appointed on a full-time basis. Geriatricians should be appointed on a part-time basis only where the hospital has a small number of consultant physicians (three or four) and the geriatrician is required for some general medical duties. This arrangement does not seem to work, however, in hospitals where the geriatrician is one of only two physicians, as the amount of time available for geriatric medicine is inadequate.

85. In the long-term the Council believes that all geriatricians should be employed on a full-time basis as an enlarged community hospital sector will require significant support from geriatricians if it is to operate properly.

86. The future of day hospitals for geriatric medicine in general hospitals should be reviewed by the Department of Health. Beyond the larger Dublin hospitals this recommendation has been ignored and, it seems, rejected. The Council believes that all Departments of Medicine for the Elderly require on-campus day hospital facilities if they are to have meaningful contact with community residing older people living in the hospital's catchment area.

87. The Council recommends that the hospital liaison role outlined in *The Years Ahead* report be reviewed by the Department of Health. The Council feels that dedicated hospital-community liaison workers responsible for overseeing discharge of older patients and liaising with Public Health Nurses and General Practitioners, are necessary in all acute general hospitals. The liaison worker should be equipped to respond quickly and appropriately to discharge. A liaison

worker should be available seven days per week. The liaison worker should have at least as close a relationship with community care staff as with the hospital staff. They should be prepared and trained to accompany the older person to their home, and to visit and assess home situations where necessary. The liaison worker should have a car for this purpose if an ambulance journey is not necessary.

The community hospital

88.   The community hospital sector is developing belatedly and looks set to grow significantly in the coming years. It is unclear, however, whether the sector is to be developed in the manner envisaged by the Working Party. Most hospitals are not converted long-stay facilities and are not seen as modern replacements for the other long-stay facilities such as welfare homes. Community hospitals provide very few long-stay beds compared to the private nursing home sector, which has expanded significantly since the *Health (Nursing Homes) Act* of 1990. Nor do they all provide assessment and rehabilitation facilities, originally envisaged as a core function of the community hospital. The emphasis tends to be on low technology services such as day and respite care.

89.   The availability of geriatricians is essential if community hospitals are to provide high quality medical services at a local level. Unfortunately, there are not enough full-time geriatricians, particularly outside Dublin, to guarantee that this will occur. Geriatricians have a particularly important role in the development of day hospitals, which should be attached to community hospitals if they are not to be developed in general hospitals.

90.   While it is clear that welfare homes are being slowly eradicated, it is not clear how the health boards plan to provide alternative welfare accommodation. Across the country a number of options are mentioned (sheltered housing, boarding out, bed and breakfasts) but no overall target for the desired mix is apparent. From a historical point of view it may be argued that welfare accommodation for older people in Ireland has a poor history. This was in part due to the willingness of authorities to institutionalise frail, destitute and homeless older people, rather than offering them some form of independent living.

91.   The number of places and criteria for entry to various long-term facilities are not clear and vary significantly from health board to health board. This is in part due to historical variations in the type of facilities available, but is also linked to different admission policies across the health board regions.

Recommendations

92.   The Council recommends that the community hospital sector continue to grow in the manner envisaged by the Working Party, replacing geriatric hospitals and welfare homes where possible. It is essential that these hospitals are equipped

with assessment and rehabilitation facilities for the disorders associated with old age and that they receive weekly visits from consultant geriatricians.

93. For the sake of equity the Council recommends that national guidelines on the placement of older patients in long-term care be established by the Department of Health. At local level, these guidelines should then be translated into clear policies for admission to specific public, voluntary and private facilities. Placement guidelines for welfare accommodation should also be developed, taking account of the alternatives advocated by the proposed national plan on social housing for older people.

94. The long-stay bed norms advocated by *The Years Ahead* report must be addressed by the Department of Health. In general they seem to bear only a coincidental relationship to the situation on the ground and are not seriously used to plan services. They are viewed by most health boards as both inappropriate and unfeasible. If local formulae are to be used as an alternative to the national norms, the Department of Health should give guidance on the admission criteria that should guide these calculations.

95. The Council is concerned at the ongoing growth in the private nursing home sector and the rising costs to the State associated with this increase. While private nursing home homes undoubtedly meet an existing need, the Council feels that the long-term solution to the care of dependent older people must be in community care. The Council would urge that more resources be given to community care services. For older people at the highest risk of institutionalisation the option of sheltered housing should be available.

96. The Council welcomes the recent establishment of a Social Services Inspectorate within the Department of Health to develop an expertise in promoting high standards of care in institutions. The Council believes that the Inspectorate should have executive responsibility for the organisation of an inspection system of all types of long-term care institutions, public and private, where older people reside. At present there is a clear discrepancy in the system as nursing homes are formally inspected and governed by a Code of Practice, while health board facilities are not. The Inspectorate should have responsibility for the formulation of protocols governing the inspection and intervention process, and the training of those responsible for the inspections at community care area level.

Care of older people with a mental disorder
97. There has been a move since 1984 to reduce the number of older people in psychiatric facilities. In addition, some patients, particularly those with dementia, are no longer routinely treated in psychiatric hospitals and units, and are generally cared for in a community facility or in nursing homes. A recent Council report

(Keogh and Roche 1996) confirmed a significant psychiatric morbidity among older Irish people and also raised questions about the extent to which this morbidity was being adequately detected and treated at the primary care level.

98. No clear plan for the desired mix and role of different care settings exists, with the result that older people with a mental disorder may be treated in very different settings depending on where they live. There has been very slow progress on the development of specialist services in this area. Only four consultants in the psychiatry of old age have been appointed and the number of dedicated facilities for dementia or functional mental illness in old age is very small.

99. Progress on the recommendations on community care for older people with dementia has been very poor. The health boards do not currently have the resources to screen older people for the early signs of dementia, and the number of day care and day hospital places for people with dementia is significantly lower than required. The recommendation on the provision of welfare and high support hostel accommodation for older people with dementia has been rejected as inappropriate by the health boards.

100. *The Years Ahead* report made some recommendations on the care of older people with dementia which have been met with widespread disapproval. It is now accepted that welfare and hostel type accommodation is not an appropriate residential option for people with dementia.

Recommendations
101. The Council reiterates its recommendation that a national strategy for the future of mental health services for older people be developed by the Department of Health in consultation with all concerned parties in this area. Action in this area has been particularly disappointing since *The Years Ahead* report, leading to an unacceptably high rate of institutionalisation of older people with mental disorders, and significant regional variations in care policies and the quality of care (Keogh and Roche 1996).

102. The Council is concerned at the slow rate of progress in the appointment of consultant psychiatrists in the psychiatry of old age. There are currently four old age psychiatrists, three in Dublin and one in Limerick. The Council believes that consultant-led old age psychiatry should be at the core of the development of mental health services for older people. The specialist assessment, rehabilitation and treatment services offered by these consultants, and the ancillary services they develop are recognised as a model for good practice. It is inequitable then that only four districts in the country can avail of these services. In the absence of a feasibility study on the establishment of a national old age psychiatry service, the

Council would recommend that the Royal College of Psychiatrists (Jolley and Wattis 1994) planning norm of one consultant in the psychiatry of old age per 10,000 older people be urgently adopted.

103. The Council believes that the ability to detect mental health problems such as depression and dementia should be a part of the training of all care professionals so that treatment can be delivered as early as possible. General practitioners and public health nurses in particular should be able and willing, as part of a routine assessment or ongoing care programme, to screen for mental disorders using the simple measures that are available. A training programme to achieve this should be organised by the Irish College of General Practitioners and An Bord Altranais.

104. Major investment is needed in all community care services but the following areas are of particular importance to older people with mental disorders and their carers:

- 24 hour a day, seven days a week community services
- specialised day centres for people with severe dementia with transport to the centres available when needed
- day hospitals capable of treating older people with mental disorders, again with transport when needed
- flexible respite care services, capable of accepting patients at short notice, for day or night care
- in-home respite care services.

105. It is clear from this and other research (Keogh and Roche 1996) that the supply of designated community residential beds for older people is very low. In a context where patients are being resettled from psychiatric institutions into the community or not being accepted in the first place, there is an urgent need to:

- Increase the supply of housing and hostel accommodation for older patients suitable for discharge to the community.
- Ensure that older people who are left behind in psychiatric facilities are not left in buildings with falling standards of care as younger patients are discharged. If older patients are to remain, these buildings must be adapted to their needs in accordance with established principles of good design and environment.
- Increase the supply of long-stay beds in non-psychiatric facilities dedicated to the care of older people with dementia but without behavioural problems.
- Increase the supply of beds in appropriately designed secure psychiatric units for dementia patients with behaviour problems.
- Increase the supply of beds in geriatric units and hospitals for dementia patients with physical illnesses.

Partnership

106. There is no doubt that family carers make an enormous contribution to care of older people in the community often at a substantial personal cost in terms of opportunities foregone, as well as physical and mental strain. Yet there is very little recognition by policy-makers of the role played by informal carers. Indeed certain community services are refused to dependent older persons on the grounds that a relative is present in the household. There is widespread agreement that this approach should be replaced by one that sees formal service providers and home carers as complementary or mutually supportive.

107. Policy-makers should not assume that the current levels of care provided by families to older people will continue to exist in the future. There are conflicting views on the future demand for care and supply of carers, but the majority of factors involved seem likely to exacerbate rather than alleviate the current situation. The future demand for informal care depends on a number of factors. A 1996 report by the Joint Committee on Women's Rights estimated that based on current morbidity patterns, population growth and care provisions, between 100,000 and 110,000 older people will require informal care by the year 2011, an increase of 30 per cent. This will increase however, if the Department of Health's targets for the balance between community and residential care are to be achieved. In the health strategy document *Shaping a Healthier Future* a target of at least 90 per cent of persons aged 75 years or more living in their own homes is outlined. According to the Council's population projections, there will be an extra 60,000 people over 75 years living in the community, if this target is reached (Fahey 1995).

108. The future supply of carers is also open to a number of influences, most of which seem to be exerting a downward pressure on the number of carers available. A crude measure of caretaker potential is the ratio of women aged 45 to 69 years (given that the majority of carers are in this group) to the number of people aged 70 years or more (O'Shea 1993). In 1991 the ratio was 1.4 and is projected to rise to 1.6 by 2011. Thereafter it is expected to decline, reaching 1.3 by 2021. In the short-term, therefore, the supply of traditional carers is expected to rise slightly but declining numbers (in relative terms) are projected for the medium to long-term. This assumes that current caring patterns will not change, but it is possible larger numbers of men and younger people will begin to engage in a caring role. Such a development would be welcome, not only to enlarge the pool of carers but also on the grounds of equity.

109. A further downward pressure is the increasing proportion of married women in the labour force. While much of this work is part-time, and increases the ability of carers to purchase other forms of care, it is likely in many situations to reduce the amount of time, especially during the day available for care of relatives. A number of influences also seem set to fragment Irish families, making regular

contact more difficult. Increased urbanisation and geographic mobility mean that the distance that people live from their relatives is likely to increase, making contact and caring arrangements more difficult. Divorce may fragment families, and may have particular effects on the level of care provided by spouses. This of course may be desirable in many circumstances, given that poor relationships may result lead to physical and psychological abuse.

110. It is apparent that the relationship between the voluntary sector and the statutory authorities is still far from ideal. Funding remains limited and co-ordination is often carried out on an ad-hoc basis. Given that many of the co-ordination structures recommended by *The Years Ahead* report are not in place, this is not surprising. The Council has already noted above its main concerns in relation to this sector.

Recommendations

111. When asked, carers would wish to receive three main types of support from the State (O'Shea and Hughes 1994). Firstly, the vast majority of carers express a desire for direct payment for caring services. This would both recognise the value of the work performed by carers and allow them to purchase other forms of support (e.g. respite care) should they need to do so. Current payment rates, through the Carer's Allowance Scheme are restrictive (because of the means test) and low in comparison to the effort involved. As a result, less than 9,000 carers received the allowance in 1996. A Constant Care Attendance Allowance for people caring full-time for dependent older relatives (e.g. those suffering from advanced dementia) would be a fairer alternative. The allowance would be similar to the Domiciliary Care Allowance which is provided for parents of severely handicapped children, in that it would not be based on an assessment of the carer's means, but on the effort, and opportunity costs involved in providing full-time care at home. The allowance would be paid regardless of means, and should not be calculated in the means test for other social welfare payments. As well as providing a just reward for the effort of carers, such an allowance, especially in the context of recent Nursing Homes legislation, could go a considerable way towards equity in the deployment of limited health care resources and towards a more favourable balance between institutional and community care.

112. To ensure a more widespread coverage, the conditions surrounding the new allowance should be less restrictive than those governing the Carer's Allowance. The current conditions effectively demand that the carer perform a caring role 24 hours per day. These conditions are highly unfair given the regulations governing working hours in formal employment. The new allowance could also be used to provide full-time carers with social insurance cover. Many carers can not avail of a contributory pension in old age because of gaps in their employment histories. The Constant Care Attendance Allowance would achieve widespread coverage

and would therefore be the ideal vehicle for collecting social insurance contributions from carers and from the State (as the *de facto* employer). The Council welcomes the review of the Carers Allowance currently being undertaken by the Department of Social, Community and Family Affairs and hopes that the above recommendations are taken into account in the review.

113. The second support most frequently sought by carers in Ireland is information and advice on health and social services, and on welfare entitlements. Carers also wish to know about the long-term prognosis and treatment options related to the medical condition of the person they are caring for. Information is a relatively low cost method of providing support and it would diminish the burden of care for carers

114. The third support most frequently sought by carers is relief care of various kinds. The fact that the carer must constantly remain in the home and is therefore confined on a daily basis is the most frequently cited stress of caring. Carers could benefit from the provision of a range of respite options, including day care places, short-term relief care (for instance through community residential services), night-sitting (freeing the carer for a number of hours in the late evening), and most importantly, domiciliary relief provided by home helps during the day. Other options would be holiday beds (to enable carers to take a holiday) and 'floating beds' (accommodation with or without medical treatment for dependant older people for, say, two nights out of 14). There is also a need for secure night-time beds in community facilities, for older people with dementia. People with dementia often have disturbed sleep patterns which can create intolerable burdens on the carer.

115. A great number of family carers enjoy what they do, receiving many intangible benefits and fulfilment. Many are older people themselves and experience a great physical, financial and emotional burden as they themselves age. It would be a pity if the natural willingness of people to care for their kin was eroded by the State's response to their needs. As pointed out above, the pool of potential carers may be reduced in the future. The lack of statutory support services for carers is likely to result in a breakdown of the family caring system and a consequent increase in the demand for institutional care. Policy makers must recognise the valuable contribution of carers and become more attuned to their needs if community care is to remain a viable policy. The Council also recognises the requirement for research on the specific needs of carers for older people. This research should focus on the development of service delivery models that are designed to facilitate individual circumstances in a flexible manner.

116. To encourage the development of voluntary activity for and by older people the Council believes that community workers should be employed by the health

boards. There is currently little or no community development work for older people although the Community Work Department of the Southern Health Board is providing a lead in this regard. One of the core skills of community workers is the empowerment of marginalised groups through the creation of structures which encourage participation in the life of the community. Community workers have an expert knowledge of the statutory funding available to voluntary bodies and would be able to perform an advocacy role where it is felt that funding is inadequate. They would also identify areas where voluntary activity might flourish by canvassing the local population, and developing the skills, confidence and knowledge of those that might become involved.

Priorities

117. This review of *The Years Ahead* report has raised many issues relating to care for older people. Some of these are more important than others and the Council wishes to underline those issues which require urgent attention. The Council believes that home and community care must be the cornerstone of any health and social care strategy for older people. To this end the following services require immediate development:

- The home help service
- Respite services for carers
- Sheltered housing
- Day care centres with transport services where required
- Paramedical services at home and in the community
- A social work service dedicated to older people
- All services for older people with mental disorders
- The community hospital sector.

118. The Council is particularly concerned that structures responsible for the development and implementation of the proposed strategy on services for older people be established. The Council welcomes the recent appointment of a Minister of State at the Department of Health with responsibility for Older People. The Minister is in an ideal position to co-ordinate the activities of relevant Departments in the creation and implementation of the strategy.

119. The Council believes that an increased proportion of the total health and housing budgets should be directed towards services for older people. The Council notes the excellent detailed and costed recommendations made by the Department of Health's 1996 report of the Review Group on Health and Personal Social Services for People with Physical and Sensory Disabilities. In this review, recommendations on service development totalling more than £50m over a five-year period are made. Older people are not specifically addressed in this

document, but given that more than two thirds of disabled adults are aged 60 and over (Martin, Melzer and Elliot 1988) the Council recommends that older people benefit from a commensurate amount of the funds set aside for the implementation of this document.

References

Blackwell, J., O'Shea, E., Moane, G. and Murray, P., 1992. *Care Provision and Cost Measurement: Dependent Elderly People at Home and In Geriatric Hospitals.* Dublin: Economic and Social Research Institute.

Browne, M., 1992. *Co-Ordinating Services for the Elderly at Local Level: Swimming Against the Tide. A Report on Two Pilot Projects.* Dublin: National Council for the Elderly.

Commission of the European Communities, 1993. *Growth, Competitiveness, Employment: The Challenge and Way Forward into the 21st Century.* White Paper. Brussels: European Commission.

Department of Health, 1994. *Shaping a Healthier Future.* Dublin: Stationery Office.

Department of Health, 1997. *Statement of Strategy.* Dublin: Stationery Office.

Department of the Environment, 1995. *Social Housing - The Way Ahead.* Dublin: Stationery Office.

Evason, E. and Whittington, D., 1993. 'Community care: the quality issue explored'. *International Journal of Health Care Quality Assurance*, Vol. 6: 18-24.

Fahey, T., 1995. *Health Service Implications of Population Ageing in Ireland, 1991-2011.* Dublin: National Council for the Elderly.

Health (Nursing Homes) Act, 1990. Dublin: Stationery Office.

Interim Report of the Joint Oireachtas Committee on the Family, 1997. *The Elderly, the Family and the State in Ireland.* Dublin: Stationery Office.

Joint Committee on Women's Rights, 1996. *A Long-term Support Framework for Female Carers of Older People with Disabilities: 1996-2011.* Dublin: Stationery Office.

Jolley, D. and Wattis, J., 1994. *Guidelines for Regional Advisors on Consultant Posts in The Psychiatry of Old Age.* London: Royal College of Psychiatrists.

Keogh, F. and Roche, A., 1996. *Mental Disorders in Older Irish People: Incidence, Prevalence and Treatment.* Dublin: National Council for the Elderly.

Lundström, F. and McKeown, K., 1994. *Home Help Services for Elderly People in Ireland.* Dublin: National Council for the Elderly.

Martin, J., Meltzer, H. and Elliot, D., 1988. *The Prevalence of Disability Among Adults. Report 1.* HMSO: London.

Mulvihill, R., 1993. *Voluntary-Statutory Partnership in Community Care of the Elderly.* Dublin: National Council for the Elderly.

National Council for the Elderly., 1996. *Planning Health and Social Care Services for the Elderly: Implications of Projected Increase in Our Elderly Population (1991-2011).* Dublin: National Council for the Elderly.

O'Connor, J., Ruddle, H. and O'Gallagher, M., 1989. *Sheltered Housing in Ireland. Its Role and Contribution in the Care of the Elderly.* Dublin: National Council for the Elderly.

O'Donovan, O., Hodgins, M., McKenna, V. and Kelleher, C., 1997. *Training Carers of Older People: An Advisory Report.* Dublin: National Council for the Elderly.

O'Shea, E., 1993. *The Impact of Social and Economic Policies on Older People in Ireland.* Dublin: National Council for the Elderly.

O'Shea, E. and Hughes, J., 1994. *The Economiçs and Financing of Long-Term Care of the Elderly in Ireland.* Dublin: National Council for the Elderly.

Programme for Competitiveness and Work, 1994. Dublin: Stationery Office.

Report of the Commission on Health Funding, 1989. Dublin: Stationery Office.

Report of the Working Party on Services for the Elderly, 1988. *The Years Ahead...A Policy for the Elderly.* Dublin: Stationery Office.

Review Group on Health and Personal Social Services for People with Physical and Sensory Disabilities, 1996. *Towards an Independent Future.* Dublin: Stationery Office.

Authors' Acknowledgements

This study is the outcome of the effort, co-operation and commitment of many people. The work was carried out under the direction of Professor Joyce O'Connor. Administrative back-up was provided by Geraldine Hennessy and Mary Healy, and the fieldwork was co-ordinated by Barbara Crowley. We wish to acknowledge the Chairperson and members of the National Council on Ageing and Older People who initiated, funded and guided the study. The Consultative Committee played a vital role in the planning and execution of the study. We want to thank all the members for the information they provided, for their assistance in identifying key questions, for providing opportunities for exploration of ideas and for their constructive feedback on the various drafts of the Report. We are particularly grateful to Michael White (Chairperson of Council and Committee), Bob Carroll (Director, National Council on Ageing and Older People) and John Browne (Research Officer, National Council on Ageing and Older People) for their support, guidance and expert advice.

The key contributors to the study are, of course, all those unnamed people who took time out from busy schedules to provide us with information and to share with us their experiences and perceptions. We gratefully acknowledge the co-operation and assistance of all the respondents to the study from government departments, health boards, local authorities, voluntary organisations, nursing homes, carers groups, professional organisations and trade union and employers groups.

CHAPTER ONE

The Years Ahead - A Policy for the Elderly. Summary and New Perspectives

1.1   Introduction

The Years Ahead...A Policy for the Elderly (hereafter referred to as *The Years Ahead*), produced in 1988 by the Working Party on Services for the Elderly constitutes official government policy for the development of services for older people in this country. When the National Council for the Elderly, now known as the National Council on Ageing and Older People, was established in 1990 in succession to the National Council for the Aged, its new terms of reference included a responsibility to advise the Minister for Health on the implementation of the recommendations of *The Years Ahead*. This study was commissioned by the National Council for the Elderly to review the extent to which the recommendations of *The Years Ahead* have been implemented since the policy document was first published. In cases where recommendations have not been acted upon, the review explores the reasons for non-implementation. The review also attempts to explore the impact which implemented recommendations have had. Comprehensive evaluation of the impact of the many recommendations made would require research outside the scope of this review, but information is provided on the views of service providers. It is recognised that this is but one perspective on the value of what has been done and that for a true and complete picture feedback from the users of the services is essential.

Since experiences and perceptions of the implementation of the policy document are likely to vary, the review provides feedback from a variety of perspectives: policy-makers, administrators, service providers and representatives of older people. The overall purpose of the review is to evaluate the current situation with regard to care of older people and to identify the way forward in providing the most appropriate and effective care system for the future.

This chapter gives a context for the review by providing a summary of *The Years Ahead* policy document, of the considerations and the assumptions underlying it and of the developments in health policy which have occurred since its publication.

1.2   Report of the Working Party on Services for the Elderly, 1988

In 1988 the Working Party on Services for the Elderly, set up in 1986 under the Department of Health, published its report under the title *The Years Ahead...A Policy for the Elderly*. Since its publication the report of the Working Party has formed the basis for official policy with regard to the care of older people in this country. *The Years Ahead* made a number of recommendations for the provision of a legislative framework for the development of services for older people, but the report itself has no statutory status and there is no statutory obligation on the health boards or other agencies to implement its recommendations. In the two decades prior to the publication of *The Years Ahead*, public policy on older people was heavily influenced by *The Care of the Aged* report produced in 1968 by the Inter-Departmental Committee on Care of the Aged.

1.2.1   Policy prior to 1988

Twenty years before *The Years Ahead*, the Inter-Departmental Committee set out explicit objectives for service delivery to older people (p. 49):

The Care of The Aged report, which was predicated on the belief 'that it is better, and probably much cheaper, to help the aged to live in the community than to provide for them in hospitals or other institutions', led to a radical shift away from institutional care towards community care. In providing that care it was the Committee's view that public and family care should be regarded as complementary - not as alternatives - and that the public authority should endeavour to help the family, not take over from it (p. 13). *The Care of the Aged* report had a major influence in stimulating voluntary involvement in care of older people and following its publication there was a huge growth in voluntary Care of the Aged Committees and Social Welfare Councils throughout the country. To achieve its objectives, the Inter-Departmental Committee recommended that housing, financial assistance, health and welfare services be closely integrated to provide a comprehensive care system.

The Care of the Aged report was a major catalyst for change and many of its recommendations had been implemented and significant improvements to income maintenance, housing and health services had been brought about by the time the Working Party on Services for the Elderly was established in 1986. However, the Working Party noted in 1988 that 'despite the undoubted improvements in the care of the elderly there are still considerable shortcomings in services' (p. 24). In particular, the Working Party noted that 'many elderly people still have little choice but to seek admission to institutional care because support is not available to allow them to manage at home'; that 'the appointment of physicians in geriatric medicine and the development of specialist assessment and rehabilitation has been slow' and that 'despite progress in developing domiciliary and community services insufficient support is available to thousands of relatives caring for elderly people at home, many of whom have severe disabilities' (Working Party on Services for the Elderly 1988, p. 24). In the view of the Working Party, one of the major deficiencies in services for older people in 1986 was that too many older people were inappropriately cared for in geriatric hospitals, nursing homes and psychiatric hospitals. It was also felt that housing, health and welfare services were not sufficiently targeted at assisting the most vulnerable older people. With regard to the administration of services, the objectives of *The Care of the Aged* report for an integrated community service had not been fulfilled and the Working Party found a lack of co-ordination in the delivery of services from different statutory bodies. By the end of the 1980s not only were there still many deficiencies in the care system for older people but public expenditure cutbacks were curtailing the impetus for continued improvement. It was within this context that the Working Party sought to devise a care system for older people that would be appropriate and responsive to the challenges and changes arising in the years leading into the 21st Century.

1.2.2   Terms of reference of the Working Party

When the Working Party began to examine services for older people in 1986 they acknowledged that they were 'stand[ing] on the shoulders of the *Care of the Aged* report' (p. 26). The terms of reference of the Working Party were directly related to the philosophy and policy outlined twenty years earlier (p. ix):

(a) to enable the elderly person to live at home, where possible, at an optimum level of health and independence

(b) to enable those who cannot live at home to receive treatment, rehabilitation and care in accommodation and in an environment as near as possible to home.

Within the framework of these objectives, the Working Party was asked to review:

(i)   the role and function of existing health and welfare services in serving these objectives

(ii) the appropriateness of existing health and welfare services

(iii) the comparative effectiveness, efficiency and cost of alternative models and settings

(iv) the planning norms for services both residential and community.

In carrying out its terms of reference, the Working Party was guided by certain considerations which it described as arising from 'society's obligations towards its elderly citizens, tempered by the economic realities of the times in which we live' (p. iii). These considerations were that:

- old age demands our special respect
- improvements in life expectancy and the increasing number of elderly persons require a clear-cut public policy for the future in regard to the State's role towards the elderly
- the underlying aim of policy should be to help the elderly maintain their dignity and independence by protecting them from economic and social hardship
- the dignity and independence of the elderly can best be achieved by enabling them to continue to live at home with, if necessary, support services provided by the State
- when ill or disabled, the elderly are entitled to the same standard of treatment available to the rest of the population even if services have to be organised in ways that meet their particular needs
- when admission to long-term care is unavoidable, such care should be of the highest standard and should respect the dignity and individuality of the elderly person.

1.2.3   Objectives of services in The Years Ahead

The Years Ahead report reiterates and expands on the principle that services for older people should enable them to live in their own homes as long as possible but where it is no longer possible appropriate residential options should be made available. The objectives for public policy towards older people set out by the Working Party were as follows (p. 38):

- to maintain elderly people in dignity and independence in their own home
- to restore those elderly people who become ill or dependent to independence at home
- to encourage and support the care of the elderly in their own community by family, neighbours and voluntary bodies in every way possible
- to provide a high quality of hospital and residential care for elderly people when they can no longer be maintained in dignity and independence at home.

The services provided to meet those objectives should, according to the Working Party, be comprehensive, equitable, accessible, responsive, flexible, co-ordinated, planned and cost-effective (p. 39).

1.2.4   Emphasis and focus of The Years Ahead
The Working Party sought to consolidate the translation of the policy of community care into solid practice. To do this it made recommendations with regard to the level and types of services provided, the manner of delivery of these services and the allocation of resources.

1.2.4.1   Emphasis and focus: level and types of services
The Years Ahead report outlines detailed recommendations and norms on level of provision for an extensive range of services in regard to the following:

- housing: choice in accommodation, adaptations and repairs, sheltered housing, home income schemes, house transfer and sharing, and voluntary housing
- care at home: anticipatory care and case-finding, nursing services, medical appliances and aids, paramedical services, help at home, social work services, and alarm systems
- care in the community: transport, day care, dental, aural and ophthalmic services, and boarding out
- care in general hospitals: pre-admission and post-discharge assessment and liaison, day hospital facilities, geriatric departments, rehabilitation services, and special hospital needs
- the community hospital: development of community hospitals, assessment and rehabilitation services, extended care facilities, welfare accommodation, and nursing home services
- care of the elderly mentally ill and infirm: screening for dementia, day care facilities, high support hostels, residential accommodation, and support for carers.

In the area of service provision one of the most pronounced changes from *The Care of the Aged* report was the proposed restructuring of long-stay units - such as geriatric hospitals or homes, long-stay district hospitals and welfare homes - into community hospitals which would provide a range of services at local level including: assessment and rehabilitation, convalescent care, day hospital and day care services, respite care, facilities for highly dependent or terminally ill older people and information, advice and support services for carers.

1.2.4.2   Emphasis and focus: organisation of services
In the area of service organisation, *The Years Ahead* went much further than the *Care of the Aged* report and set out detailed proposals for a comprehensive and co-ordinated service. These proposals reflect the view that co-ordination is essential at a number of levels - national, regional and local - and involves different parties - the family, the local community, voluntary organisations and public services.

Specifically, the Working Party proposed that:

- services should be organised as far as possible in local districts serving a population of 25-30,000 people
- within each district co-ordination of services should be the responsibility of a District Liaison Nurse
- the District Liaison Nurse should be supported by a District Team for the Elderly representative of those with direct responsibility for providing services to the elderly in the district
- at community care area level, there should be an overall Co-ordinator of Services for the Elderly
- at health board level there should be an Advisory Committee on the Elderly
- at national level, the Departments of Health, the Environment and Social Welfare should agree administrative arrangements to ensure that there is a co-ordinated national policy towards the elderly
- there should be close liaison between the health boards and the local authorities in meeting the housing needs of the elderly
- a mechanism should be developed to co-ordinate voluntary activity in each community care area and national guidelines should be developed for a more constructive relationship between the voluntary and statutory sectors.

In addition to co-ordination, *The Years Ahead* emphasised the importance of assessment of the medical, social, emotional and physical circumstances of the older person in ensuring delivery of the most appropriate and effective care services. The report also spelt out the role of informal carers in the delivery of care to dependent older people in the community and made specific recommendations for services to carers in their own right.

1.2.4.3   *Emphasis and focus: resourcing of services*
With regard to resourcing of the proposed care system, *The Years Ahead* provided an advance on *The Care of The Aged* report by making specific monetary proposals to increase the amount of resources for a number of paramedical services. The Working Party, however, acknowledged the underlying budget constraints of the time and suggested that redeployment rather than increases in resources could be used to fund improvements. The report emphasised the dependence of older people on the State for their chief or only means of income and on this basis suggested that general taxation should remain the chief source of funding for services with insurance playing a minor role.

1.3   Government commitment to the policy of community care
An indication of Government commitment to the policy of community care was provided in the 1991 *Programme for Economic and Social Progress* (PESP) which

set out provisions over a seven-year period for the development of community-based services on the assumption of satisfactory economic growth in the country. The PESP provided for an increase of £100 million in capital expenditure on these services and progressive increases in the annual level of current expenditure to a target of £90 million above the 1990 level by the end of a seven-year period. While the increased resources were to be shared with other groups besides older people, the PESP provided support for the kind of recommendations made in *The Years Ahead*. With specific regard to older people, the PESP put forward the following priorities for service development based on *The Years Ahead* (PESP 1991):

- expand home nursing and other support services for the elderly and their carers living at home
- extend respite facilities to relieve the families caring for dependent elderly at home
- provide specialist assessment and rehabilitation units associated with the main acute general hospitals
- ensure adequate numbers of extended care beds in those boards experiencing rapid increase in the elderly population, particularly in the Eastern Health Board.

The Government's *Programme for Competitiveness and Work* (PCW) drawn up in 1994 promised continued progress in implementing the health provisions agreed under the PESP. In the case of older people, the commitment in the PCW was again to continue strengthening home and community services for older people who are ill or dependent but the focus was on the provision of adequate numbers of extended care beds and staff (PCW 1994). The most recent National Programme - *Partnership 2000 for Inclusion, Employment and Competitiveness* - has specific provisions for the inclusion and equal treatment of groups such as women and people with disabilities but makes no mention of older people apart from a commitment to reviewing the tax position of pensioners.

1.4   Underlying assumptions of *The Years Ahead*

1.4.1   Growth in older population and assumed demand for services
The recommendations put forward in *The Years Ahead* were based on the number and proportion of older people in the population at the time and projected changes in the demographic situation up to the early years of the 21st Century. The Working Party stated that 'the growth in the elderly population will increase demand for health services in particular and must be a major influence on the planning of these services for the future' (Working Party 1988, p. 36). The underlying assumption was that increases in the number of people living into old age would be matched by a *pro rata* increase in the numbers who are ill or dependent.

Fahey (1995) argues that this assumption may be overly pessimistic. Fahey points out that health policy in this country has increasingly committed itself to the goal of healthy ageing and that this deliberate policy could reasonably be assumed to lead to a situation where improvements in life expectancy are associated with at least some improvements in general health and a reduction in underlying morbidity and dependency. Fahey proposes a revision of the assumption in *The Years Ahead* of a *pro rata* increase in demand with an increase in the ageing population and argues that population ageing has a double effect on health needs - a negative effect from increasing numbers of older people and a positive effect from improved health status among older people. An important qualification to Fahey's argument that the Working Party may have been overly pessimistic about demand for services is that population figures would suggest that, on the contrary, the Working Party may have underestimated demand. The actual growth in the older population by 1991 had already outstripped that projected for 1996 in *The Years Ahead* and recent population projections for the year 2011 are much higher than envisaged in 1988 (Table 1.1). Of particular importance is the growth in the number of those over 75 years, who are the greatest consumers of health care services.

Table 1.1: Population projections 1988 - 2011

	1988 CSO projections for 1996	Actual in 1991	1988 CSO projections for 2011	1995 NCE projections for 2011
Population aged over 65	394.7	402.9	437.4	521.7
Population aged over 75	158.7	162.8	155.2	227

Sources: Central Statistics Office, 1988
         Fahey, 1995

The National Council for the Elderly has also made further important qualifications to Fahey's argument and shows how need - both health and social - is likely to increase with the growing number of older people (National Council for the Elderly 1995). In the area of health need, the Council points out that health promotion and illness prevention require considerable resources and the cost of such measures can only be expected to increase as the population ages and the number of people with pre-morbid conditions increases. A second influence on future health need is that there is little evidence of improvement in the average mental health of older people and it is likely that current morbidity levels - at any one time 20 per cent of older people suffer from depression and a further five per cent from dementia - will continue. Another factor which has to be taken into account is that while increases in the number of people aged 65-75 may not lead to increased health need, people older than this are likely to continue to develop the diseases associated with advanced old age. Apart from health need, the

Council has also drawn attention to the social care needs of older people. Research has shown that many social care needs of older people are unmet at present. With the increases in the numbers of older people projected in the future, a very significant expansion in social care service provision will be required.

Apart from the fact that the projected growth in the number of older people is likely to lead to an increase in health and social care needs, there is also likely to be greater pressure on services through increased demand. The evidence is that demand for health services will increase rapidly in the future and that the scale of this increase will outstrip what might be predicted on the basis of demographic forces alone (Fahey 1995). It appears that, as it stands, the health service is driven by public policy and private demand rather than health needs. It is therefore urgent that the health needs of older people are identified, brought to the forefront and given due weight.

1.4.2   Assumed homogeneity of need

The recommendations for services in *The Years Ahead* assume a certain homogeneity of need among all people aged 65 years and over, but the heterogeneity within the older age category is becoming more pronounced. With improved health status the boundaries of this category may now need to be shifted from 65 to the later 60s. The 'old old' may now need to be distinguished as a separate group in their own right with special health and welfare needs requiring a different care system than those in their 60s. The growth in the numbers of people over 80 years and of older people living alone is likely to give rise to an increased need for community care services if these people are to be enabled to continue to live independent lives with dignity.

1.4.3   Assumption of redeployment of resources

An assumption of the Working Party was that the 'decline in birth presents an opportunity to redeploy the resources saved in social welfare, health and education to services for the elderly' (p. 32). On the basis of this assumption, it was recommended that '... the government should, in the light of the changing demographic trends, adopt a conscious long-term policy of redeploying resources to services for the elderly' (p. 175). However, the assumed opportunities to redeploy resources has not, in fact, materialised. On the contrary, experience over the 1990s has shown that there is no simple correspondence between numbers in an age group and either need or demand for health and welfare services. While it is true that the number of children in the country has been declining, the savings that the Working Party expected have been offset by a heightened awareness of the needs of children and identification of new needs in areas such as sexual and physical abuse, learning disability, educational opportunity and speech therapy. By comparison with the attention given in the 1990s to the needs of children, the needs of older people - although an increasing proportion of the population - have been relatively neglected.

1.5   Underlying model of service delivery in *The Years Ahead*

Walker proposes that different modes of service delivery may be placed along a continuum, the end points of which are a bureaucratic mode of delivery and an empowerment mode of delivery. The characteristics of these polar opposites of service delivery are as follows (Walker 1995, p. 210):

Bureaucratic	Empowerment
Service Provider Oriented	User Oriented
Inflexible	Responsive
Provider-Led	Needs-Led
Power Concentrated	Power Sharing
Defensive	Open to Review
Conservative	Open to Change
Input Oriented	Outcome Oriented

One of the criteria for deciding where on the continuum a particular mode of service delivery lies is the extent of user or customer involvement in definition of needs and development and management of services. A tacit assumption underlying *The Years Ahead* is that the needs of older people can be defined effectively by professional service providers and administrators on the basis of certain 'objective' criteria or indicators. For example, the structure recommended for the provision of a comprehensive and co-ordinated service involves a District Team for the Elderly which consists solely of service providers. Likewise, the recommended Advisory Committees consist of service providers (although it is recommended that a proportion of the members should be older people). Neither do the principles outlined for the delivery of services include service-user participation.

Several arguments have been raised against dependence on the professional view of need. A reliance only on the professional perspective, it is argued, fails to take account of people's own day-to-day experiences. It suppresses the qualitative aspects of need, can arbitrarily fragment people's needs along arbitrary lines of jurisdiction and can ignore whole areas of need by focusing only on services that are currently provided (Leiss 1976; Clayton 1984). In recent years there has been a growing emphasis on the consumer's view of need. Such an approach is seen as participative, as being grounded in people's own goals and life plans and as reflecting the overlapping and inter-connected nature of needs. The user-centred approach is rooted in the view that people are the best judges of their own situation. Frazer, in the context of social inclusion, argues, for example, that '...the views of people who depend on public services must be taken into account in the process of developing modern, accessible and people-centred public service provision' (Frazer and O'Neill 1992, p. vii).

Walker argues that consultation with users on need is not enough to empower them and that the only way that service users can be assured of influence and power over service provision, is to also have a 'voice' in the development, organisation and management of services. According to Walker, service users must be provided with a range of realisable opportunities to define their own needs and to specify the kind of services required to address these needs. A further requirement which has to be added to Walker's specifications is the need for consumer involvement in evaluating the benefits of whatever services are provided. The European Year of Older People and Solidarity Between Generations may be seen as an indicator of the shift of attitudes and values in Europe towards a recognition of the rights of older service users to participate in decisions on care provision which have a significant impact on their lives. In this country too there are several indications of a shift in public policy towards a consumer orientation. (This is discussed more fully in Chapter Twelve.) For example, the National Economic and Social Forum highlighted customer orientation as a key principle underpinning the delivery of a quality social service (National Economic and Social Forum 1995). Similarly, the Government's Strategic Management Initiative and the 1994 Health Strategy document, *Shaping a Healthier Future*, both emphasise the importance of consumer orientation.

Up to recent times older people have not been prominent in demanding a 'voice' in the care decisions that are vital to their lives. However, developments in Europe - the Grey Party in Germany, a 'pensioners' party in Belgium, a party of older people in Portugal and pensioner action groups in the UK - and in this country - the Irish Senior Citizens National Parliament, Active Retirement Associations, the Irish Association of Older People and Pensioner Associations - point to a growing self-confidence on the part of older people. The importance of service-user participation is highlighted in a Eurobarometer study on age and attitudes which found that people over 65 years of age emphatically rejected the term 'the elderly' in favour of terms such as 'older people' and 'senior citizens' which emphasise integration and participation rather than separation (Walker 1993). But participation by older people in the decisions which affect their lives cannot happen unless structures for service delivery incorporate provision for service user involvement. Positive action in the form of information, resources and staff training is needed to support both users and providers in working toward service user involvement. In the case of frail older people, user participation may require advocates who are committed to articulating their needs. Informal carers are well placed to act as advocates for older people, but it must be recognised that carers are also service users in their own right and are entitled to an equal right to participation in service organisation.

Judged against the criterion of user involvement, the mode of service delivery in *The Years Ahead* appears to belong more to the bureaucratic than the empowerment end of Walker's continuum. The recommendations of *The Years Ahead* provide few opportunities for older people or their carers for genuine participation in needs assessment, and in the planning, delivery and evaluation of services. At an even more fundamental level, *The Years Ahead* paid no attention to structures for provision of basic information to older people on the services available, the means of access to them and changes that may occur. Failure to address the issue of provision of information and the delineation of pathways to care is remarkable in the context of a document which advocated the establishment of many new services and structures and wide-ranging changes in existing services. However, evaluation of *The Years Ahead* against other criteria in Walker's model shows that the mode of service delivery proposed belongs to the empowerment end of the spectrum. For example, the emphasis on local teams, liaison between different service providers, integration and co-ordinated effort, appropriate assessment and provision of options, characterises a mode of delivery that is responsive, encourages power-sharing and is open to review and change.

1.6 Recent influences on policy on care of older people: The 1994 Health Strategy

The present central policy document on overall health services in this country is *Shaping a Healthier Future: A Strategy for Effective Healthcare in the 1990s* (Department of Health 1994) hereafter referred to as *Shaping a Healthier Future*. An analysis of this document reveals a number of differences in policy orientation and emphasis compared to that outlined in *The Years Ahead*. Re-orientations are evident with regard to the services, the framework of management and organisational structures and the participants in the system. The principles underpinning this re-orientation are equity, quality of service and accountability.

1.6.1 Services re-orientation

Shaping a Healthier Future shifts the focus of health strategy away from level of provision to the provision of a positive outcome. Health services must now have a demonstrable benefit in terms of health gain (concerned with health status) and social gain (concerned with broader aspects of quality of life). Reflecting this emphasis, in 1995 the Chief Executive Officers of the health boards founded the Office for Health Gain with the aim of working together to achieve measurable health gain. The emphasis on health and social gain adds a dimension to service provision not addressed in *The Years Ahead*, that is, the collection and analysis of comprehensive and good quality data on the benefits of the services implemented. The Institute of Public Administration points out that we need uniform health indicators to know what progress is being made towards the goals of health and social gain (Health Services Development Unit 1995). Information is needed on

life expectancy, death rates, patterns of lifestyle and ᴗ
present much of the requisite information on trends in heᴗ
influence health is not available in this country. In assessiᴗᵤ
Institute of Public Administration highlights the importance of evaᴗ
technology before it is introduced and the need for a questioning attituᴗ
new programmes and treatments with regard to their benefits. Evaluaᴗ
equally important to current interventions so that those producing the greatest gᴗ
can be identified. Assessing health and social gain poses a considerable challenge.
Shaping a Healthier Future proposed clinical audit - which is defined as a
systematic critical analysis of the quality of medical care from the first point of
contact through to assessment of outcome - as an essential element in assessing
gain. But much remains to be done to develop appropriate evaluation measures.
Part of the responsibility of the new posts of Directors of Public Health Medicine
is to identify health outcome measures that can be used to assess the achievement
of health gain and social gain.

Another aspect of the re-orientation of services in *Shaping a Healthier Future* is
the increased emphasis on provision of the most appropriate care. This could
involve providing community-based rather than institutional care for a person
who, as a result could continue to live at home, or it could mean providing the
most appropriate option from a number of different types of institutional care.
Provision of the most appropriate care was a concern also of *The Years Ahead* and
the sum of its recommendations spell out a continuum of care options which
would address different care needs. However, six years after the publication of
The Years Ahead, *Shaping a Healthier Future* acknowledged that community-
based services are not as yet developed to the extent that they can appropriately
complement and substitute for institutional care, or provide adequately for those
in the community who are dependent on support.

1.6.2 Re-orientation of management and organisation of services

Provision of the most appropriate care depends on effective linkages between
services. This was a major concern of the Working Party but six years after the
publication of *The Years Ahead*, and its recommendations on co-ordination of
services, *Shaping a Healthier Future* notes that the health care system is still too
compartmentalised. In particular, there is '...a significant problem in relation to
the lack of integration between services for the elderly in the community and those
in hospitals' (Department of Health 1994, p. 26). In addressing the area of
linkages, *Shaping a Healthier Future* proposed a new organisation for the health
boards but it also returned to certain recommendations of *The Years Ahead* such as
the development of specialist departments of old age in general hospitals.

1.6.3 Re-orientation towards users of the system

Perhaps one of the most radical shifts of focus between *The Years Ahead* and
Shaping a Healthier Future is the emphasis in the latter on a consumer orientation.

When the Commission on Health Funding reported in 1989, one of the key problems it noted in the organisational structures of the time was the '...inadequate effective representation of the interests of individual patients and clients within the structure' (Commission on Health Funding 1989, p. 151). This was not an issue which was addressed in *The Years Ahead. Shaping a Healthier Future* offers some redress by emphasising that the system exists to serve the patient or client. A new dimension brought by *Shaping a Healthier Future* to the organisation of services is that they must be user-oriented and take account of user satisfaction and participation. The document acknowledges that '...there is much room for improvement in that respect' (Department of Health 1994, p. 39). The Charter of Rights for Hospital Patients, noted in *Shaping a Healthier Future,* is seen as a first step in re-orienting services towards greater user responsiveness and further charters are promised, including one for older people. A second mechanism put forward for ensuring quality of services is the clinical audit and here again *Shaping a Healthier Future* emphasises the importance of taking into account the user's perspective. A further indication of the re-orientation of services towards the user is the proposed legislation for reform of the organisation of services which includes the following measures (Department of Health 1994, p. 40):

- the establishment of advisory groups in each health authority area to provide an input to the authority from the users of the various services
- a requirement on all health authorities to put appropriate complaints procedures in place
- the introduction of a statutory function of the boards of the health authorities to act as a channel to the Minister of the views and concerns of their populations.

In addition, health authorities will be required to include formal evaluations of patient satisfaction levels as part of their annual performance report to the Minister.

1.6.4   Priorities for older people: 1994-1997

The approach to care of older people in *Shaping a Healthier Future* is focused on the 'ill and dependent elderly'. Although the document notes that the rapid rise in the number of people in the oldest age groups poses a special challenge to health services, there is little to indicate how these challenges are to be met. In the case of child care, *Shaping a Healthier Future* highlights the urgency of children's needs arising from the growth of social problems affecting children and families and it specifies a whole range of new services to address the care needs involved. By contrast, in the case of older people, there is no evidence in *Shaping a Healthier Future* of any heightened awareness of the needs of this group and the document identifies no new areas of need not already identified in *The Years Ahead.* The document, in fact, reiterates the objectives of health and personal

social services laid down in 1988 in *The Years Ahead*. The docu
'while considerable progress has been made in the past few yea
services for ill and dependent older people, much remains to be
objectives of *The Years Ahead* are achieved' (Department of Hea
The overall goal set down for the period 1994-1997 is to str
community and hospital services to provide much needed support to elderly
people who are ill or dependent, and to assist those who care for them'. The
priorities set out for the period are:

- promoting healthy ageing
- strengthening the role of the general practitioner, the public health nurse, the
  home help and other primary care professionals in supporting older people
  and their carers who live at home
- increasing the number of specialist departments of medicine of old age so
  that every general hospital either has such a department or has access to one
- providing additional places for convalescent care
- ensuring that adequate funding is available to meet in full the requirements
  of the *Health (Nursing Homes) Act, 1990* by the end of 1996
- providing eight small-scale nursing units in the community by the end of
  1997.

The target of the action plan for older people is to ensure that no less than 90 per
cent of those over 75 years of age continue to live at home.

Differences in approach to care between children and older people are
particularly evident with regard to the legislative framework for care services. In
the case of children, the enactment of the *Child Care Act 1991* imposes a clear
statutory duty on the health boards to provide a range of child care and family
support services, including several services not in existence prior to 1991.
Shaping a Healthier Future promised that all sections of the *Child Care Act*
would be implemented by the end of 1996. A major programme of investment
was instigated by Government in order to implement the Act, including an
additional £10 million in each of the years 1993-1996 for new service
developments. In 1993, for example, over 100 new posts of social worker and
child care worker and 20 new posts in child psychology were appointed and three
new consultant-staffed child and adolescent psychiatric services were initiated.
The legal underpinning of child care services and consequent investment in them
is in stark contrast to the situation of care services for older people. For example,
there is no statutory obligation on the health boards to implement the
recommendations of *The Years Ahead* and the plan in *Shaping a Healthier Future*
for 'the ill and dependent elderly' does not have a specific programme of
investment for upgraded or new services. Whereas it is clear in the case of child
care that there are a number of services that are considered so essential that their

rovision is enshrined in legislation, *Shaping a Healthier Future* makes no such clear case for the care of older people.

The National Council for the Elderly has argued for the concept of core services, defined as support services which are essential to maintain quality of life and functional autonomy among older people. While certain services such as acute hospital care, home nursing and GP services are a recognised part of essential provision for older people and are mandatory, the National Council for the Elderly argues that there are other services - such as home help, day care facilities and appropriate housing - which are also so essential to the basic welfare and survival needs of older people that they too must be seen as part of the core service provision with legal obligation for their provision and appropriate statutory funding (Mulvihill 1993, p. 12)

1.7   Structure of review

This introductory chapter has provided a context for the review by summarising *The Years Ahead* and outlining the current policy focus for the care of older people. The next chapter describes the research procedures and data-gathering measures employed in carrying out the review. Chapters Three to Eleven follow the structure of *The Years Ahead* examining, in sequence, the extent to which recommendations have been implemented with respect to:

- A Comprehensive and Co-ordinated Service (Chapter Three)
- Maintaining Health (Chapter Four)
- Housing (Chapter Five)
- Care at Home (Chapter Six)
- Care in the Community (Chapter Seven)
- Care in General Hospitals (Chapter Eight)
- The Community Hospital (Chapter Nine)
- The Care of the Mentally Ill and Infirm (Chapter Ten)
- Partnership between Carers, Volunteers and Statutory Agencies (Chapter Eleven).

In Chapter Twelve, the focus is on current needs and priorities in the care of older people. These issues are explored from two perspectives: organisations representing older people and service providers. The final chapter provides an overview of the findings obtained; raises the key issues which have to be addressed; and puts forward suggestions for a future strategy for the care of older people.

CHAPTER TWO

Methodology

2.1   Introduction

This chapter gives details on the aims and objectives of the study, the methodology employed, the organisation of the fieldwork and the respondents to the review.

2.2   Aims and objectives

The aim of the project was to review the progress on the implementation of the recommendations of *The Years Ahead* report. The specific objectives were to elicit:

- factual information on the recommendations that have been implemented
- factual information on the recommendations that are in the process of being implemented
- factual information on the recommendations that have not been implemented
- perceptions of the effects of recommendations implemented
- reasons for the non-implementation of recommendations.

2.3   Project management

Management of the project was conducted by the Project Director, the research team, the fieldwork supervisor and the panel of fieldworkers. Regular meetings were held between members of the research team and a Consultative Committee appointed to oversee the project on behalf of the National Council for the Elderly.

2.4   Methodology

2.4.1   Securing co-operation

The two main statutory agencies providing services to older people are the health boards and local authorities. In addition, other significant service providers are voluntary organisations, nursing homes and professional bodies.

2.4.1.1   Health boards
Under the *Health Act, 1970*, local health administration was removed from the local government system and assigned to eight regional health boards. The Act empowered health boards to make arrangements with other bodies to provide health services. The work of each health board is divided into three broad programmes covering community care services, general hospital services and special hospital services (mostly psychiatric hospitals). In the larger boards there is a separate Programme Manager for each of these services but in the smaller boards one Programme Manager covers the general and special hospital programmes (see Chapter Three). Programme Managers report to the Chief Executive Officer (CEO) of the health board.

The counties covered by each health board are as follows:

Eastern Health Board	Dublin, Kildare, Wicklow
Midland Health Board	Laois, Longford, Offaly, Westmeath
Mid-Western Health Board	Clare, Limerick, Tipperary NR
North Eastern Health Board	Cavan, Louth, Meath, Monaghan
North Western Health Board	Donegal, Leitrim, Sligo
South Eastern Health Board	Carlow, Kilkenny, Tipperary SR, Waterford, Wexford
Southern Health Board	Cork, Kerry
Western Health Board	Galway, Mayo, Roscommon.

In order to secure the co-operation of the health boards, the CEOs of each health board were approached and their agreement sought for involvement in the study. CEOs were asked to provide the name of a liaison person who was then approached for lists of appropriate personnel who were required for interview. Using lists supplied, personnel were targeted and sent a letter enclosing the appropriate questionnaire. Follow-up interviews were then carried out.

2.4.1.2   Local authorities
The Irish local government system operates through a network of directly elected local authorities. These authorities are corporate bodies constituted by or under statute to discharge functions in their administrative areas. Local authorities have responsibility for a wide range of functions. These include housing, road transport and safety, water and sanitary services, development incentives and controls, environmental protection, and recreation and amenities.

With regard to securing the co-operation of the local authorities, the Department of the Environment's representative on the Consultative Committee and a county manager who heads a housing committee for older people provided lists of city and county managers in all urban and rural authorities. From these lists a stratified random sample design was employed to ensure that proportionate numbers of local authorities in all the categories, that is county councils, county boroughs, boroughs and district councils, were selected and that their distribution by health board was also taken into account. A sample, therefore, of 44 per cent was drawn covering each local authority. In addition, letters endorsing the review were sent by the Department of the Environment's representative with each questionnaire.

2.4.1.3 Professional bodies

Representatives of professional groups were contacted for their lists of members. Once lists were supplied, samples of respondents were drawn from these. As with the local authorities above, these samples covered all health boards. Geriatricians were identified as crucial to the health care of older people so a coverage of 100 per cent of their professional body was taken. For Consultants in the Psychiatry of Old Age, coverage of 100 per cent was also taken as there are only four in the country. In some instances, the groups themselves requested permission from the research team to distribute questionnaires. This was the situation with the Irish College of General Practitioners (a member of whom was on the study's Consultative Committee), the Irish Chiropodists' Association and the Irish Nutrition and Dietetic Institute.

2.4.1.4 Nursing homes

The Irish Registered Nursing Homes Association represents over 185 private nursing homes. It was founded in 1973 and is the only national body which exclusively represents the interests of private nursing homes. The Federation of Catholic Voluntary Nursing Homes represents 34 voluntary nursing homes which are run by Catholic religious orders. Both groups were invited to supply lists of their members. Once these lists were supplied, nation-wide samples were drawn from them and questionnaires distributed.

2.4.1.5 Voluntary organisations

Health boards were asked to provide lists of voluntary organisations providing 'core' services, such as meals services and day care centres, in their areas. Samples of voluntary organisations were drawn from these lists. In addition, major voluntary organisations in the country who are involved in providing services to older people, such as the Society of St. Vincent de Paul, were sent questionnaires. Voluntary organisations representing the interests of older people were invited to send in submissions, according to a standardised format.

2.4.2 Data collection

Several policy areas were covered in *The Years Ahead* which concerned different services and providers. Taking each recommendation, therefore, and assigning it to the appropriate policy-makers and service providers, a questionnaire was drawn up for each relevant grade or level. Due to the nature of the data being collected both quantitative and qualitative methods were used. Drafts of the questionnaires were circulated in advance of Consultative Committee meetings which reviewed the appropriateness and suitability of questions. Questionnaires were then pre-tested and piloted with representatives of the respondent grades. Once pre-tested and piloted, the re-drafted questionnaires were again circulated to the respondents in the pilot tests as well as to the members of the study's Consultative Committee. Once these were approved and agreed upon, final drafts, both comprehensive and valid, were drawn up for distribution. (Copies of interview schedules and questionnaires can be obtained from the National Council on Ageing and Older People, if required.)

Data collection involved face-to-face interviews, questionnaires, written submissions and available literature. Different methods were chosen for the sake of efficiency and to maximise the resources which were available. A study of this size must ensure that responses are effective as well as drawn from a wide range of service providers and practitioners. In some instances, therefore, group interviews were conducted where members of the professional body held a regular meeting which they agreed to make accessible to the researchers (medical and psychiatric social workers, Environmental Health Officers, physiotherapists, Age Action annual general meeting, Care Alliance meeting). In some cases questionnaires or submissions were also sent after these group interviews (Age Action, physiotherapists, psychiatric social workers). Face-to-face interviews were carried out with most government departments and health board personnel, where practical, while most professional groups were sent questionnaires and were followed up by phone. This latter method was also used with local authorities, nursing home proprietors, carers' groups and voluntary organisations.

2.4.3   Sampling and response rates

Different management and service providers were sampled in the health boards and in the different professional areas. Tables 2.1 to 2.6 give the sampling methods used and response rates achieved for Government Departments, health boards, professional groups involved in service provision to older people, local authorities, nursing homes, carers' groups and voluntary organisations.

Difficulties were encountered at several levels of the data collection phase. Gaining access to lists from health boards and professional bodies was one of the first. Once respondents were identified difficulties were also encountered in arranging interviews. This was due, on the most part, to problems with respondents' other work commitments. This was a factor too in getting questionnaires back from respondents and delays were encountered despite many follow up requests. In some instances, respondents did not have access to the data which was required. This led to further delays and also contributed to non-response rates.

Table 2.1: Sampling and response rate in government departments

Level/grade	Sampling methods	Research method	Attempted sample	Response
Principal Officers in Departments of Health, Social Welfare, Environment, Finance, Education, Transport, Energy and Communications	One relevant officer from each	Questionnaire plus interviews where required	All	Interviews with Departments of Health and Environment (Dept. of Health also covered Finance and Transport). In addition written responses from Education, Social Welfare as well as Transport, Energy and Communications

Table 2.2: Sampling and response rate in health boards

Level/grade	Sampling methods	Research method	Attempted sample	Response
CEOs	From each health board (Two CEOs take responsibility for two health boards each - therefore six)	Questionnaire plus individual interviews	All	Interviews with NEHB, SEHB. Written responses from MHB. Interviews with representative for CEO in SHB. Other boards - CEOs felt issues covered adequately by Programme Managers
Programme Managers Community Care, General Hospitals, Special Hospitals	From each health board	Questionnaire plus individual interviews	All	Face-to-face interviews conducted with most. Written responses from Programme Manager General Hospitals, Programme Manager Special Hospitals (WHB) and Programme Manager General Hospitals (NEHB)
Directors of Community Care	All from each health board	Questionnaire plus individual interviews	All (31)	19 (61%) (included one group interview with 2 Directors of Community Care in SHB and 6 written responses - EHB, MHB, NEHB, SHB, WHB)
Co-ordinator of Services for the Elderly at board level	Eastern Health Board	Interview	1	1

Table 2.2: Sampling and response rate in health boards (ctd)

Level/grade	Sampling methods	Research method	Attempted sample	Response
Co-ordinators of Services for the Elderly	Where appointed. If no one in place, person who takes responsibility for this function	Individual interviews	All (21)	16 (76%). This included one group interview with 3 x Co-ordinator of Services for the Elderly in NEHB; 3 written responses - EHB, MWHB, WHB and phone follow-ups
District Liaison Nurses	Where appointed*	Individual interviews	All (40)*	24* (60%) (included 5 written responses - EHB, MHB, NWHB, SHB)
Superintendent Public Health Nurses	One from each community care area in each health board	Individual interviews	All (30)	26 (included 2 written responses - EHB, SHB)
Senior Public Health Nurses	From each health board	Individual interviews	46* (56% of all Senior PHNs)	23* (50%) (included 2 written responses - MHB, SHB)
Chief Nursing Officers - Psychiatry	From each health board	Interviews	29**	17 (58%). This included 4 written responses - EHB, MHB, MWHB, SEHB
Environmental Health Officers	One from each health board	Group interview	Group	Group interview
Medical Social Workers	From each health board	Group interview through Irish Association of Social Workers	Group	Group interview and one written response
Psychiatric Social Workers	From each health board	Represented at group interview with Irish Association of Social Workers and individual questionnaires	Group	Group interview and individual questionnaires (4)

Table 2.2: Sampling and response rate in health boards (ctd)

Level/grade	Sampling methods	Research method	Attempted sample	Response
Superinten-dent Community Welfare Officers	From each health board	Individual interviews	39**	23 (59%). This included 3 written responses - EHB, MHB, WHB
Home Help Organisers	From each health board	Individual interviews	37**	22 (59%). This included 3 written responses - NEHB, SHB, MHB
Chief Ambulance Officers	One from EHB	Individual interview	1	1
Hospital Liaison Officer	SHB and EHB only†	Interviews	11**	7 (63%). This included 2 written responses - EHB, SHB

*In some Health Boards (Southern and Mid-Western) the District Liaison Nurse function is carried out by Senior Public Health Nurses. From lists supplied by Health Boards, 23 Senior Public Health Nurses were identified who carry out District Liaison Nurse function, the majority of these (20) were in the Southern board. Accordingly, the samples of District Liaison Nurses and Senior Public Health Nurses were as follows: 'Pure' District Liaison Nurses sample = 40, Response = 24; Senior PHN = 46 (23 of whom were District Liaison Nurse/Senior Public Health Nurse), Response = 23 (15 of whom were District Liaison Nurse/Senior Public Health Nurse). Therefore, valid District Liaison Nurse responses = 39.

**For all of these groups, the sample chosen was based on total coverage of lists of names supplied by each health board. The sample was chosen with coverage across each health board and greater coverage in the Eastern board.

†According to lists supplied by each health board, there are designated hospital liaison personnel in only two boards (see Chapter Eight). In interview, however, it emerged that in the SHB only are there liaison personnel designated for this function, as the responsibility in the EHB is taken on by hospital managers or matrons along with other responsibilities.

Table 2.3: Sampling and response rate among professional groups

Level/grade	Sampling methods	Research method	Attempted sample	Response
GP Liaison Officers	One representative from one ICGP faculty from each health board area	Questionnaire distributed through ICGP	8	7 (87%)
Physicians in geriatric medicine	All	Questionnaire (list from professional body)	All (21)	14 (66%)
Consultants in Psychiatry of Old Age	All	Individual interviews	All (4)	4

Table 2.3: Sampling and response rate among professional groups (ctd)

Level/grade	Sampling methods	Research method	Attempted sample	Response
Physiotherapists	From each health board	Group interview through professional body	Group	Group interview and two written responses
Occupational Therapists	One from each health board (and more from EHB)	Questionnaire (list from professional body)	11 (7%)*	7 (63%)
Chiropodists	One from each health board	Questionnaire through professional body	8 (2%)†	4 (50%)
Speech Therapists	One from each health board (and more from EHB)	Questionnaire	11 (30%)¥	7 (63%)
Dieticians	One from each health board	Questionnaire through professional body	8 (60%)§	Group response from special interest group for older people in professional body; 8 returned questionnaires (100%)
Consultant Orthopaedic Surgeons	Representative from Orthopaedic Surgeons professional body	Questionnaire	1	1
Consultant Ophthalmologists	Representatives from Ophthal-mologist professional body	Questionnaire	2	2

* There are 320 occupational therapists in the country, 260 of whom are members of the Association of Occupational Therapists of Ireland; two thirds of these work with older people, but not exclusively. Our sample, therefore represented seven per cent.

† Distributed through the Irish Chiropodists' Association of whom there are over 400 members. One in each health board was selected by the Secretary of this Association, representing a sample size of two per cent.

¥ There are 43 principal speech therapists in the country, five of whom work exclusively with children. From the remainder (38), 11 were chosen to give national coverage (with greater numbers in the EHB region), representing a sample size of 30 per cent.

§ A list of 13 community dieticians was supplied by the special group for older people in the Irish Nutrition and Dietetic Institute. From this a sample of eight, representing each health board, was chosen. In addition, a response was received from the special interest group for older people in the Institute.

Table 2.4: Sampling and response rate in local authorities

Level/grade	Sampling methods	Research method	Attempted sample	Response
Local Authorities: City and County Managers	From each local authority	Questionnaire	42 (44%)	30 (71%)

Table 2.5: Sampling and response rate among nursing home proprietors

Level/grade	Sampling methods	Research method	Attempted sample	Response
Representatives from Irish Registered Nursing Homes Association and Federation of Catholic Voluntary Nursing Homes	Sample drawn from each health board from lists supplied by Irish Registered Nursing Homes Association (N=185) and Federation of Catholic Voluntary Nursing Homes (N=34)	Questionnaire	53 Irish Registered Nursing Homes Association (28%) 8 Federation of Catholic Voluntary Nursing Homes (23%)	30 (49%)

Table 2.6: Sampling and response rate among carers' groups and voluntary organisations

Level/grade	Sampling methods	Research method	Attempted sample	Response
Representatives from Carers' Association and Soroptimist International	Sample drawn from each health board, from lists supplied by Carers' Association and Soroptimist International (N=56)	Questionnaire	26 (45%)*	22 (84%)
Voluntary housing organisations	Small sample drawn from lists supplied	Questionnaire	20	14 (70%)
Representatives of voluntary bodies providing services for older people	Major/national voluntary organisations and voluntary organisations providing services to each health board (N=280)	Questionnaire	60 (21%)	35 (58%)

Table 2.6: Sampling and response rate among carers' groups and voluntary organisations (ctd)

Level/grade	Sampling methods	Research method	Attempted sample	Response
Representatives of voluntary bodies representing older people, including the 'old old'	Major/national voluntary organisations	Group interviews with members of Care Alliance and at Age Action AGM; Invited submissions	10	Group interview (2) Submissions from Age Action; Age and Opportunity; Alzheimer Society of Ireland; Carers' Association; Dublin Port and Docks' Pensioners' Group; Irish Association of Older People; St. Vincent de Paul; Soroptimist International; Retired Workers' Committee. (9)

* The sample chosen was based on total coverage of lists of names supplied by the Carers' Association and Soroptimist International and reflected coverage across each health board. In addition, contact was made with Irish Business and Employers Confederation, Irish Congress of Trade Unions, the Health and Safety Authority; PAMBO, the Transport Co-Operative Society Limited (in relation to transport for older people); National Rehabilitation Board (in relation to aids and appliances); the Dental Council (about dental recommendations); Institute of Public Administration (about health promotion fact sheets); the Institute of Public Health Nursing (about communication between Public Health Nurses and General Practitioners) and all the Universities with Departments of Medicine (in relation to Chairs of Geriatric Medicine).

2.5 Timescale

The study commenced in December 1995 and was carried out over a period of nine months, comprising four months of fieldwork. The fieldwork was complex, involving a multiplicity of different agencies, groups and different professional levels. The heavy workloads of several respondents, in the Eastern Health Board in particular, and of all Programme Managers, were also factors which had to be taken into consideration in the fieldwork planning and implementation.

2.6 Summary

This chapter has outlined the methods used in data collection and the approaches taken. The following chapters are devoted to an analysis of the results produced.

CHAPTER THREE

A Comprehensive and Co-Ordinated Service

3.1   Introduction

A major focus of the Working Party was to ensure that the policy of encouraging older people to live in their own homes for as long as possible was implemented in as effective a manner as possible, given the level of resources available. Accordingly, one of the first chapters in *The Years Ahead* was concerned with setting out a detailed framework for the management and co-ordination of the delivery of services. The purpose of this chapter is firstly to outline the recommendations made by the Working Party for a co-ordinated service, to describe the context and thinking which led to these recommendations and to explore recent policy in this area. The second purpose is to examine the extent to which the recommendations of the Working Party with regard to service delivery structures have been implemented. Later chapters of the review explore further the experiences of different service providers in attempting to provide a co-ordinated service.

3.2   Data sources

In setting the context for discussion of the recommendations for the provision of a comprehensive and co-ordinated service, the chapter draws primarily on the National Council for the Elderly study of two pilot projects on co-ordination of services at local level but also includes recent Government policy documents. Data on the implementation of the recommendations was obtained from interviews and/or questionnaires from:

- Principal Officers of the Departments of Health, Environment and Social Welfare
- Programme Managers of community care, general hospitals and special hospitals
- District Liaison Nurses (39)

- Co-ordinators of Services for the Elderly at community care area level (16)
- Co-ordinators of Services for the Elderly at board level (1)
- CEOs/representatives of CEOs in all health boards.

3.3 Context of recommendations

3.3.1 The case for co-ordination of services

Concern about the co-ordination of services for older people was articulated for several years before the establishment of the Working Party. The desirability of establishing structures for the co-ordination of services was accepted in principle in *The Care of the Aged* report in 1968. This report stated that '...unless services are carefully planned, there will be wasteful duplication of effort in respect of some of the aged, while others will receive little, if any, of the help they require' (Inter-Departmental Committee on the Care of the Aged Report 1968). In the view of the Inter-Departmental Committee, co-ordination had to occur within the public services and between the public and the voluntary services and this co-ordination was needed both at national and at local level. Since 1983, the National Council for the Aged (now the National Council on Ageing and Older People) has argued in several reports - related to community services, institutional care, housing and informal care in the home - that an effective care system for older people could only be delivered if appropriate co-ordinating mechanisms were established (National Council for the Aged 1983,1985a, 1985b, 1989). The case for co-ordination of services, put forward by the National Council for the Aged in 1985, was based on two considerations (National Council for the Aged 1985a):

- the needs of older people rarely fall into watertight compartments to be met by one service or one department only
- limited resources are likely to be best used where there is a joint approach resulting in appropriate collaboration and co-ordination of services and the consequent elimination of duplication and overlap in service provision.

The Commission on Health Funding, in 1989, made a similar argument for the connection between cost-effectiveness and the way services are delivered: 'The kernel of the Commission's conclusions is that the solution to the problem facing the Irish health services does not lie primarily in the system of funding, but rather in the way services are planned, organised and delivered' (Commission on Health Funding 1989, p. 15).

3.3.2 Problems of co-ordination identified by the Working Party

The issue of co-ordination was taken up and developed by the Working Party in 1988. At the time, the Working Party noted that considerable resources were already committed to the care of older people, but the problem was how to weld these resources into an integrated care delivery system. *The Years Ahead* highlighted many instances of lack of co-ordination in the services operating at the time (p. 40):

- no formal co-ordinating link between local authorities and the health boards
- no formal reporting relationship between General Practitioners (GPs) and Public Health Nurses (PHNs)
- the acute hospital sometimes discharging an older person with a severe disability and in need of continuing attention without notifying those responsible for community care services or the General Practitioner
- little or no support from health board personnel to people caring for older relatives at home
- separation of responsibility for community care, acute hospital, psychiatric and long-term care into two or three administrative programmes of health boards
- private nursing homes operating with the minimum amount of co-ordination with the health board services
- inadequacy of working arrangements between voluntary bodies working with older people and the health boards and the absence of a formal method whereby voluntary bodies can influence policy or the direction of services.

Six years later in 1994, *Shaping a Healthier Future* again noted that one of the weaknesses in the health care system was '...inadequate linkages between complementary services, such as hospitals, general practitioners and other community services' (Department of Health 1994b, p. 10).

3.3.3   Problems of co-ordination identified by the National Council for the Elderly

The Years Ahead identified one of the major obstacles to the co-ordination of services as being the separation of responsibility for community care, acute hospital, psychiatric and long-term care into two or three administrative programmes within health boards. A 1992 report by the National Council for the Elderly reiterates some of the concerns of the Working Party and also provides further elucidation on the obstacles to co-ordination. The report contends that we do not have an 'ethos of co-ordination' in this country and identifies the particular difficulties we have to address as follows (National Council for the Elderly 1992, pp. 14-15):

- the separation of responsibility for assessing and meeting housing needs from responsibility for providing health and personal social services in the home and community
- the divisions of the health boards into separate programmes based on functional responsibility, such as the hospital programme and the community care programme, rather than a more integrated model

- the extent of the reliance on the voluntary housing and personal social services sector and the lack of adequate mechanisms for consultation about planning, provision and funding between voluntary and statutory agencies and within the voluntary sector itself

- the special difficulties for co-ordination entailed by the independent status of general practitioners which manifests itself in various ways, including, for example, difficulties in attending meetings and insufficient liaison between Public Health Nurses and General Practitioners

- insufficient collaboration between health care professionals and sectors, particularly as this affects older people with a mentally infirmity

- the increasing reliance on the private nursing home sector which requires improved liaison between it and the statutory sector

- generally, a lack of focused collaboration at inter-departmental level to deal with a range of welfare and service areas, such as transport needs, carers' allowances, developing voluntary organisations and fostering new services.

3.4 Structures of co-ordination proposed in *The Years Ahead*

The model for co-ordination of services recommended in *The Years Ahead* (Figure 3.1 below) takes account of co-ordination between different agencies within health boards, co-ordination between different agencies within the public service

Figure 3.1: Administrative structure for the organisation of housing, health and welfare services for older people as recommended in *The Years Ahead* report

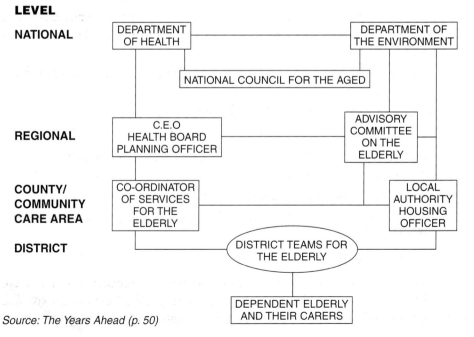

Source: The Years Ahead (p. 50)

sector (e.g. health boards and local authorities) and co-ordination between the public sector and the voluntary sector. The model covers co-ordination at district, community, regional and national levels.

The Working Party endorsed recommendations made in 1986 in the Consultative Statement on Health Policy for a change in the unit of management of health boards from care programmes to the administration of services by geographical area (Department of Health 1986). The Working Party argued that responsibility for the delivery of a service should, in general, be located as close as possible to the operational level. Since, in the case of most services for older people, the operational level is very local, the Working Party's recommended delivery structure is based on the geographical district serving a population of approximately 25-30,000 people.

3.5   Factors found to facilitate effective co-ordination
Based on the findings of a number of its reports, the National Council for the Aged in 1985 proposed that the Department of Health should provide 'funding to establish two pilot projects which would develop and evaluate the concept of co-ordination of services for the elderly in terms of both planning and provision at local level' (National Council for the Elderly 1985a, p. 80). These pilot projects were initiated at the time the Working Party was making its deliberations and were in operation during 1988-1991. Through the experience of the pilot projects the factors outlined below were identified as predisposing towards effective co-ordination (National Council for the Elderly 1992, p. 171):

- an ethos of co-ordination which would permeate administrative and institutional arrangements starting from national level and filtering down to regional and district levels
- a shared understanding of the co-ordination task and shared belief in the value of co-ordination
- organisational arrangements favourable to co-ordination
- adequate resources to promote co-ordination
- joint planning to facilitate joint working rather than simply joint discussion of separate plans
- partnership involving all partners vital to services for older people
- inter-disciplinary team approach with ongoing training and education for co-ordination
- key worker to facilitate co-ordination.

The evaluation of the pilot projects endorsed the recommendations for a co-ordinated service made in *The Years Ahead*, but emphasised the complexity and challenge involved and warned that the impediments to co-ordination should not be underestimated. The National Council for the Elderly recognised that the co-ordinated approach can effectively mean 'swimming against the tide' of traditional practices and, accordingly, recommended that health boards and local authorities should pool resources to develop a comprehensive education and training programme in inter-agency co-operation and inter-disciplinary working. Within the health boards, the National Council for the Elderly recommended that adequate resources, personnel and administrative structures should be made available to ensure that co-ordination mechanisms are established in the districts proposed in *The Years Ahead* and, at community care area level, that the recommended Co-ordinator of Services for the Elderly should be given the resources to ensure liaison between community care services, acute hospital services and extended care services.

3.6   Case management in co-ordinated delivery

The recommendations for local service delivery made by the National Council for the Elderly on the basis of the pilot projects added a new dimension to the co-ordinated delivery structure proposed in *The Years Ahead,* that is the development of co-ordinated packages of care. Such packages of care would be individually tailored for older persons in need of high levels of care and would involve the optimal use of available support services. The National Council for the Elderly recommended careful piloting of this approach so that a model of case management could be developed.

The care package approach was also advocated in a 1992 analysis of community and institutional care (Blackwell *et al.* 1992). The care package approach requires having people in the community whose specific responsibility is the care of vulnerable older people and who would undertake assessment, plan appropriate care and monitor outcomes. 'This would allow information about actual and potential need to be generated so that services might be planned in an orderly manner. It would also help overcome one of the weaknesses of current provision, where divisions of responsibility between those in charge of institutional care and those in charge of community care services are likely to lead to lack of coherence between services' (Blackwell *et al.* 1992, p. 212). A 1993 study on care of Alzheimer's Disease/dementia sufferers again recommended the appointment of case managers who would take responsibility for the assessment of needs and the planning and delivery of services and support (Ruddle and O'Connor 1993).

3.7   *Shaping a Healthier Future* and co-ordination

Shaping a Healthier Future proposed that new health authorities with greater autonomy should replace the current health boards so that decisions relevant at the regional level are taken at regional level and so that operational decisions reflect regional needs and priorities. While the details of future management structures will vary between the health authorities, a special emphasis is to be placed on providing structures which encourage the development of linkages between services. For example, proposals provide for a legislative framework to guide the relationship between voluntary agencies and the health authorities. This legislation will, however, be general in nature and the more detailed day-to-day arrangements for putting it into practice are to be sufficiently flexible to reflect local requirements. Larger voluntary organisations are to have service agreements with the health authorities which will link funding by the authorities to agreed levels of service to be provided by the voluntary bodies.

One of the aims in setting up new health authorities is to achieve maximum integration of hospital and community services. It is not clear from *Shaping a Healthier Future* how this aim is to be achieved. It is suggested that the planned reorganisation of the health boards will address fragmentation in the organisation of services but no specific structures for linkages are mentioned apart from specialist departments of old age in general hospitals. The responsibilities of the hospital and community programmes have been changing over the years and, in this situation, specific structures are particularly urgent in order to provide for clarity in lines of communication and operational decision-making leading to effective action further down the line at district level. The slow implementation of the planned new management structures has led to a state of flux which has delayed action on co-ordination and has prevented assessment of the extent to which the proposed structures will, in fact, address the continuing problems of compartmentalisation in service delivery. Another factor contributing to the state of flux with regard to co-ordination is the phasing out of Director of Community Care posts and delays in the introduction of the new post of General Manager of Community Services.

3.8 Implementation of *The Years Ahead* recommendations on co-ordination

A chart of the overall co-ordination structure for services for older people in each health board is provided in Appendix 3.1 at the end of this Chapter. The following sections outline the implementation of the specific recommendations made for different levels of service-delivery at district, community care, health board and national levels.

3.8.1 *District organisation of services*

In the delivery structure proposed by the Working Party, the district is the basic operational unit. The recommendation for co-ordination at this level was that:

- **(R3.12) services for the elderly be organised as far as possible in districts serving a population of approximately 25-30,000 people**.

In three of the eight health boards, services for older people are organised in districts, which in the majority of cases serve populations of approximately 25-

Table 3.1: District organisation of services

Health board	District organisation of services (25-30,000 people)	Districts coterminous with psychiatric sectors
Eastern	No: community care area basis	In most cases
Midland	No: county basis	—
Mid-Western	Yes	Yes
North Eastern	No: community care areas	No
North Western	Yes	Yes
Southern	Yes	No
South Eastern	No: community care area basis	—
Western	No: community care area basis	—

Source: Interviews with Programme Managers of Community Care, CSEs and board level CSEs

30,000 people. In two of these health boards, the districts, as recommended, are coterminous with the sectors established for the psychiatric services under *Planning for the Future* (Department of Health 1994b). In the Eastern Health Board, services for older people have traditionally been organised in line with community care area divisions rather than in districts; these areas coincide in almost all cases with the psychiatric care sectors. Within community care areas health services are grouped around health centres; each area having a number of health centres. Similarly, in the North Eastern, South Eastern and Western Health Boards, services are presently organised according to community care area. The North Eastern Health Board is currently putting in place a district co-ordination system where each county in the board is to be divided in two. Up to now, lack of resources has prevented the implementation of a district structure in this board. The South Eastern Health Board is currently reviewing its existing system and it is likely that a district structure will be put in place in the future. In the Western Health Board the tradition has been to centre services in the geriatric hospitals in each county. At present homes for older people are being enhanced and extended to give a greater geographical spread and enable more local service delivery. In the Midland Health Board, services are presently organised on a county basis (four counties), but the plan is to set up six districts which will coincide with the sectors established under *Planning for the Future*.

3.8.2   *Appointment of District Liaison Nurses*
The Working Party recommended that:

- **(R3.13) the function of co-ordinating services in each district should be the responsibility of a District Liaison Nurse**.

It was envisaged that the District Liaison Nurse would normally be a Senior Public Health Nurse. The specifications for the post made by the Working Party were that the person chosen should have a commitment to older people and should have the ability to work successfully with other professionals.

As will be seen from the discussion below there is wide variation in the manner in which the different health boards have attempted to implement this recommendation. The fact that most boards have not implemented a district structure has impacted on the appointment of District Liaison Nurses. There are few specifically designated District Liaison Nurses in the way *The Years Ahead* recommended. In all boards there are people who perform a co-ordination function but, in most cases, they have a wider remit than services for older people. The co-ordination function is usually carried out by a PHN but not always at senior level. A wide variety of terms are used in the different boards to indicate the people who carry out the co-ordination function. For ease of communication, the term District Liaison Nurse is used in the following discussion to cover what in reality is not a uniform but a diverse group.

Among the health boards with a district structure, three different types of co-ordination arrangements are evident (Table 3.2). In the North Western Health Board there is a District Co-ordinator of Services in each district. This function is carried out mostly by the Matrons of the community hospitals rather than by

Table 3.2: Appointment of District Liaison Nurses

Health board	Whether at a district level	Who fulfils the function of District Liaison Nurse?	Time devoted to older people
Eastern	Not at district level	Public Health Nurses with special designation as District Liaison Nurses (community care area: 10)	60%-100%
Midland	Not at district level	Public Health Nurses with special designation as liaison (county basis: 4)	75%-90%
Mid-Western	No	Senior Public Health Nurses (carry many of the co-ordinating functions: 3)	50%-60%
North Eastern	Not at district level	Liaison Nurses in acute hospitals (3)	75%-90%
North Western	Yes	District Co-ordinators of Services (15)	Almost 100%
Southern	Yes	Senior Public Health Nurses (20)	Approximately 50%
South Eastern	Not at district level	Geriatric Liaison Nurses (community care area: 4)	65%-100%
Western	Not at district level	General Liaison Public Health Nurses (county basis and Galway City: 4)	75%-95%

Source: Interviews with Programme Managers of Community Care

Senior PHNs and their responsibility includes: taking referrals from general practitioners, arranging assessments, accepting patients into in-patient care, arranging reviews and transferring and discharging from in-patient care. They are also responsible for co-ordinating arrangements between in-patient services and the community services and for ensuring the most effective and efficient use of all resources in the district in each individual case. In the Southern Health Board, a Senior PHN with co-ordination duties has been appointed in each district. The role incorporates that of District Liaison Nurse, but is wider than services for older people alone (approximately 50 per cent of their time is devoted to older people). In the Mid-Western Health Board, there are no District Liaison Nurses, but Senior PHNs are seen to fulfil this function to a certain extent.

In the boards without a district structure, different arrangements for co-ordination are also evident. The North Eastern Health Board does not have District Liaison Nurses as such, but it does have liaison nurses in the acute hospitals in each of its community care areas responsible for facilitating discharge from hospital care. In the Eastern and South Eastern Health Boards, there are District Liaison Nurses (called Geriatric Liaison Nurses in the latter board), but they cover a community care area rather than the district of 25-30,000 people envisaged by *The Years Ahead*. The Western Health Board has PHNs who act as General Liaison Nurses for a community care area. In the Midland Health Board, there are no District Liaison Nurses as such, but there are specially designated PHNs in each of the four counties in the board who interface between hospital and community services and who devote between 75-90 per cent of their time to older people.

3.8.2.1   Responsibilities of the District Liaison Nurse
The Working Party identified certain tasks which it considered were best carried out at district level. It was envisaged that the District Liaison Nurse would take responsibility for co-ordinating these tasks which include (p. 44):

- ensuring that older people in need are identified
- supporting caring relatives
- mobilising home nursing, home help, day care and other services
- arranging for repairs and adaptations to older person's homes
- developing a boarding out scheme
- recommending access to extended nursing or residential care
- monitoring standards in private nursing homes
- mobilising the resources of local voluntary bodies.

There are somewhat differing views on the responsibilities of the District Liaison Nurse among those carrying out this function both between and within the different health boards. In some cases - usually in the boards where a district structure is well defined - those carrying out the district co-ordination function spell out the following responsibilities: ensuring smooth discharge from hospitals, arranging follow-up care in the community; arranging respite and rehabilitation admissions; making arrangements for long-stay care; liaising between hospitals and public health nurses. A general function of liaison between hospital and community services is noted as being important by most of those involved. Few, however, speak of their role - as does *The Years Ahead* - as including the support of caring relatives or as mobilising the resources of local voluntary bodies.

With regard to liaison with local authorities, most of those performing the district liaison function report that they have either no contact at all or only informal contact. Liaison with local authorities appears to happen through the Environmental Health Officer, through a PHN other than the District Liaison Nurse or, less frequently, through the social worker. While some liaison personnel are happy with the current situation, many note problems arising from the lack of liaison. These latter report that they need more information from the local authorities on, for example, housing vacancies for older people and they need an established link so that when problems arise there is an established contact. These liaison personnel also believe that since they are familiar with the needs of older people they could have an important input on the lay-out of housing and could prevent the problems that arise from inappropriate siting or design.

3.8.2.2   Factors influencing effective district liaison

The feedback from liaison personnel operating at district level indicates the importance of having the support of a designated co-ordinator at the wider community care area or board level. In the Eastern Health Board, where the co-ordinating structure is well-defined, most of the District Liaison Nurses report regular and effective meetings with Medical Co-ordinators of Services for the Elderly responsible for community care areas. In other boards where there are also Co-ordinators of Services for the Elderly (CSEs), contact with the District Liaison Nurses appears to be less structured but is still usually perceived as satisfactory. Feedback from liaison nurses who do not have a CSE to consult with at community care area level suggests that, as a result, the care system provided for older people is more fragmented and less equitable.

3.8.2.3   Problems with liaison

Most District Liaison Nurses report problems with their role. Those carrying out the district liaison function often find they do not have access to the services they need, particularly transport facilities, but also respite services, crisis beds, long-term beds and home help services. It is also evident that there can be communication problems with different care providers within health boards and with outside agencies such as local authorities and voluntary organisations. Problems can also arise when there is reluctance on the part of carers to take responsibility for home care of older people on discharge from hospital. In terms of their administrative needs, individuals note the lack of back-up support such as secretarial assistance and technological support.

3.8.3 District teams for the elderly
The Working Party recommended that:

- **(R3.14) district teams for the elderly should be formed to support the district liaison nurse in her co-ordinating role. The teams should be representative of those with direct responsibility for providing services to the elderly in the district**.

The core members of the team should include the District Liaison Nurse, Area Medical Officer, matron of community hospital, medical officer of the community hospital, representative of the GPs nominated by the local faculty of the Irish College of General Practitioners, housing official of the local authority, administrator (to service the team), Environmental Health Officer, representative of local voluntary organisations and Community Welfare Officers. It was envisaged that other professionals would be involved as the need arose. The Working Party emphasised that the purpose of the team was co-ordination, with individual service providers retaining responsibility for their particular services.

None of the health boards has established district teams in the way *The Years Ahead* report envisaged (Table 3.3). The North Western Health Board has a loose arrangement of teams in each community hospital. The Western Health Board also has loosely structured teams providing services out of six health care centres. In the Southern and South Eastern Health Boards there are teams in a few districts. In the North Eastern Health Board, it is seen that service providers such as the PHN, the GP, the occupational therapist and the CSE do work together but without being recognised or officially labelled as a team. In the Eastern Health Board, there are two types of team, one of which - the district care team - corresponds to

Table 3.3: Establishment of district teams for the elderly

Health board	Whether teams established
Eastern	Yes, but at community care area level
Midland	No
Mid-Western	No
North Eastern	No
North Western	Yes (in each community hospital)
Southern	Not in every district
South Eastern	Not in every district
Western	No (but loosely structured teams operate out of 6 health care centres)

Source: Interviews with Programme Managers of Community Care, CSEs and board level CSEs

that described in *The Years Ahead*. The district care teams meet four times a year and comprise PHNs, representatives of community, psychiatric and hospital services, GPs, representatives of voluntary bodies and local authority housing officers. These teams have an administrative and planning focus and deal with general problems affecting older people. While these teams are close to that recommended in *The Years Ahead* they cover a community care area rather than a district. In some boards there is an Assessment Team or Committee for Admission to hospital or nursing home at community care area level (Mid-Western, South Eastern, Southern and Western Health Boards). The second type of team established in the Eastern Health Board is the community ward team which is focused on service provision. The community ward teams provide outreach medical, nursing, paramedical services and domiciliary care on a multi-disciplinary basis. The team is led by a project leader, usually a PHN, and also has physiotherapists, occupational therapists, care attendants and GPs. At present there are 17 community ward teams across 10 community care areas and the plan is ultimately to have three teams for each community care area.

3.8.3.1   *Reasons for non-establishment of district teams*
As already indicated, district organisation of services has been implemented in only three of the boards and this has made the establishment of district teams impossible. Feedback from Programme Managers in boards where local teams had been tried but discontinued, reveals further problems. These include a perception that district teams can be unwieldy, that it can be difficult to get commitment from team members and that it can be difficult to get the appropriate composition.

In one board it is felt that a district team is unrealistic and that effective liaison between Senior PHNs and CSEs is sufficient. In another board the emphasis is on liaison between the GP and PHN. The role of the GP is seen as critical and the GP unit is being reviewed to see if liaison can be further developed and improved in this way. In a third board, the GP is also seen as being the first point of contact and the emphasis is on liaison between the GP, the PHN and the CSE. In some cases the formation of district teams is seen to be impractical because of the geographical spread of population and small population size. In speaking of their plans for future service delivery, several Programme Managers speak of the establishment of a 'seamless service'. However, the central element in such a service is seen to be the management of care packages by a specified person, such as the PHN, and the district team is not mentioned as having any role to play in this. Even those who see district teams as being feasible and useful sometimes raise a note of caution about their management. In one board where there are currently some district teams, one Programme Manager cautions that they can be seen as 'talk shops' and, if they are to be of any value, the roles and responsibilities involved must be clearly defined.

3.8.3.2   Views on the district team among District Liaison Nurses and Co-ordinators of Services for the Elderly

Feedback from district liaison personnel working without support from a team is mixed on the consequences of this lack of structure. Some say they experience no problems in not having a district liaison team, that existing communication networks work effectively, and that further team meetings could be time-consuming. Some say they manage without because there is no choice or they do not miss them since they never had them. Others, however, note the lack of support they feel in not having the back-up of a team and feel they are working in isolation. These liaison nurses perceive that without a team it is difficult to establish an effective service and difficult to determine the appropriate level and type of care required. Without a team, there is a lack of co-ordination and certain groups of older people - such as those with psychiatric problems - may not be given appropriate attention. Feedback from CSEs in one board where teams had previously been tried but disbanded described them as not being conducive to quick decision-making.

Among liaison personnel working with a team structure, the feedback is typically positive, but there is a concern that district teams can be difficult to keep going. Other important factors are the regularity and frequency of meetings and the openness of the communication that occurs. Some feel that meetings are too infrequent but acknowledge that scheduling more is probably not feasible. Among CSEs in boards where there are teams, it is felt that district teams can be an ambitious undertaking and require much work to be effective. Some of the major benefits of having district teams noted among both liaison nurses and CSEs are that:

- they provide a multi-disciplinary perspective
- they provide a forum for inter-agency liaison
- they have a specific focus on older people
- they provide a forum to identify gaps in services and discuss ways of meeting needs
- they are close to older people and thus have better knowledge of their problems and needs
- they can ensure greater access to services
- they enable feedback to be given
- they enable joint decisions to be made; joint decisions can carry more weight than individual decisions
- they provide support.

Compared with the district teams, feedback on the community ward teams in the Eastern Health Board - which, as already indicated, have a specific focus on

service-provision - is uniformly positive. Both the CSEs and District Liaison
Nurses in the Eastern Board note the establishment of the community ward team
as one of the most valuable developments in the care of older people. In the view
of the Programme Managers of community care and general hospital care in this
board, it is these teams which have had the greatest impact on the care of older
people. In addition to the benefits of district teams noted above, the community
ward teams are regarded as providing the following particularly positive
outcomes:

- they provide on-going monitoring of progress of care
- they enable appropriate decisions to be made about the choice of care
  options
- they can ensure that inappropriate admission to hospital does not occur
- they enable rehabilitation of older people discharged from hospital
- they can ensure older people remain in the community for as long as
  possible.

3.8.3.3   Review of district co-ordination
The Working Party had recommended that:

- **(R3.15) the role of the district liaison nurse and the district team for the
  elderly be reviewed three years from the date of being put in place**.

Because the district structure has rarely been fully implemented, no reviews (or
only informal ones) have been carried out in any of the health boards on the roles
of the District Liaison Nurse and the district team for the elderly.

3.8.4   Co-ordination at community care area level: appointment of
            Co-ordinators of Services for the Elderly
At a larger geographical area level than the district the Working Party
recommended that:

- **(R3.17) in each community care area, health boards appoint a Co-
  ordinator of Services for the Elderly**
- **(R3.20) in current circumstances, the task of co-ordinating services for
  the elderly should be assigned to a community physician**.

The Working Party envisaged that the task of co-ordination would initially be a
full-time responsibility but that once co-ordination was working smoothly, a part-
time commitment would be sufficient.

The structures in the Eastern, North Eastern and North Western Health Boards are
the closest to that proposed in *The Years Ahead* with designated full-time CSEs in
each area (Table 3.4). The Southern Health Board has a full-time person

Table 3.4: Appointment of Co-ordinators of Services for the Elderly

Health board	Whether Co-ordinator appointed
Eastern	Yes: in each community care area (called Medical Co-ordinators of Services for the Elderly
Midland	No (Director of Community Care used to fulfil the function; sector managers planned)
Mid-Western	Not for every community care area (one for the board)
North Eastern	Yes: in each community care area (called Area Co-ordinators of Services)
North Western	Yes: in each community care area (called Area Co-ordinators of Services)
Southern	Yes (but not designated as such)
South Eastern	Not for each community care area (one in the board)
Western	Not for each community care area (one in the board)

Source: Interviews with Programme Managers of Community Care

undertaking the co-ordination of services in one area (but not yet officially designated as such) while the co-ordinating function in the other three community care areas is part-time and carried out by people not designated as co-ordinators. In three of the boards (Mid-Western, South Eastern and Western) there is just one co-ordinator in the whole board (a Senior PHN in the Mid-Western and a medical officer in the other two boards). In the Western Health Board, it was felt that there were insufficient medical officers to enable this function to be fulfilled in each community care area. The Midland Health Board plans to appoint Sector Managers and a Director of Care Services for the Elderly to fulfil the co-ordination role.

With three exceptions, the co-ordinating role in each board is carried out by a medical officer such as a Director of Community Care, Senior Area Medical Officer or Area Medical Officer. Two of these boards note, however, that it may not necessarily be a medical officer who holds the post in the future. In the North Eastern Health Board the co-ordinators have come from a nursing background but are now in managerial roles. They are seen to have a key function and manage both budgets and resources. In the North Western and Western Health Boards the co-ordinating role is also carried out by nursing professionals.

3.8.4.1   Review of Co-ordinator of Services for the Elderly role
The Working Party recommended that:

- **(R3.20) the appointment of community physicians as co-ordinators of services for the elderly be reviewed three years after arrangements have been established to co-ordinate services at district and community care level**.

Although current arrangements have been in place for a number of years, just one board has carried out a review of the role of the CSE at community care level. In two other boards, a review is currently underway. In one of the boards two of the people identified by management as CSEs do not see themselves as officially having this role while in another board the CSEs perceive that their function is, as yet, not adequately developed.

3.8.4.2   Responsibilities of the Co-ordinator of Services for the Elderly

The responsibilities of the CSE set down by the Working Party include:

- planning the development of services for the elderly in the community care area
- ensuring that the district teams achieve their objective of supporting elderly people with health or welfare needs at home for as long as possible
- encouraging the provision of a range of services for the elderly and their carers in each district
- ensuring co-operation between health board services and the activities of housing authorities and voluntary housing bodies
- agreeing with the general hospital and the psychiatric services policies for the admission and discharge of elderly people to hospital
- liaising with voluntary organisations at county level
- being the main source of information and advice on services for the elderly in the community care area
- enforcing legal requirements in respect of private nursing homes
- servicing a board-wide Advisory Committee on the Elderly
- co-ordinating transport to day care and hospital services.

In most health boards, from the perspective of management, the main functions of the CSE are to assess needs, be aware of options and resources and facilitate decisions on the most effective form of care. This is seen to involve liaison with other service providers, in particular the GP and PHN, but also Community Welfare Officers, social workers, housing officials, and voluntary bodies. In several of the boards, there is a special emphasis on liaising with nursing homes and carrying out assessments for admission to them. In some boards, the CSE is also expected to monitor trends in demands for services, to audit existing services and plan for future development. Most CSEs see themselves as having a generic role in evaluating, planning, developing and co-ordinating services. In addition, they describe specific responsibilities such as carrying out assessments for placement in extended care, nursing home inspection and assessments for subvention, chairing committees and being a central point for information related to elderly care.

3.8.4.3   Liaison between Co-ordinator of Services for the Elderly and other service providers
Where there are a number of designated CSEs in a board, such as the Eastern, North Eastern and North Western Health Boards, they meet regularly, once per month, and also have frequent phone contact. In cases where those fulfilling the function are not officially designated as CSEs, liaison tends to be informal and irregular. Similarly, where there are specifically designated District Liaison Nurses, such as in the Eastern board, the CSEs work very closely with them and have regular formal meetings and informal contact. The Working Party had envisaged that part of the function of the CSE would be to ensure co-operation between health board and housing authority services, but feedback reveals that while CSEs and housing officials are sometimes co-members of committees and have informal contact, no formal arrangements exist in any board to enable the CSE to fulfil this responsibility. It is suggested by the co-ordinators in one board that because co-ordination does not happen at Government Department level, the ethos of co-ordination does not filter down to local level.

3.8.4.4   Factors influencing the effectiveness of Co-ordinator of Services for the Elderly function
With one exception, all of the CSEs indicate that they have encountered some obstacles in carrying out their role. In three of the boards (North Eastern, North Western and Southern), one of the problems has been failure to define the role properly and it is perceived that it is only now that it is being appropriately developed. In the Eastern and Western Health Boards the main problem appears to be work overload and the broad scope of the CSE's remit. Pressure of work is also an issue for CSEs in the Southern and South Eastern Health Boards. In individual cases, the CSE experiences difficulty because of the lack of services required or because of not having a local budget for services. It is noted that it can be difficult to motivate others to work towards co-ordination and that there can be conflicting agendas between different people and different agencies. It is also noted that free flow of information is vital to the CSE's function but that such information is not always made available.

3.8.5   Co-ordination at health board level
At health board level, *The Years Ahead* recommended that co-ordination be achieved through a systematic approach to planning. One of its specific recommendations was that:

- **(R3.24) the health and welfare needs of the elderly be considered as a distinct but integral part of a new planning system for the health services**.

All of the health boards indicate that older people are treated as a distinct group in planning health services for the board's region. The Working Party envisaged that, at least in the larger health boards, the planning and development of services for older people would require the full-time attention of a designated person. In seven of the health boards one of the Programme Managers takes board-wide responsibility for older people, while in the other board overall responsibility is carried out by the CEO. In the Eastern Health Board there is also a board-wide, full-time administrative Co-ordinator of Services for the Elderly who has cross-programme responsibility to co-ordinate services and with whom the Area CSEs liaise. In the North Eastern Health Board there is a General Manager of Services for the Elderly and in the Midlands there is a Health Strategy Facilitator who takes overall responsibility for older people. There is a move now among a number of the health boards to focus service delivery on 'Care Groups' such as older people, children and people with mental handicap, and to access services across programmes rather than focus on Care Programmes.

A second recommendation on board-wide co-ordination was that:

- **(R3.26) health boards be obliged to appoint an Advisory Committee on the Elderly**.

This committee would include the CSEs, public representatives nominated by the health board and local authorities, a consultant physician in geriatric medicine (where such posts exist), the housing officers of the local authorities, GPs nominated by the relevant faculties of the Irish College of General Practitioners, PHNs and representatives of voluntary organisations working on behalf of older people in the area. A proportion of the members would be older people. The functions of the advisory committee set down by the Working Party were to:

- advise on health and welfare needs and how they can be met
- represent the views of those working with or on behalf of the elderly
- recommend the planning and provision of services for the elderly; in particular to agree each year a plan for the development of services
- encourage co-ordination between statutory and voluntary bodies.

Only two health boards have established an advisory committee on the elderly (Western and North Eastern, Table 3.5). Both of these committees adhere to the requirements of the recommendation with membership comprising health board members, public representatives, GPs, geriatricians (recently appointed in the North Eastern), PHNs and members of voluntary organisations. The Midland Health Board has an action planning committee which does not have the same composition recommended in *The Years Ahead* but does address the care of older people. In the North Eastern Health Board the remit of the advisory committee includes not just older people but also children and people with a disability. At management level, the committees that have been established are perceived as fulfilling a useful function, particularly in relation to guidance of policy making.

Table 3.5: Establishment of advisory committee on the elderly

Health board	Whether advisory committee established
Eastern	No
Midland	No (has action planning committee)
Mid-Western	No
North Eastern	Yes
North Western	No
Southern	No
South Eastern	No
Western	Yes

Source: Interviews with Programme Managers of Community Care and CSEs

From the perspective of some of those CSEs who have an advisory committee, the committee allows interchange of information and leads to convergence on aims and priorities. In the Midland Health Board the action planning committee has produced an 'Action Plan for Health and Social Gain for the Elderly' and acts to oversee its implementation.

Several Programme Managers in boards without advisory committees express reservations about the usefulness of such a committee. It is perceived, for example, that it can be hard to manage effectively, it can be difficult to get commitment and its function can be usurped for political purposes. The advisory committee, it is sometimes felt, could add another level of bureaucracy without adding much in terms of effective care for older people. In one case it is noted that finding other more effective means of hearing the voice of older people is currently being explored.

3.8.6 *Co-ordination at national level*
At national level, the Working Party recommended that:

- **(R3.27) the Departments of Health, the Environment and Social Welfare agree administrative arrangements to ensure co-ordination of policy towards the elderly at national level and monitoring of progress towards the implementation of the recommendations of *The Years Ahead* Report.**

There is agreement in the Departments that there is a high level of co-operation between them on matters related to older people. It is noted, for example, that the Department of the Environment is represented on the National Council for the Elderly (now the National Council on Ageing and Older People) and, on the other hand, representatives of the Department of Health are on the Task Force on Special Housing Aid for the Elderly. Likewise, the Departments of Health and the

Environment were included in the review of the Supplementary Welfare Allowance Scheme by the Department of Social Welfare and representatives of other Departments were also on the Task Force on Security for the Elderly set up by the Department of Social Welfare. Department of Health officials describe the arrangements for liaison which currently exist between these Departments as mostly informal in nature; with meetings occurring as the need arises, rather than being proactive. Officials in all Departments perceive current arrangements as satisfactory. For example, the Department of the Environment sees the existing approach as allowing flexibility in relation to specific matters of mutual interest. There is a sense, however, in the Department of Health that meetings should probably be held on a more structured and regular basis.

A recent development of relevance to inter-departmental co-ordination is the Government's Strategic Management Initiative (SMI) launched in February 1994. A significant theme of the SMI is the development of inter-departmental links and the improvement of communication between Government Departments. The SMI acknowledges that many of the most pressing issues facing the country require the expertise and commitment of a number of Departments and agencies and effective action necessitates new approaches to understanding, developing and managing links. The SMI notes that currently there are limited structures for consultation, co-ordination and co-operation across departments and that the present system rewards 'territorial protection' at the expense of active co-operation (Co-Ordinating Group of Secretaries 1996, p. 15). In recognition of the essential need for inter-departmental co-operation, the SMI proposes, for example, the creation of dedicated cross-departmental teams, with co-ordination by a Minister/Minister of State and with a nominated lead Department to tackle jointly issues of major national importance. *Shaping a Healthier Future* also promises that the possibilities for changing organisational arrangements between the Departments of Health and Social Welfare, in the interest of better service co-ordination, will be examined as an integral part of the implementation of the strategy.

3.8.6.1   Legislation for co-ordination

The Working Party considered that the function of co-ordinating and planning services for the elderly was so important that it should be given a firm foundation in legislation and recommended that:

- **(R3.29) health boards be obliged by law to co-ordinate and plan health and welfare services for the elderly, to appoint co-ordinators of services for the elderly and to establish advisory committees on the elderly**.

While health boards are encouraged by government to plan and co-ordinate services, they are not obliged by law to liaise with other agencies, nor are they obliged to appoint Co-ordinators of Services for the Elderly or to establish advisory committees.

3.8.6.2   Terms of reference of National Council for the Elderly
A further recommendation at national level was that:

- **(R3.28) the terms of the National Council for the Aged be broadened to cover all aspects of the welfare of the elderly and that it be an advisory body, not just to the Minister for Health, but to all Ministers with responsibility for the elderly**.

In 1990 the National Council for the Elderly was established to succeed the National Council for the Aged. In its new terms of reference, the National Council for the Elderly remained responsible only to the Minister for Health. As with the National Council for the Aged, the National Council for the Elderly advised the Minister for Health on all aspects of ageing and the welfare of older people and in particular on:

- methods of ensuring co-ordination between public bodies at national and local level in the planning and provision of services for the elderly
- ways of meeting the needs of the most vulnerable elderly
- ways of encouraging positive attitudes to life after 65 years and the process of ageing
- ways of encouraging greater participation by elderly people in the life of the community
- models of good practice in the care of the elderly.

The terms of reference of the National Council for the Elderly were broadened compared with those of the previous Council to include advice on:

- measures to promote the health of the elderly
- the implementation of the recommendations of *The Years Ahead - A Policy for the Elderly*
- ways of encouraging greater partnership between statutory and voluntary bodies in providing services for the elderly and
- action, based on research, required to plan and develop services for the elderly.

In 1997 the National Council for the Elderly was re-established as the National Council on Ageing and Older People. While it remains an advisory body to the Minister for Health, its terms of reference have again been broadened to include work on the following:

- measures to promote the social inclusion of older people
- the implementation of the recommendations contained in policy reports commissioned by the Minister for Health.

The new Council will also assist the development of national and regional policies and strategies designed to produce health gain and social gain for older people by:

- undertaking research on the lifestyle and the needs of older people in Ireland
- identifying and promoting models of good practice in the care of older people and service delivery to them
- providing information and advice based on research findings to those involved in the development and/or implementation of policies and services pertaining to the health, well-being and autonomy of older people
- liaising with statutory, voluntary and professional bodies involved in the development and/or implementation of national and regional policies which have as their object health gain or social gain for older people.

The new Council will also work directly on the promotion of the health, welfare and autonomy of older people and on the promotion of a better understanding of ageing and older people in Ireland.

3.9   Summary and conclusions

A summary of the extent of implementation of recommendations concerning provision of a comprehensive and co-ordinated service is presented in the table below.

Co-ordination is an issue of central concern in *The Years Ahead*. The Working Party identified a number of problems with co-ordination in the delivery system operating at the time. In order to remedy these, the Working Party set out a structure for co-ordination which took account of different spheres and levels of operation. With regard to spheres of operation, the Working Party was concerned with co-operation between: different agencies within the health board; different agencies within the public sector; and the public and voluntary sectors. The different levels taken into account were district, community care area, regional and national levels.

In the delivery structure proposed by the Working Party, the district serving a population of around 25-30,000 people was the basic operational unit. Only three health boards have organised their services in this way for a variety of reasons including tradition, population spread and lack of resources. Different health boards have evolved different systems to suit their own particular circumstances but all boards now appear to be moving towards a district structure. There are several background factors contributing to a state of flux in the health boards which are likely to be impeding progress in organising services at district level. One factor contributing to a state of flux is the slow implementation of the new management structures proposed in *Shaping a Healthier Future*. A second factor is that *Shaping a Healthier Future* did not set out specific structures for linkages

Table 3.6: Extent of provision of a comprehensive and co-ordinated service

Recommendation	Current situation
Services for the elderly to be organised in districts of 25-30,000 people	District organisation in three health boards
Co-ordination of services in each district should be the responsibility of a District Liaison Nurse	Nurses with a co-ordinating function in all boards. Often operate at larger than district level. Not always dedicated to co-ordination nor devoted to older people
District teams should be formed to support the District Liaison Nurse in her co-ordinating role	Two boards have teams at community care area level. Two further boards have teams in a few districts
Role of District Liaison Nurse and district team should be reviewed after three years	No formal reviews carried out
Co-ordinators of Services for the Elderly should be appointed in each community care area	Co-ordinators of Services for the Elderly in each community care area in four health boards. One co-ordinator for all areas in three boards
Health boards should be obliged to appoint an an advisory committee on the elderly	No obligation on the health boards to appoint an advisory committee. Advisory committees in two boards
Department of Health, the Environment and Social Welfare should agree administrative arrangements to ensure co-ordination of policy towards the elderly	No formal administrative arrangements. Structures for interdepartmental co-ordination being examined as part of the Strategic Management Initiative and *Shaping a Healthier Future*
Terms of reference of the National Council for the Aged should be broadened to cover all aspects of the welfare of the elderly. Should be an advisory body to all ministers with responsibility for the elderly	Terms of reference broadened with establishment of National Council for the Elderly (1990) and the National Council on Ageing and Older People (1997). Still an advisory body only to Minister for Health
Health boards should be obliged by law to co-ordinate and plan health and welfare services for the elderly	Not obliged by law

between community and hospital programmes both of which have been undergoing changes in responsibility over the past number of years. A third contributing factor is the phasing out of the post of Director of Community Care and the slow introduction of the post of General Manager of Community Services. Another factor is the difficulty in setting out boundaries that distribute hospitals and other permanent facilities in an equitable manner.

At district level, *The Years Ahead* recommended that co-ordination should be carried out by Senior PHNs who would be titled District Liaison Nurses. All the health boards have nurses -given a variety of titles - who perform a co-ordinating function but because a district structure is not always in place they often operate on a larger than district level (five boards). Contrary to the Working Party's recommendation they are not always dedicated to co-ordination work and few are devoted full-time to older people. Different definitions of the role of the District Liaison Nurse are evident across the boards but liaison between hospital and community services is noted as an important function by most of those involved. There have been changes in the responsibilities borne by the community and hospital programmes and, as yet, there are no structures in place which would lead to clarity of function and better co-ordination between them.

The Working Party had envisaged that the District Liaison Nurse would also liaise with agencies outside the health board including caring relatives, private nursing homes, voluntary organisations and local authorities. However, the focus for most liaison nurses appears to be on intra-health board liaison and little or no contact occurs with, for example, local authority officials. This situation at district level may reflect the circumstances prevailing at wider regional and national levels where there is little liaison on policy and planning between health boards and local authorities and little liaison at Departmental level. Without the support of a wider ethos of liaison it is difficult for nurses and local authority officials to implement liaison at district level.

Within the health board, the role of District Liaison Nurse was intended by the Working Party to be part of an overall co-operation structure. The reality is that many liaison nurses do not have such a structure and are without the support of a CSE at community care level. District Liaison Nurses indicate the difficulties involved in trying to provide a cohesive and equitable service without a CSE. Another problem which can prevent the District Liaison Nurse from carrying out co-ordination effectively is lack of access to the services required to meet identified needs.

In its overall co-ordination structure, *The Years Ahead* recommended that the District Liaison Nurse should have the back-up support of a district team but many do not have such support. Two boards have established teams that approximate those envisaged by the Working Party although in one of these boards the teams cover a community care area rather than a district. Two further boards have teams in a few districts. Many benefits are noted among District Liaison Nurses who work with district teams including support, better knowledge of needs, identification of service deficits and multi-disciplinary input into care decisions. Questions are also raised, however, about the effectiveness of such teams.

Liaison nurses and particularly CSEs note that teams can be difficult to operate effectively and are a challenging undertaking. Unless carefully managed, teams can be time-consuming and can hinder effective decision-making. Doubts about

EASTERN HEALTH BOARD

CEO

Programme Manager Community Care	Programme Manager Special Hospital Care	Programme Manager General Hospital Care

Board level

Board-Wide Co-ordinator of Services for the Elderly (full-time post)

Community care level (10 community care areas)

Medical Co-ordinators of Services for the Elderly: One in each community care area (10)	District Care Team (10: One in each community care area)
District Liaison Nurses: At least one in each community care area (10)	

District Level _____

Note: Second type of team in Eastern Health Board which is the community ward team. Focus on care provision; multi-disciplinary team providing outreach services.

☐ Takes overall responsibility for older people

MIDLAND HEALTH BOARD

CEO

Programme Manager Community Care	Programme Manager Hospital Care

Board level

Board-wide Health Strategy Facilitator

Community care level (Two community care areas)

District level (two districts in each community care area)

District Liaison Nurse function: Carried out by PHNs with special designation as Liaison Nurses (4)

☐ Takes overall responsibility for older people

MID-WESTERN HEALTH BOARD

```
        ┌─────────────┐
        │     CEO     │
        └─────────────┘
```

Board level	Programme Manager Community Care	Programme Manager Special Hospital Care	Programme Manager General Hospital Care

```
┌──────────────────────────────────────────────────────────┐
│   1 Co-ordinator of Services for the Elderly:  Senior PHN  │
└──────────────────────────────────────────────────────────┘
```

**Community care level
(Three community
care areas)**

_____

**District Level
(10 districts)**

```
┌──────────────────────────────────────────────────────────┐
│  District Liaison Nurse function: Senior PHNs carry        │
│  out this function and spend up to 60% of their time       │
│                on older people (3)                         │
└──────────────────────────────────────────────────────────┘
```

☐ Takes overall responsibility for older people

NORTH EASTERN HEALTH BOARD

CEO

Advisory committee on the elderly

Board level

| Programme Manager Community Care | Programme Manager Special Hospital Care | Programme Manager Acute Hospitals |

General Manager of Services for the Elderly

Community care level (Three community care areas)

Area Co-ordinators of Services for the Elderly (3)

Liaison nurses based in acute hospitals in each community care area (3)

District Level

☐ Takes overall responsibility for older people

NORTH WESTERN HEALTH BOARD

CEO

Board level

Programme Manager
Community Care

Programme Manager
Hospital Care

**Community care level
(Two community care
areas)**

Area Co-ordinators of Services for Elderly (2)

**District level
(15 districts)**

District Co-ordinators of
Services for the Elderly: 15

District Liaison Nurse function:
Carried out by district CSEs

District
care
teams for
the
elderly

☐ Takes overall responsibility for older people

SOUTH EASTERN HEALTH BOARD

CEO

Board level

| Programme Manager Community Care | Programme Manager Special Hospital Care | Programme Manager General Hospital care |

Community care level (Four community care areas)

Co-ordinator of Services for the Elderly: 1 (Waterford)

District Liaison Nurse function: Carried out by Geriatric Liaison Nurses (4)

District Level

☐ Takes overall responsibility for older people

SOUTHERN HEALTH BOARD

```
                          ┌──────────────┐
                          │     CEO      │
                          └──────────────┘


Board level       ┌──────────────┐  ┌──────────────┐  ┌──────────────┐
                  │  Programme   │  │  Programme   │  │  Programme   │
                  │   Manager    │  │Manager Special│ │Manager General│
                  │Community Care│  │ Hospital Care│  │ Hospital care│
                  └──────────────┘  └──────────────┘  └──────────────┘
```

Community care level   ┌──┐
(Four community   │ Co-ordinator of Services for the Elderly in each │
care areas)   │   community care area: (4)   │
                                │   (Not official designation)   │
                                └──┘

District Level   ┌──┐
(20 districts)   │ District Liaison Nurse function: Carried out by │
                                │   Senior PHN in each district (20)   │
                                └──┘

☐ Takes overall responsibility for older people

WESTERN HEALTH BOARD

CEO

Advisory Committee on the elderly

Board level

| Programme Manager Community Care | Programme Manager Special Hospital Care | Programme Manager General Hospital Care |

Community care level (Three community care areas)

*Co-ordinator of Services for the Elderly: one in Galway community care area

District Liaison Nurse function: Carried out by General Liaison PHNs, one in each community care area and two in Galway community care areas (4)

District Level

_____

* In Mayo and Roscommon this function is shared by Directors of Community Care and consultant geriatricians

☐ Takes overall responsibility for older people

CHAPTER FOUR

Maintaining Health

4.1   Introduction

The second issue taken up in *The Years Ahead*, following co-ordination of services, was health promotion, thereby emphasising its importance in providing for the well-being of older people.   The Working Party took its definition of health promotion from an earlier (1987) document, *Promoting Health Through Public Policy,* which was 'a process which aims at altering and developing fundamental features of society with a view to promoting good health and removing hazards and obstacles in the way of doing so. It seeks to mobilise resources in health and to pursue healthy public policy.   The concept of health promotion is based on an understanding that health is more than an absence of disease' (Health Education Bureau 1987, p. 1).   The Working Party, following the World Health Organisation (1985), identified three objectives of health promotion: to add life to years by enabling as many people as possible to remain healthy and active throughout the years of their life; to add health to life by reducing the occurrence of illness and accidents; and to add years to life by increasing the average life expectancy of the individual.   In regard to each of these aims, the conclusion of *The Years Ahead* was that health promotion among older people left much room for improvement.

This chapter reviews the implementation of the recommendations made by the Working Party to address the gaps identified in health promotion among older people.   Data on implementation was obtained from two sources: written documents and submissions from bodies such as the National Council for the Elderly, Irish Congress of Trade Unions, Irish Business and Employers Confederation, Age and Opportunity and interviews and/or questionnaires from health board personnel including Programme Managers of Community Care, CSEs and Superintendent and Senior PHNs.   Information was also obtained in written form from officers in the Department of Education and from professional bodies representing physiotherapists, occupational therapists and GPs.

4.2   Health promotion

4.2.1   *Inter-departmental links and health promotion*

The Years Ahead recognised that health promotion is a multi-faceted process influenced, for example, by housing, security, social cohesion, air quality, road safety, retirement and income. Accordingly, the report recommended that health promotion among older people should be a primary concern of the existing inter-departmental Cabinet Sub-Committee on Health Promotion. In a 1993 discussion of measures to promote health and autonomy for older people, Kelleher noted that this Cabinet Sub-Committee was under-utilised and recommended that it be exploited more fully as a mechanism for addressing such complex issues as health promotion, 'where there is no real option but to involve all sectors and interests at policy level' (Kelleher 1993, p. 27). In Kelleher's view, the single most obvious barrier to health promotion for older people is that those with different responsibilities and roles do not talk to each other enough. As indicated in Chapter Three, there is now an increased emphasis through the Strategic Management Initiative on inter-departmental working links in many areas of the public service and this should help to create the kind of multi-sectoral approach needed in effective health promotion. The *Health Promotion Strategy* (Department of Health 1995a) recognised the shortcomings in current arrangements for multi-sectoral co-operation and proposed a National Consultative Committee on Health Promotion which would submit periodic reports to the Cabinet Sub-Committee on Health Promotion. The National Consultative Committee on Health Promotion was established in late 1995 and represents the Departments of Agriculture, Enterprise and Employment, Education, Justice, and Transport, Energy and Communications; the Health and Safety Authority, the Irish Cancer Society, the Irish Heart Foundation, the health boards and the Health Promotion Unit of the Department of Health.

4.2.2   *National programme on healthy ageing*

The Years Ahead report recommended the development of a national plan for health promotion. Its specific recommendation was that:

- **(R4.8) the promotion of health among the elderly be a primary concern of the Cabinet Sub-Committee to co-ordinate policies affecting health, the Health Promotion Council, and the Health Promotion Unit of the Department of Health and that this concern be made explicit in a national plan to promote health**.

A number of steps have been taken to implement this recommendation (Figure 4.1).

The Healthy Ageing programme which is currently being developed by the National Council on Ageing and Older People has three strands. The first strand

Figure 4.1: Steps in developing a programme on healthy ageing

National Council for the Elderly appointed in 1990
New term of reference: to advise on measures to promote health of the elderly

↓

National Council for the Elderly Consultative Committee on Measures to Promote the Health and Autonomy of the Elderly in Ireland

↓

National Council for the Elderly Report on Health and Autonomy Among the Over-65s in Ireland (1994)

↓

National Council for the Elderly Recommendation for Programme for the Promotion of the Health of Older People

↓

Priority given to promotion of healthy ageing in *Shaping a Healthier Future* (1994) in conjunction with the National Council for the Elderly

↓

Health Promotion Strategy published by Department of Health: includes goal to develop a national programme to promote 'healthy ageing' (1995)

↓

National Council on Ageing and Older People currently developing Healthy Ageing programme

is the preparation of a health promotion strategy specifically for older people. The existing national *Health Promotion Strategy* is concerned with the whole population. However, it must be recognised that while health and well-being in older life cannot be separated from efforts at health promotion and disease prevention in earlier stages of life, there are health issues specific to old age. It must also be recognised that the settings for health promotion for younger age groups, for example schools and workplaces, are often irrelevant to older people. A health promotion strategy is therefore needed to address the issue of health promotion and disease prevention particular to later life and to determine the best means of reaching older people. The strategy will:

- assess the needs of older people and identify the key priority areas
- identify key settings and priority population groups
- set national targets and goals for improving health and well-being
- identify the actions which are most likely to improve health and well-being.

The second strand of the Healthy Ageing programme involves the development of an information and support network for promoting the health and well-being of older people. The network will play an important role in ensuring that the health promotion needs of older people are addressed. It will also have a role to play in fostering an integrated approach to health promotion for older people across all sectors. It will act as a resource on healthy ageing by providing services such as:

- a database on health promotion initiatives, good practice in healthy ageing and materials on healthy ageing
- factsheets and information updates on healthy ageing issues
- seminars on priority areas in health promotion for older people.

In the third strand of the Healthy Ageing programme the evaluation of new or existing initiatives designed to promote the health and well-being of older people will be encouraged. This is one way in which the Healthy Ageing programme will seek to identify models of good practice for healthy ageing which will be promoted through its support and information network.

4.2.3 *Creation of supportive environment for health promotion*

The national *Health Promotion Strategy* (Department of Health 1995a) emphasises that health promotion goes beyond disease prevention and health education and recognises - as did *The Years Ahead* - that environmental and socio-economic factors influence the health choices the individual makes. Accordingly, health promotion operates at two levels: the individual level and the wider community, regional and national level. At the individual level, health promotion requires information, education and skills development to enable people to make good decisions in relation to their health. At the wider level, health promotion involves the development of appropriate policies, structures and support systems so that the healthier choice becomes the easier one to make. At health board level, one of the structures proposed in the national *Health Promotion Strategy* is regional inter-sectoral consultative committees on health promotion. The establishment of Departments of Public Health Medicine and of Health Promotion in the health boards provides opportunities for the enhancement of health promotion. Another important development is the establishment by the health board Chief Executive Officers of the Office for Health Gain, which supports joint work by the boards on health promotion.

With regard to the creation of a supportive environment for health promotion among older people, housing is clearly a crucial issue (see Chapter Five) and so also is a sense of personal safety - an issue which is further discussed in Chapter Six. Another significant issue is the attitudinal culture which surrounds the health measures introduced. Kelleher, for example, suggests that 'we need to question whether the culture is covertly ageist or whether it enhances a genuinely positive approach to ageing' (1993, p. 27). Similarly, the National Council for the Elderly argued that in considering the situation of older people it is necessary to adopt 'a value-critical perspective' where we ask basic questions about our attitudes to, and perceptions of, ageing and older people (National Council for the Elderly 1994b, p. 10). According to the National Council for the Elderly we need an attitude shift whereby people are seen not as old first and people second but rather as persons who happen to be old. In this way older people would no longer be seen primarily as a 'social problem' but as people with a wealth of talents, skills and experience which are to be cherished and prized. The national *Health Promotion Strategy* also takes up this issue; one of its planned actions being to promote self-respect, dignity and a positive role for older people in society.

4.3   Health education

The national *Health Promotion Strategy* identifies lifestyle as a key determinant of health. In turn, lifestyle is determined, on the one hand, by the person's social, economic, cultural, physical and ethical environment and, on the other hand, by the person's levels of information and skill in relation to health. Accordingly, health education is critical in enabling the person make good decisions about health. While recognising that prevention of many of the diseases of older life requires action in childhood or early adult life, the Working Party considered that it was within the capacity of most older people to take action to postpone the onset of some diseases and reduce the disabilities associated with other diseases. The Working Party argued that older people, no less than other age groups, need health education. This approach is corroborated by the National Council for the Elderly study on *Health and Autonomy Among the Over-65s in Ireland* which found that although it may be more difficult to change the lifestyle of a lifetime, health promotion initiatives are likely to find a receptive audience among older people (Fahey and Murray 1994).

4.3.1   *Development of health education policy for older people*

According to the Working Party, health education for the elderly should provide information on issues directly affecting health such as nutrition and exercise, as well as useful advice on cooking, heating, insulation, accident prevention and security and it should also give information on coping with particular problems of ageing such as strokes, arthritis and incontinence. The Working Party suggested that, as far as possible, health education should be integrated with social activities of older people in clubs, community and parish centres. Its specific recommendation was that:

- **(R4.11) the Health Promotion Unit of the Department of Health, in consultation with those organisations working with or on behalf of the elderly develop directly or indirectly, a health education policy for the elderly. It should be the responsibility of the Co-ordinator of Services for the Elderly in each area to ensure that an appropriate health education service for the elderly is available.**

Most existing health education programmes are aimed at young or middle-aged people. While prevention of many of the diseases of older life requires action in earlier life, it must also be acknowledged that as people grow older particular health concerns and problems begin to arise which require specific health education input. Two existing health education programmes which are relevant to the needs of older people are *Lifewise* and *Health, Well-Being and Empowerment for Older People*. *Lifewise* is a community health education course, available in a number of areas around the country, which covers topics such as stress, healthy eating, exercise and fitness, heart disease, tobacco and alcohol use. *Lifewise* is designed for adults of all ages but the topics covered are relevant to the health of older people and are readily adaptable to their particular needs. The second programme - *Health, Well-Being and Empowerment for Older People* - was developed by the Cork Social and Health Education Project and is carried out mainly in the Southern Health Board region. This programme covers topics related to physical health but is concerned particularly with maintaining self-esteem and with continuing involvement and contribution among older people.

While there has been positive feedback on both of these programmes, to date neither has been systematically evaluated. The National Council for the Elderly has suggested that before developing any new national health education programmes, these existing programmes should be evaluated. Such evaluation would enable assessment of the effectiveness of the programmes, their possible role in national efforts at health education among older people and their potential for informing and guiding local programmes and campaigns.

4.3.2   Health education services provided by health boards
The Years Ahead identified the CSE as the person who should be responsible for ensuring appropriate health education services for older people at local level. Feedback from CSEs indicates that current health education services for older people vary across health boards in content, in mode of delivery and delivery agents (Table 4.1). The Public Health Nurse appears to be the primary deliverer of current health education services although other professionals, such as occupational therapists, physiotherapists, nutritionists and Environmental Health Officers are also sometimes involved. Because of the way in which health education services are currently being provided, it is very difficult to assess their effectiveness. Feedback from the PHNs suggests that their services in this regard are often unrecognised and they are given neither the time nor the resources needed for the task. Many perceive current services as informal, unco-ordinated and opportunistic rather than proactive. These nurses call for development of a more formalised and coherent service which is available to all. The importance of co-ordination, particularly in regard to the work of voluntary organisations, is frequently noted.

Table 4.1: Health education services for older people

Health board	Content (examples, not complete listing)	Mode of delivery	Delivery agent
Eastern	Safety, hygiene, diet entitlements, relaxation, continence promotion	PHN visits, day care centres, social clubs, age-well clinics (in some areas), campaigns	PHN mainly, nutritional advisor, occupational therapists, physiotherapists, CSEs, board CSE, voluntary groups
Midland	Diet, healthy lifestyle, maintaining mobility, relaxation, maintaining social contact, self-esteem	PHN visits, day care centres, leaflets, *Lifewise* programme	PHNs, invited speakers, physiotherapists, local authority officials
Mid-Western	Diet, healthy lifestyle, safety, socialising	PHN visits, day care centres, leaflets, *Lifewise* programme	PHNs mainly
North Eastern	Healthy lifestyle, diet, exercise	PHN visits, day centres, day hospitals	PHNs, invited specialists
North Western	Diet, exercise, safety, continence promotion, aids and appliances	Community hospitals, day care centres, PHN visits, leaflets	PHNs, occupational therapists
Southern	Healthy lifestyle, nutrition, continence promotion, self-esteem, assertiveness, safety	PHN visits, talks, leaflets, day-care centres, *Lifewise* programme, *Health, Well-Being and Empowerment with Older People* programme	PHNs, Assistant Medical Officers, physiotherapists, Environmental Health Officers, Cork Social and Health Education Project
South Eastern	Diet, exercise, security, entitlements, aids and appliances, continence promotion	PHN visits, day centres, leaflets, day hospitals, local radio	PHNs, occupational therapists, physiotherapists, Community Welfare Officer, CSE and voluntary groups
Western	Healthy lifestyle, valuing capacities and resources	PHN visits, talks at health centres	PHNs, GPs, nutritionist

Sources: Interviews with CSEs and PHNs

The feedback from the CSEs and PHNs highlights the need for a national healthy ageing strategy which would guide the development of a coherent and comprehensive health education service throughout the country. But, in addition to a national strategy, health boards must develop their own systematic structures for the delivery of a health education service dedicated to the needs of older people. Seven of the health boards indicate that through their health promotion departments definite plans are being developed for health promotion and health education. The Eastern Health Board plans to develop a health promotion team in each community care area. The new Departments of Public Health Medicine in the health boards also have a potentially significant role to play in health education. Across the health boards, an important development is the establishment of the Office for Health Gain. But, while structures may be developing, an important issue still to be addressed is the lack of a comprehensive, reliable, accurate and up-to-date body of information which could be used to guide health promotion and health education efforts.

4.3.3 Health education and carers

In recognition of the crucial role of informal carers in addressing the well-being of dependent older people, *The Years Ahead* highlighted the need for a specific health education service geared to the needs for carers. In a number of studies, the carers themselves have identified advice and information as one of their key needs (O'Connor and Ruddle 1988; Blackwell *et al.* 1992; Ruddle 1994). One of the Working Party's recommendations was that:

- **(R4.13) the Department of Health should direct health boards to provide a health education service for carers of elderly people and provide guidelines on the content and operation of such a service**.

While this recommendation has not yet been implemented, the national *Health Promotion Strategy* proposes the development of a specific programme for carers in its action plan for older people.

4.3.3.1 Formal training and education of carers

A recent National Council for the Elderly report (O'Donovan *et al.* 1997) found overwhelming support for the provision of training for both formal and informal social care workers who work with older people. This support was based on a belief that training is likely to benefit older people by contributing to improved standards of care and to increased health and social gain. It is also likely to benefit the carers by equipping them with the skills necessary to cope with the tasks of caring. A review of existing courses in social care in Ireland found that there has been much development in this area in recent years. Courses available include:

- Certificate/Diploma in Applied Social Studies in Social Care - Regional Technical Colleges/National Council for Educational Awards
- Certificate/Diploma in Social Care - University College Galway
- Course in Community and Health Services - National Council for Vocational Awards
- Course in Community Care Practice - FÁS

- Certificate in Caring for the Sick/Voluntary Care - Irish Red Cross and Institute of Community Health Nursing.

The report highlights the fact that although the majority of carers of older people are mature women, most of the courses available are targeted at school leavers. Furthermore, many of the courses are full-time and offer general training in social care rather than focusing on the care of older people. In the report the Council expressed concern that, in the absence of a national policy on training in the care of older people, the needs of those who care for older people may be overshadowed by the needs of those who care for other groups. The Council recommended that the Department of Health should take responsibility for formulating a national policy on training for formal social care workers and informal carers who care for older people and for introducing a standardised system of training.

4.3.3.2   Health board education services for informal carers
A second recommendation of the Working Party on education services for carers was that:

- **(R4.13) in each community care area, the Co-ordinator of Services for the Elderly should ensure that support and advice are available to carers and that carers have sufficient information and advice to carry out their task**.

Feedback from CSEs reveals that, in the absence of a health education policy, current health education services for carers are, for the most part, unstructured, uneven, uncoordinated and opportunistic. Most services are provided through the PHN's visits (Table 4.2). In the North Eastern and North Western Health Boards carers are now being involved in pre-discharge planning and are given information and advice on providing care post-discharge. In the Eastern Health Board a course on caring is provided through carers support groups in some areas by a voluntary organisation. The Mid-Western board appears to have the most structured service for carers but it operates only in a certain area. This is the Caring for the Carers project operated through Soroptimist International Republic of Ireland in conjunction with other voluntary organisations (such as Clare Care and the Irish Red Cross Society). Among other activities, the Caring for the Carers project provides information and advice on benefits and services (including an information booklet and a telephone Helpline) and education and training services (including courses such as Caring for the Sick, Voluntary Care in the Community and Personal Development).

Feedback from PHNs reveals much dissatisfaction with the health education they provide to carers. Many describe what is currently provided as unfocused, unstructured and informal. The nurses perceive that while they do what they can,

Table 4.2: Health education services for carers

Health board	Content (examples)	Mode of delivery	Delivery agent
Eastern	Courses on caring (in some areas), advice on caring tasks	Carers support groups, one-to-one contact	Voluntary organisations, PHNs
Midland	Nothing structured, provided on demand	One-to-one contact, written materials	PHNs mainly
Mid-Western	Caring for Carers project (in some areas), entitlements, services available	Carers support groups, one-to-one, written materials	Voluntary organisations in partnership with board, PHNs, occupational therapist, Community Welfare Officer
North Eastern	As part of discharge planning information given on caring at home, practical nursing care	One-to-one contact, carers support groups	PHNs mainly
North Western	Pre-discharge plans include information and advice to carers, carers involved in planning care, hospitals have information bulletin for carers	One-to-one contact, written materials	Community hospital mainly; occupational therapists, physiotherapists, PHNs
Southern	Safety, lifting techniques, diet, entitlements	One-to-one contact, day care centres	PHN mainly, GPs, Community Welfare Officers, CSEs
South Eastern	Information and talks as requested	One-to-one contact, talks, day care centres, written materials and local radio	PHNs, carers support groups
Western	Services available, entitlements	Health centres, PHN and GP visits, leaflets	PHNs and GPs mainly

Sources: Interviews with CSEs and PHNs

the time they can give is limited and the resources are not there for the service they would like. The nurses call for resources for development of a comprehensive, equitable, widely available service for carers, and also highlight the need for a co-ordinated approach.

4.4   Professional attitudes to ageing and older people

The Years Ahead highlighted the role of health professionals in health education for older people and their carers. In particular, the report noted the importance of the medical practitioner, PHN, dentist, physiotherapist, occupational therapist and chiropodist. The Working Party identified a number of issues which were preventing these professionals from playing their full part in health education. Most professional training courses at the time were perceived as paying little attention to the problems of ageing, training for each profession took place in isolation and there was little awareness of the contribution of informal carers and the strain that caregiving can entail. To remedy these deficiencies, the Working Party recommended that:

- **(R4.15) the teaching authorities of the professions concerned encourage more positive attitudes to caring for the elderly among students and trainees and that more attention be given to ageing in professional training**.

In particular, the Working Party argued that there should be a greater emphasis on caring for the elderly in the vocational training of GPs and PHNs and there should be closer links between the training programmes of the two professions. Most PHNs perceive that their training does give sufficient attention to ageing and that positive attitudes towards caring for older people are encouraged. Apart from a suggestion that more emphasis could be given to the development of assessment skills, no other training issues in regard to older people are identified by the nurses. Feedback from GPs also reveals a general perception that their training gives sufficient attention to caring for older people and provides adequately for health problems associated with ageing. It is accepted, however, that the sociological and psychological problems of older people receive little attention and that there is a need for greater emphasis on the multi-factorial nature of the problems experienced by older people. From the perspective of the GPs, the absence of any formal links between GP and PHN training leads to a lack of communication between the two professions and poor appreciation of each other's knowledge and expertise. The roles of GPs and PHNs are seen as interdependent and if this interdependence is not recognised then the care of the older person suffers.

Physiotherapists and occupational therapists perceive that their training gives adequate attention to care of older people with particular modules being devoted to this area, but there is a suggestion that more practical placements may be necessary. The Irish Society of Chartered Physiotherapists places particular emphasis on continuing education with regard to care of older people. In the context of professional training a second recommendation made by the Working Party was that:

- **(R4.15) professorial chairs of geriatric medicine be established in all medical schools**.

To date, the situation remains as it was in 1988 with only Trinity College Dublin having a chair of geriatric medicine. Two of the medical schools (University

College Galway and the Royal College of Surgeons) indicate that they have no plans to establish such a post because the necessary funding is not available. The other medical schools have plans for such a post but there is no specific timeframe in the case of University College Dublin while University College Cork awaits the appointment of the necessary accompanying consultant post.

4.5 Retirement

The Years Ahead draws attention to the fact that retirement is a time when many new adjustments are required and when an individual's health may be particularly vulnerable. In a society where people are judged in terms of their social usefulness or productivity, retired people may lose their sense of purpose and value as contributing members of society. The Working Party acknowledged· the importance of the work of the Retirement Planning Council of Ireland in pioneering pre-retirement courses which prepare people approaching retirement for another stage in life. At present, in addition to its *Planning for The Years Ahead* and other company in-house courses, the Retirement Planning Council of Ireland offers a free pre and post-retirement counselling service, a volunteer service and a newsletter.

In recent years there has been a rapid growth in the number of Active Retirement Associations across the country. A directory of services produced by Age Action Ireland lists 80 Active Retirement Associations. This development is taking place even in those rural and urban areas where such self-help groups are not often found. The national *Health Promotion Strategy* acknowledges the importance of preparation for older life at the pre-retirement stage and includes in its action plan for older people the development of programmes that encourage pre-retirement age groups to remain fit, active and independent for as long as possible.

4.5.1 Pre-retirement services provided by employers and trade unions

The Working Party argued that there is an obligation on employers and trade unions to ensure that their employees and members are well prepared for retirement. Their recommendation in this regard was that:

- **(R4.18) the Federated Union of Employers and the Irish Congress of Trade Unions advise their members to give greater priority to the development of a comprehensive pre-retirement service**.

It appears that this is not an area in which the present-day Irish Business and Employers Confederation is very active although it does collaborate with the Retirement Planning Council of Ireland with regard to policy-making. The Irish Congress of Trade Unions is involved in a number of initiatives related to retirement. In 1990 the Irish Congress of Trade Unions Retired Workers' Committees were established to advise on matters of special concern to older people, to promote the development of trade union structures for retired members and to organise and participate in activities specifically related to retired workers. The committees consist of retired trade union members, members of the Irish Congress of Trade Unions Executive Council and representatives from the National Federation of Pensioners' Associations (and the Northern Ireland Pensioners Convention). The Irish Congress of Trade Unions has also produced Guidelines on Retirement Planning designed to secure comprehensive Retirement Planning Agreements with employers. One aspect of such an agreement would be the provision of a Retirement Planning Programme. The guidelines suggest that a retirement planning programme should be carried out in four stages: mid-life planning; planning for retirement; pre-retirement; and post-retirement. The different stages would have different foci and emphases but generally the content would cover topics such as financial advice, health assessment and advice, coping with change, benefits and entitlements, legal matters and activities and interests.

The Working Party also recommended that:

- **(R4.18) the proposed Authority for Occupational Safety and Health when established, should ensure that a comprehensive pre-retirement service is available to all employees and to self-employed people**.

The Health and Safety Authority - established after *The Years Ahead* was published - indicates that it was unaware that any such recommendation had been made concerning its brief.

4.6   Labour force participation among older people

In recent years, both national policy documents and reports of the Commission of the European Communities have taken up the issue of social exclusion. One of the factors in social exclusion is non-participation in the labour force. In this regard, a report of the Commission of the European Communities states that: 'the prospect of a group of the population being 'retired', sometimes with 20 years or more ahead of them, is fraught with human, social and economic difficulties' (Commission of the European Communities 1993b, p. 46). The labour force participation rate of older workers (over 65 years) has traditionally been relatively higher in Ireland because of the high proportion of the older population engaged in farming. However, a study by Ronayne and Duggan in 1993 showed that the labour force participation rate of older male workers decreased dramatically from 52 per cent in 1960 to 16 per cent in 1990 and recent labour force figures show that in 1996 the rate had decreased further to 15 per cent. The reduction in participation rate for all older people has been from 32 per cent to 9 per cent in the period 1960-1990 with a further reduction to 8 per cent in 1996. The participation rate of those in the pre-retirement age group (55-64 years) fell from 56 per cent in 1961 to 43 per cent in 1990 with a small rise to 44 per cent in 1996.

4.6.1   Unemployment and older workers

The problems of older workers have been exacerbated in recent years by the growth in unemployment. The focus in dealing with the unemployment problem has been on job creation among the younger age groups and, when older workers become unemployed, it is frequently almost impossible for them to re-enter the labour market. It has been suggested that there is a tacit agreement between the social partners that older workers should bear a disproportionate share of the burden of unemployment in a labour surplus economy (O'Shea and Larragy 1993). In an examination of the extent to which the older long-term unemployed are targeted in state training and employment programmes, Ronayne and Duggan found that over two-thirds of participants in such programmes are under the age of 25 years (1993). A Eurobarometer Survey shows that among the Irish general public there is a widespread view that older workers are discriminated against with regard to job recruitment, job training and job promotion (Commission of the European Communities 1993a). The marginal labour market position of the older long-term unemployed is reinforced by the educational and occupational backgrounds of older people.

4.6.2   Early retirement schemes

At the present time, many workers are retiring before the conventional retirement age of 65 years (National Pensions Board 1993). While many make an argument for flexible retirement, this increase in early retirement reflects not so much flexibility as an orientation of policy towards withdrawal of older people from the labour force. The growth in unemployment has led to early retirement policies, redundancy packages and improved pension schemes. For example, in 1990, the Department of Social Welfare introduced the Pre-Retirement Allowance Scheme for persons then aged 60 years or over who are in receipt of the long-term rate of unemployment assistance. The scheme allows those eligible to opt to retire from the labour market and receive a weekly allowance instead of unemployment assistance. This Pre-Retirement Scheme is now open to those aged 55 years and over. Since its introduction, the number availing of this scheme has increased very rapidly from 6,513 in 1991 to 14,050 in early 1997.

The National Council for the Elderly has argued that ideally there should be 'a half-way house between working and retirement/redundancy and that job sharing by older workers should be explored' (National Council for the Elderly 1994b, p. 33). The National Council for the Elderly suggests that workers should be facilitated in gradual withdrawal from full-time employment over a number of years by providing the option of beginning to draw down pension entitlements.

4.7   Social involvement and attitudes towards ageing

The Working Party noted that the health and welfare of older people is greatly affected by whether or not they consider themselves to be valued members of the community. As discussed above, disengagement from an active work-life can be a significant factor in older people feeling that they no longer have a useful contribution to make. But, apart from disengagement from work, a second very important factor in whether or not older people remain actively involved in society is social attitudes towards ageing. As indicated above, the National Council for the Elderly has argued strongly that a fundamental change in attitude is a prerequisite for the effective social integration of older people. What is needed is a perspective where the talents, skills and experiences of older people are valued and channelled into the ongoing process of social and economic development and progress. The focus of such a perspective 'would be on the potential of older people to bring stimulation and creative challenge to others as distinct from making demands on the social services' (National Council for the Elderly 1994b, p. 12). In recognition of the need for this kind of perspective, the National Council for the Aged in 1988 initiated a National Day on Ageing. The Working Party recommended that:

- **(R4.20) the National Day on Ageing become an annual event**.

This initiative of the Council led to the establishment of Age and Opportunity, a national agency whose aim is to promote positive attitudes towards ageing and older people, to encourage participation of older people in all areas of society and to encourage inter-generational understanding. There are a number of other agencies currently in existence whose aim also is to promote and develop this kind of positive approach to ageing and older people. These include Age Action Ireland, Age Alliance, the Federation of Active Retirement Associations, the Irish Association of Older People, the Retirement Planning Council of Ireland and the National Federation of Pensioners Associations. In the absence of evaluation studies it is not possible to determine the contribution made by such bodies and whatever programmes they have developed to promoting participation of older people and inter-generational understanding.

Guided by the philosophy of 'adding life to years' a target of the World Health Organisation is that by the year 2000 people should have the basic opportunity to utilise their health potential to live socially and economically fulfilling lives (World Health Organisation 1985). With regard to older people the World Health Organisation has stressed that 'adding life to years' (or 'social gain' in the terms of *Shaping a Healthier Future*) is influenced greatly by empowerment, participation, and social involvement (World Health Organisation 1989). In the interests of 'social gain' the National Council for the Elderly recommends that initiatives offering older people the chance to deploy their skills and experience in a socially useful way should be actively promoted (Fahey and Murray 1994, p. 33). Examples given by the National Council for the Elderly of the kinds of involvement that would tap the knowledge and skills of older people and at the same time provide an ongoing social role for them are as follows (National

Council for the Elderly 1994b, p. 32):

- working with and supporting younger parents who are experiencing difficulties
- retired public servants working with voluntary bodies (as a number already do) to foster the concept of voluntary-statutory partnership
- working with younger people to maintain, develop, and in some instances to rediscover, crafts of the hands
- working in schools in varying capacities, for example, in pre-employment courses or with individual students in a one-to-one support/counselling role
- acting as trainers/tutors on community employment development programmes
- participating in the trade union movement (this would have the advantages of giving older people a say in the development of social and economic structures while also availing of their insights, skill and experience) and
- health promotion by older people for older people.

One initiative of this type currently in operation is a mentoring scheme developed by the National Social Services Board called The Social Mentor Project. Through this scheme retired experts in many fields (mainly business) give advice to voluntary organisations on a voluntary basis. Two more schemes are being considered for the future; one is the Health Mentor scheme, through which older people will advise their peers about health promotion. The other scheme which is a pilot venture developed by Community Technical Aid, involves older people acting in an advisory capacity with young unemployed people on interview skills, application forms and *curriculum vitae*.

4.8   Education and involvement

In the context of promoting the continued involvement of older people in society, the Working Party also recommended that:

- **(R4.21) the Department of Education encourage schools to promote positive attitudes to ageing and the elderly within the school curriculum.**

Research shows that there is little evidence of inter-generational conflict in this country (O'Shea and Larragy 1993). It is of note that the 1993 Eurobarometer Survey on Age and Attitudes showed that, within the European Community, Ireland had the highest proportion of older people who said they felt more respected as they got older. Similarly, the great majority of Irish older people (82 per cent) endorsed the view that younger people were generally helpful towards older people (Commission of the European Communities 1993a). In 1993, as part of its contribution to the European Year of Older People and Solidarity between

Generations, the National Council for the Elderly produced two programmes for use in schools aimed at promoting the themes of the positive contribution of older people, solidarity between young and old and meeting the challenge of older life. These were *Bearing Fruit* (a programme for primary schools) and *In Due Season* (a programme for post-primary schools).

The Department of Education indicates that attitudes to ageing and older people, at primary school level, are covered in the context of a programme of social, personal and health education. One goal of this programme is to teach students about the different groupings in their local community - such as young and old - and the inter-dependence of such groupings. At second level, a programme of civic, social and political education is being introduced in 1996/1997 as part of the junior cycle curriculum. Certain elements of this programme which deal with concepts such as human dignity, citizenship and the community are considered to be of relevance to the development of positive attitudes towards ageing and older people. At senior cycle level, the syllabus in Home Economics includes 'care of the aged' as an area of study. The transition year is also seen by the Department of Education as providing an opportunity where students can become more socially aware of the needs of different groups in their community including, among others, older people.

O'Shea and Larragy argue that education has long played a powerful role in the social integration of younger people and that it is now time for it to be accorded a similar role in the social integration of older people (O'Shea and Larragy 1995, p. 14). Older people are largely absent from the formal education system and their learning needs are poorly met. Age and Opportunity is active in promoting the concept of 'lifelong learning' and has produced a guide to educational opportunities for older people in Ireland. This is the first such resource designed directly for the use of older people in this country. It is of note that of the many learning opportunities listed in the guide, fewer than ten are designed especially for older people. An important development noted in the guide is the University of the Third Age, also known as U3A. The U3A movement basically involves self-help groups of older people who decide themselves the subjects they will study either using people within the groups as tutors or negotiating with local colleges or universities. Age Action Ireland has been given a grant to promote U3A in Ireland. O'Shea and Larragy recommend that greater efforts be made to attract older people into third level courses, that learning programmes designed to help combat exclusion and marginalisation be developed and that older people themselves determine the nature and content of whatever adult education courses are provided for them (1995).

4.9   Summary and conclusions

A summary of the extent to which recommendations in relation to maintaining the health of older people have been implemented is presented in Table 4.3 below.

Table 4.3: Summary of provisions for maintaining health

Recommendation	Current situation
Promotion of health among elderly be a primary concern of the Cabinet Sub-Committee to co-ordinate policies affecting health, the Health Promotion Council and the Health Promotion Unit of the Department of Health	Cabinet Sub-Committee under-utilised in health promotion among older people. National Consultative Committee on Health Promotion proposed in National Health Strategy established in 1995. Strategic Management Initiative promoting inter-departmental working links
The primary concern with health promotion among the elderly be made explicit in a national plan to promote health	Healthy Ageing programme incorporating a health promotion strategy currently being developed by the National Council on Ageing and Older People
Health Promotion Unit should develop directly, or indirectly, a health education policy for the elderly. CSEs in each area should be responsible for ensuring that an appropriate health education service for the elderly is available.	Health education policy for older people not yet in existence. Most existing health education programmes are aimed at young or middle-aged people. Two existing programmes are of relevance to older people but their possible contribution to national efforts at health education not yet evaluated. At health board level, health education services vary widely and are unstructured, uncoordinated and ad hoc. Potentially important developments are the establishment of health promotion departments and departments of public health medicine within the health boards and the establishment of the Office for Health Gain by the health boards. An important issue is the continuing lack of comprehensive, reliable data to underpin health education
Health boards to provide a health education service for carers of elderly people. Department of Health to provide guidelines on the content and operation of such a service. CSEs should ensure support and advice are available to carers	Current health education services for carers are patchy, unfocused and unstructured. No guidelines for the service provided but national Health Promotion Strategy promises a specific programme for carers
More positive attitudes to caring for the elderly should be encouraged and more attention given to ageing in professional training	Professions concerned are mostly satisfied with the attention given to care of older people in their training
Professorial chairs of geriatric medicine to be established in all medical schools	Situation remains as in 1988 with one medical school having a chair of geriatric medicine
Employers, trade unions and the Health and Safety Authority should develop pre-retirement services	A number of initiatives related to retirement established by the Irish Congress of Trade Unions
There should be an annual National Day on Ageing	National agency - Age and Opportunity - set up to promote positive attitudes towards ageing and older people
Schools should be encouraged by the Department of Health to promote positive attitudes to ageing	Two school programmes developed by the National Council for the Elderly. Existing primary and second-level curriculum contains elements of relevance to the development of positive attitudes towards ageing

Health promotion among older people was a critical concern of the Working Party. As a result, when the National Council for the Elderly was established in 1990 as a successor to the National Council for the Aged, one of its new terms of reference was to advise the Minister for Health on measures to promote the health of the elderly. The Working Party recognised that health promotion is a multi-faceted process and, in the interests of intersectoral co-operation, had recommended that this issue should be a primary concern of the Cabinet Sub-Committee on Health Promotion. The Cabinet Sub-Committee has not been very active in health promotion but a potentially important development is the Government's Strategic Management Initiative which sets out to create effective inter-departmental working links. Another development is the establishment of the National Consultative Committee on Health Promotion which reports to the Cabinet Sub-Committee on Health Promotion. At health board level, structures intended to support health promotion include the new Departments of Public Health Medicine and Health Promotion. Across the health boards, an important development in co-ordination of health promotion efforts is the establishment by the Chief Executive Officers of the Office for Health Gain.

The Working Party recommended that a national plan to promote health among older people should be developed. Since its establishment in 1990, the National Council for the Elderly has taken a number of steps in this regard. Based on a recommendation from one of the Council's reports, *Shaping a Healthier Future* promised, as a matter of priority, a health promotion programme for older people; a promise taken up in the later national *Health Promotion Strategy*. As a result, the National Council for Ageing and Older People is now developing a Healthy Ageing programme, one strand of which is the development of a health promotion strategy. The value of a health promotion strategy specifically for older people is to enable the health problems specific to older life to be properly addressed and to enable detection of the most appropriate channels and means of access for health promotion among older people.

One dimension of health promotion is health education which seeks to increase the person's information and skill levels so that healthy choices can be made. Two health education programmes currently in existence are of relevance to the needs of older people: *Lifewise* and *Health, Well-Being and Empowerment among Older People*. Neither programme has yet been evaluated and their effectiveness and potential contribution to a national health education programme have yet to be determined. While progress is evident in developing a national Healthy Ageing programme, at local level much remains to be done. The health boards do provide some health education for older people but the service is patchy and varies widely across boards. The PHNs, who are the primary deliverers of the service, raise many concerns about current health education for older people. The services are perceived as unstructured, uncoordinated and *ad hoc*, but the PHNs have been given neither the time nor the resources for a more coherent service. Health boards must develop specific structures for the provision of a comprehensive, coherent health education service dedicated to the needs of older people. In this regard, the development of the healthy ageing strategy is essential to guide and inform the programmes provided at local level.

The Years Ahead had also recommended a specific health education service for carers. Such a service is promised in the action plan for older people in the national *Health Promotion Strategy*. But, as in the case of older people, current health education services for carers are perceived by the PHNs as largely unfocused, unstructured and informal. One example of a local structured service for carers is the Caring for Carers project operated by Soroptimist International, Republic of Ireland in conjunction with other voluntary organisations and the health board in the Mid-Western region.

The Years Ahead identified the development of positive attitudes towards ageing and older people as an important dimension of health promotion. According to the National Council for the Elderly there is a need to question the culture surrounding ageing and fundamental changes in attitudes and perceptions are needed so that older people are seen not as a burden on society but as actively contributing members. A number of agencies have been formed to promote continued social involvement and active contribution among retired older people; including, for example, the Retirement Planning Council of Ireland, Active Retirement Associations, Age Action Ireland and the Irish Association of Older People. A major development in this regard has been the establishment of Age and Opportunity which is a national agency for the promotion of positive attitudes towards older people. Research is needed to evaluate the effectiveness of these different efforts at promoting positive attitudes. The Irish Congress of Trade Unions has responded to the Working Party's recommendation in regard to retirement planning by setting up Retired Workers' Committees and by producing guidelines on retirement planning. Other agencies which might be considered to have an important part to play in relation to retirement - such as the Irish Business and Employers Confederation and the Health and Safety Authority - have not as yet been very active in the area.

The National Council for the Elderly has provided a number of examples for the continued social and economic involvement of older people including mentoring schemes, training and tutoring schemes and involvement in trade union and health promotion activities. One practical implementation is the mentoring scheme developed by the National Social Services Board. An important concern now being identified relates to evidence of age discrimination at work and pressure towards early retirement. These are issues which must be addressed in the interest of the continued involvement of older people in society.

The Working Party highlighted the important role of education in promoting positive attitudes towards ageing and older people. As part of its contribution in this regard, the National Council for the Elderly developed two programmes for use in schools among primary and post-primary students. The existing primary and second-level school curriculum is seen by the Department of Education to contain elements of relevance to the development of positive attitudes.

With regard to the education needs of older people themselves, it has been pointed out that older people are, at present, largely absent from the formal education system. Age and Opportunity actively promotes the concept of 'lifelong learning' and has produced a guide to educational opportunities for older people in this country. However, few of the opportunities listed are designed specifically for older people and despite growing acceptance of the concept of 'lifelong learning' little practical effort is evident in the education system to encourage and enable the participation of older people.

CHAPTER FIVE

Housing

5.1   Introduction

For many years the close relationship between health policy and housing policy has been recognised, especially in respect of older people. *The Care of the Aged* report (1968) argued that the provision of suitable housing for older people was one of the most important factors in enabling older people to continue to live in the community. *The Years Ahead* fully endorsed that proposition and contended that housing policy should aim to ensure that older people have an opportunity to live in accommodation suited to their needs. *Shaping a Healthier Future* restated the importance of the housing environment for older people; in so doing it made clear its commitment to maintaining older people in dignity and independence at home in accordance with the wishes of older people, 'as expressed in many research studies', and restoring to independence at home those older people who become ill or dependent. One of the targets of *Shaping a Healthier Future* is to ensure that 90 per cent of those over 75 years of age continue to live at home.

According to the 1991 Census 91.5 per cent of older people were living in private households. The following estimates are available concerning the tenure of those living in private households.   In 1993 the great majority (89.7 per cent) of households in which a person 65 years or older was present were residing in housing which was owned outright or being purchased. Minorities of older households were either renting from a public authority or from a private landlord, 6.6 per cent and 2.9 respectively. The remaining 0.8 per cent were living in rent free accommodation (Fahey and Murray 1994).

Housing types available to older people can be considered to comprise a continuum ranging from conventional housing to high support hostels. Housing options between these extremes can be seen to include conventional housing modified by adaptations or extensions, old persons dwellings (OPDs) - mainly one bedroom houses built by local authorities for older people - and sheltered housing, which could be further subdivided according to the degree of support made available. Sheltered housing can range from a few houses with limited support services to larger groups of houses supported by alarm and warden services, and a wide range of support services. These models of sheltered housing are described in detail in an advisory document published by the Irish Council for Social Housing (1993). Some sheltered housing has been provided by local authorities, but most new projects are provided by voluntary housing organisations, and to a small degree by private ventures. High support hostels, mainly intended to accommodate older people who need psychiatric support, are usually provided by health boards - often in collaboration with voluntary groups.

5.1.1 Structure of the chapter

In this chapter the implementation of the recommendations of *The Years Ahead* report relating to housing is reviewed. These recommendations can be grouped under a number of headings: assessment and planning, priorities and criteria for letting, voluntary and sheltered housing, homelessness, repairs and adaptations to housing, and equity release and house exchange schemes. Recent developments in housing are then described; reference is made to the main ways in which housing is delivered to older people, the number of new (and acquired) housing units provided directly by local authorities for older people in recent years, evidence concerning changes in the quality of housing generally and in that of the housing of older people in particular. Some of the results of a 1996 assessment of housing need are presented. Following this the implementation of the recommendations of *The Years Ahead* is examined under the headings listed above. Finally some conclusions are presented.

5.1.2 Data sources

Several data sources are used in this chapter. They include a memorandum submitted by the Department of the Environment; extracts from interviews with health board officers including Chief Executive Officers, Community Care Programme Managers, Co-ordinators of Services for the Elderly and District Liaison Nurses. A postal survey of local authorities and voluntary housing organisations is also used to supplement the other information available. Approximately half (43) of the local authorities in Ireland (county councils, county boroughs, boroughs and urban district councils) were included in the survey of local authorities. In selecting local authorities stratified random sampling design was employed to ensure that proportionate numbers of local authorities in each of the categories listed above were selected and that their distribution by health board was also taken into account. Thirty respondents replied, a response rate of 70 per cent. The distribution of respondents and non-respondents to the local authority survey by health board area was as shown in Table 5.1.

Lists supplied by the Irish Council for Social Housing were used as the sampling frame for the survey of voluntary housing organisations. A small sample of 20 organisations were randomly selected from this list proportionate to the number of

Table 5.1: Distribution of respondents to the local authority survey

Health board region	Co. Councils	Co. Boroughs	Urban District Councils and Boroughs	Non-Response
Eastern	—	Dublin	Naas	Co.Council (2) Urban District Council (1)
Midland	Offaly	—	Tullamore	Co.Council (1)
Mid-Western	Clare	Limerick	Thurles	Co.Council (1) Urban District Council (1)
North Eastern	Louth, Meath	—	Dundalk, Navan, Carrickmacross	Urban District Council (1)
North Western	Leitrim	—	Sligo	Co.Council (1) Urban District Council (1)
Southern	—	Cork	Mallow, Skibbereen, Tralee, Youghal	Co. Council (1)
South Eastern	Carlow, Kilkenny, Tipperary SR	Waterford	Dungarvan, Tipperary	Borough (2) Urban District Council (1)
Western	Mayo, Roscommon	Galway	Ballinasloe, Westport	—
Total	10	5	15	13

Source: Local authority survey

organisations in each health board area. Fourteen replies were received, a response rate of 70 per cent.

Most (8) of these voluntary housing organisations have been operating since 1900 with seven since 1960. Virtually all are small in scale; ten had less than 40 housing units, three had between 40 and 75 units but the biggest has one thousand units. Most (12) of these organisations provide housing for older people only. The average age of tenants was estimated by eleven organisations: in two cases it was estimated to be in the late 60s, in eight cases 70 or more years and in one case 80 or more years. Most (10) provide sheltered housing only and one provides a mix of sheltered and conventional housing. Most (9) of the organisations providing sheltered housing organise visiting and on-site support on behalf of the residents. Respondents were located in four health board regions: Eastern (7), Southern (4), South Eastern (2) and Western (1).

5.2   Housing in *The Years Ahead*

Several recommendations were made in *The Years Ahead* in regard to the provision of housing for older people. In regard to overall housing policy, *The Years Ahead* recommended that the main emphasis should be to enable older people to choose between adapting their homes to the increasing disabilities of old age, or to move to accommodation which was more suited to them. Where it is not possible to maintain older people in their own homes or in ordinary local authority housing, sheltered housing should be the first choice. Close liaison between local authorities and health boards in the planning of sheltered housing was strongly recommended. Moreover, it was recommended that domiciliary services should be provided by health boards for the older residents of such schemes, and where appropriate, for their associated day centres.

While *The Years Ahead* was being prepared it was evident to the Working Party that a reduction in the overall supply of housing by local authorities was taking place. Accordingly, it was considered that the existing quota guidelines, whereby 10 per cent of all local authority housing consisted of old persons dwellings (OPDs), would no longer be adequate, and it was recommended that in future housing provision for older people should be based on factual assessments of need undertaken by local authorities.

The Years Ahead strongly supported the further development of voluntary housing organisations in providing housing for older people and made recommendations in respect of the funding of such housing, both capital and on-going. Recommendations were also made in respect of the broadening of letting criteria, the accommodation needs of homeless older people, increasing and simplifying the funding of repairs and adaptations schemes, and the exploration of equity release and house exchange schemes.

5.3   Developments in housing

Since the publication of *The Years Ahead* considerable change has occurred in the housing environment. The legislative framework broadened the scope for dealing with older people with the passing of the *1988 Housing Act*; their accommodation needs are addressed by local authorities under Section 9 of that Act. The publication of *A Plan for Social Housing* in 1991, and *Social Housing - The Way Ahead*, in 1995 by the Department of the Environment provided further policy responses to cater for the diverse needs of those assessed by local authorities for accommodation. The goal of *A Plan for Social Housing* was to ensure that every household has a dwelling suited to its needs; the strategy underlying the plan was diversification and it embraced all sections of the housing market. Within the strategy of diversification the voluntary housing sector was identified as a key provider of social housing and several improvements relating to the voluntary housing sector were introduced. These included raising the limit of the capital

Table 5.2: Housing provision for older and disabled people* 1988-1995

Year	Local authorities	Voluntary organisations**	Total
1988	432	366	798
1989	233	237	470
1990	233	301	534
1991	234	538	772
1992	192	456	648
1993	237	339	576
1994	414	193	607
1995	403	427	830
Total	2,378	2,857	5,235

Source: Department of the Environment
*Numbers for older people only are not available.
**The number approved in any year is given here; all units were built - though not necessarily in the year approved.

assistance payable, providing grants for communal facilities in grouped housing and providing a rental subsidy scheme which redirected the subsidy away from the building to the occupant of the dwelling (Department of the Environment 1991).

As can be seen in Table 5.2, 2,378 units were provided for older or disabled people by local authorities over the period 1988-1995, an average of 279 new (or acquired) housing units per year; this constituted 19.2 per cent of all units directly provided by local authorities during a time of reduced production (Department of the Environment 1997). This compares unfavourably with the level of provision during the earlier period 1972-1987 when 11,776 units for older and disabled people were provided, an average of 736 units per year, constituting 11.9 per cent of all housing units directly provided by local authorities during the period (O'Connor and Ruddle 1989). However, comparing local authority housing provision only for these periods does not take into account the effects of the policy of diversification introduced under *A Plan for Social Housing*. Over the period 1988-1995 approximately 2,857 units of accommodation for older and disabled people (an annual average of 357) were provided under the capital assistance scheme, by voluntary housing organisations. Moreover, it is not clear how many more houses occupied by older people were rescued by the various repairs and adaptation schemes during the 1988-1996 period thus obviating the necessity for new housing. In 1995 the total local authority housing stock of 95,700 included about 13,200 local authority dwellings especially built for older people or disabled people (Department of the Environment 1996a).

5.4   The quality of housing

It was recommended in *The Years Ahead* that:

- **(R5.29) priority should be given to improving the accommodation of the elderly lacking the basic amenities of an indoor toilet, hot and cold water and a bath or shower**.

Fahey and Murray (1994) have reported significant improvements in the housing circumstances of older people. The proportions of the homes of older people having a bath or shower increased from 60.6 per cent in 1977 to 90.6 per cent in 1993 and the proportion with an indoor toilet increased from 67.2 per cent in 1977 to 93.7 per cent. Dwelling ownership, whether owned outright or mortgage being repaid, increased from 80 per cent in 1977 to 89.7 per cent in 1993. These improvements are reflected in the increasing satisfaction of older people with their housing. For example, satisfaction with dwelling size ('about right size') increased from 78.5 per cent in 1977 to 84.4 per cent in 1993; overall satisfaction with accommodation ('very or fairly satisfied') increased from 88.7 per cent to 93.3 per cent; the proportion who would not like to move, if given the opportunity to do so, increased from 88.6 per cent to 90.8 per cent.

5.5   Estimates of the number of older people requiring accommodation

It was recommended in *The Years Ahead* that

- **(R5.18) the Minister for the Environment should monitor the implementation of the Housing Bill, 1988 and the position of the elderly requiring local authority accommodation to ensure that their needs are met comprehensively**.

Under Section 9 of the *1988 Housing Act* local authorities are obliged to 'have regard to' ten categories of housing need. Older people constitute one of these categories but it should be noted that the ten categories are not mutually exclusive, so that an older applicant can be included in other categories such as 'living in unfit or materially unsuitable accommodation'. Under the returns made to the Department of the Environment in 1996, 2,140 applicant households (7.8 per cent of all applicants) were categorised as older people. This was a slight reduction on the number of older people household applicants recorded in 1993 (2,289) which in turn was less than the number recorded in 1989 (2,349).

Fahey and Watson (1995) reported that 15 months after an assessment of housing stock carried out in March of 1993, 72 per cent of those categorised as in need because of advanced age were still seeking accommodation. Only 6 per cent had been housed by a local authority or voluntary housing association while 5 per cent had provided accommodation from their own means. Sixty four per cent of older applicants had been waiting for accommodation for more than two years and the median waiting period was 33 months. The authors noted that some of these applicants may have refused an earlier offer of housing.

5.6   Assessment and planning

5.6.1   Factual assessment of the housing conditions of older people

It was argued in *The Years Ahead* that, given the projected increase in older households and the much reduced level of the local authority building programme, meeting the needs of older people could no longer be guaranteed by achieving a target of 10 per cent of new local authority accommodation, as had been recommended in the *Care of the Aged Report*. It was accordingly recommended that:

- **(R5.30) in future, housing provision for the elderly be based on the factual assessment of need carried out by housing authorities**.

It was also recommended in *The Years Ahead* that:

- **(R5.5) the Department of the Environment should carry out a comprehensive survey into the housing conditions of the elderly to establish more precisely the housing status of the elderly**.

Fahey and Watson (1995) reported that four fifths of local authorities announced an assessment of housing stock to be carried out in 1993 and that most of them also notified other statutory bodies and voluntary organisations that the assessment was being conducted. They noted that each local authority assessed its need by counting its stock of applications on a specific day and by classifying that stock according to the set of categories specified in the *1988 Housing Act*. They noted also that housing need was equated by local authorities with need for local authority housing (Fahey and Watson 1995, p. 104).

Fahey and Watson concluded that the 1993 assessment of housing need was inadequate 'if the assessment is to be regarded as a forward-looking instrument for exploring the underlying level of housing need and guiding future housing policy'. They proposed 'a comprehensive assessment of all types of housing deficiency in the population, along with a classification of those deficiencies on the basis of the remedies which are most appropriate to deal with them'. They further proposed that a national survey of housing standards should include an assessment of the housing circumstances of households in the community as a whole (Fahey and Watson 1995, p.187).

The local authorities contacted in the present survey indicated that no factual assessment of the housing needs of older people had been undertaken by their authority since the publication of *The Years Ahead* other than the kind of statutory assessment referred to above. All local authorities also undertook a further statutory assessment. It should be noted that the 1996 assessments took account of some of the recommendations made by Fahey and Watson, in that applicants suited to accommodation other than local authority housing were identified and quantified.

5.6.2   A plan of action for implementing the recommendations of
          The Years Ahead
It was recommended in *The Years Ahead* that:

- **(R12.27) the Departments of Health and the Environment request the health boards and housing authorities to draw up a plan of action to implement the recommendations of the report**.

Most (28 of 30) respondents to the local authority survey indicated that their authority had not prepared a plan of action for implementation of the recommendations of *The Years Ahead* with regard to the accommodation needs of older people. Most (16) of these respondents gave no explanation why a plan had not been prepared. Those who gave an explanation usually referred to a lack of resources or suggested it was unnecessary.

5.7   Priorities and criteria for letting
It was recommended in *The Years Ahead* that:

- **(R5.34) the following factors, in addition to overcrowding and unfitness of dwellings, be taken into account by local authorities in relation to letting accommodation to the elderly: age, with special reference to those over 75 years; whether or not the elderly person is living alone or in isolation; the suitability of housing for those in long stay institutions; homelessness; tenants in private rented accommodation unable to pay rent, the medical condition of the elderly person**.

5.7.1   Main emphasis in housing policy for older people
Over a third (12 of 30) of respondents to the local authority survey gave no reply or a vague reply only to the question concerning the main emphasis of their authority in housing policy for older people. Vague replies included such responses as 'suitable environment', and 'adequate dwellings' etc. Some of the 18 who indicated their authority's emphasis listed more than one consideration; these are listed in Table 5.3 below. Many respondents indicated in addition that the authority was concerned with the quality of the housing units in terms of their size, condition and suitability. The responses to this question are listed in Table 5.3. Many respondents also noted that their authority was concerned with the quality of the housing units in terms of size, condition and suitability.

5.7.2   Priority groups within the older population
Six (of 30) respondents to the local authority survey identified their priority groups according to a single criterion while 15 identified at least two; the numbers referring to each criterion are listed in Table 5.4.

Table 5.3: Main emphasis in housing policy for older people

Authority's main emphasis	Number
Access to services, amenities	9
Voluntary housing	7
Security	4
Sheltered housing	4
Opportunities for social contact	2
Affordable rents	1

Source: Local authority survey

Table 5.4: Priority groups among older people

Priority group	Number	Priority group	Number
Unfitness (of dwelling)	18	Isolation	2
Overcrowding	9	Single-living in flat	1
Medical/compassionate	9	Surrendering family house	1
Homelessness	7	Leaving institutional care	1
Lack of resources/high rent	6	Danger	1
Involuntary sharing	4	Waiting time	1
Physical disability	4	Living conditions	1
No tenure	2	Evicted	1

Source: Local authority survey

Most respondents to the local authority survey included older people living in unfit conditions as a priority group. One third or more of those who identified any priority group within the older population included those living in overcrowded conditions, or the homeless, or those who had applied on compassionate/medical grounds.

Respondents to the local authority survey were also asked to indicate which if any of a number of criteria were taken into account in letting accommodation to older people. These criteria, and the number taking them into account are presented in Table 5.5.

Overcrowding, unfitness of dwelling, medical/compassionate grounds, or inability to pay for private rented accommodation were the most common criteria mentioned. It should be noted that only 20 local authorities have points schemes in operation for allocating housing and therefore most authorities have considerable flexibility in weighting the above criteria (Fahey and Watson 1995).

Table 5.5: Criteria taken into account in letting accommodation to older people

Criteria	Number
Overcrowding	29
Unfitness (of dwelling)	29
Age of person (special reference to 75+)	26
Living alone/isolation	24
Suitability of housing for those in long-stay institutions	25
Homelessness	28
Inability to pay private rented accommodation	29
Medical/compassionate	29
Other*	9

Source: Local authority survey
*Under 'other' four referred to involuntary sharing, two referred to time on waiting list, one in each case referred to special problems, income and other (unspecified).

In *The Years Ahead* it was recommended that:

- **(R5.31) local authorities give special attention to the elderly on low incomes in substandard private rented accommodation in planning and allocating accommodation for the elderly**.

All respondents to the local authority survey indicated that older people on low incomes in substandard rented private accommodation were taken into account in the planning and allocation of relevant housing. Most (17) respondents provided estimates of the proportion of housing for older people given to such persons. Five gave no answer and eight indicated this information was unknown/unavailable. Of those who provided estimates, 11 indicated that at least 50 per cent of older residents had previously lived in substandard private rented accommodation. Four indicated that smaller proportions had lived in such housing. In general, county councils reported that smaller proportions had been living in such housing.

5.8 Voluntary housing

5.8.1 The extent of voluntary housing

It was recommended in *The Years Ahead* that:

- **(R5.42) the role of voluntary housing organisations be expanded to meet the housing needs of the elderly**.

In 1985 it was estimated by the National Council for the Aged (1985b) that 1,850 dwelling units were provided by voluntary associations; approximately two thirds of these were provided for older people and many of them had been built for some time. Over the seven year period 1981-1987 a total of 469 units, an annual average of 67, were constructed by voluntary housing organisations under the capital assistance scheme run by the Department of the Environment. This figure includes all such housing, not only housing for older and disabled people (separate figures for older and disabled people are not available). In contrast over the eight year period 1988-1995, 5,097 units were approved for construction by voluntary organisations under the Capital Assistance Scheme, an annual average of 637 (Department of the Environment 1997). This includes 2,857 units for older and disabled people as detailed in Table 5.2. Clearly the provision of housing by voluntary housing organisations has increased substantially since 1988 and the capital assistance scheme, and improvements to it, has made a major contribution to this increase. It has been estimated that the non-profit/voluntary and co-operative sector approved bodies currently manage a rental stock of over 8,500 dwellings, including special needs/sheltered housing and hostel accommodation. It has also been estimated by the Irish Council for Social Housing and the Department of the Environment (1996b) that in recent years such approved housing bodies have been providing 20-25 per cent of the new dwelling units added to the national rented social housing stock. While the non-profit/voluntary housing sector as a whole is expanding, with more dwellings being provided for general housing needs, the proportion of new voluntary housing designated for older people being built each year is not expected to increase very much in coming years, unless funding supports are improved (Irish Council for Social Housing 1996).

Most (22) respondents to the local authority survey indicated that their authority collaborates with voluntary organisations engaged in the provision of housing for older people. Most (17) of these provided some information on the nature of the collaboration; in seven cases it related to finance or advice concerning sites, planning permission and other related matters; in seven cases it related to informal contact, regular meetings or committee membership and in two cases it was through participation in identifying those in need of housing. While detailed information about the nature of the above collaboration is not available it would appear that where it is practised at all it is generally rather limited. Thirteen respondents indicated that their authority was currently providing capital assistance for voluntary housing schemes.

5.8.2   *Capital funding of voluntary housing*
It was recommended in *The Years Ahead* that:

- **(R5.42) the current Department of the Environment scheme to assist voluntary housing schemes be amended to increase the capital loan facility to 95 per cent**.

The maximum grants available under the voluntary housing capital assistance scheme in 1988 were £20,000 per unit of accommodation or a maximum of 80 per cent of the overall cost of the project, whichever was the lesser. These maxima were increased to £22,000 and 90 per cent respectively in 1991 with a new grant of £25,000 being introduced for family type units. Further increases were announced in May 1995 with the result that the current maximum grants are as follows: £27,000 for each accommodation unit designed for occupation by one or two persons, and £33,000 for each accommodation unit designed for occupation by three or more persons. Both these amounts are subject to the grants not exceeding 90 per cent (95 per cent where the project is for the homeless) of the overall costs of the project. Grants were also introduced in 1991 for the provision of communal facilities in voluntary housing projects. These grants, which are financed out of National Lottery funds, cannot exceed £2,000 per unit of accommodation in a project or a maximum of 90 per cent of the costs of providing the facilities, whichever is the lower. In relation to older people, local authorities can also charge to the capital cost of the scheme certain extras where the size of the scheme warrants it. These include the cost of providing a common room and the fixtures and facilities normally needed as part of a sheltered housing scheme, the cost of providing an appropriate alarm system and suitable heating facilities, and the cost of ensuring that housing schemes are designed to maximise safety and security for residents, especially for older people or disabled people (Department of the Environment 1996b).

5.8.3   *Financial assistance with maintenance and running costs*
In order to meet the management, caretaking, repair and maintenance costs of housing it is necessary for voluntary housing organisations to charge reasonable rents. The Department of Social Welfare has approved the payment by Community Welfare Officers of supplementary welfare allowances towards the housing rent charges due from qualified tenants to voluntary housing organisations for their accommodation. Typical guideline rents are up to £25 per week before subsidy. Qualified tenants would be persons in receipt of social welfare income allowances, including pensioners.

Apart from the ordinary housing management insurance, caretaking, repair and maintenance costs which are usually met from the rent charges, the provision by voluntary housing organisations of supportive/sheltered housing involves additional staff, caretaking, repair equipment and other running costs, including the cost of providing elements of care, short of full institutional care.

It was recommended in *The Years Ahead* that:

- **(R5.42) the Department of Environment should consider ways in which the voluntary housing organisations could be assisted with the cost of maintaining housing schemes**.

The Department of the Environment does not contribute towards the maintenance or other running costs of projects funded under the capital assistance scheme.

Arrangements, including financial arrangements, can be made by a local authority with an approved voluntary housing organisation for the accommodation of a person deemed to be homeless. Such financial arrangements consist of payments made by the local authorities to an approved housing/hostel organisation under Section 10 of the *1988 Housing Act* towards the running costs incurred in accommodating homeless persons, and this may include some older homeless persons. Such payments are confined to the accommodation of persons in the homeless category and are not applicable to any other special needs/disadvantaged categories. The cost of such Section 10 payments by local authorities is substantially recouped by the Department of the Environment. These funds are used by voluntary housing organisations to assist towards the additional running costs incurred in providing sheltered/supportive housing and hostel services for homeless persons but are not available for other approved projects of this type such as those for older people.

Health boards may contribute towards the running costs of bodies providing services which are ancillary to those of a health board under section 65 of the *Health Act 1953*. There is no defined scheme of funding under this section to assist towards the running costs of housing organisations in providing various elements of care and social support services in sheltered housing projects on an ongoing basis. Some organisations have negotiated the payment of such grants on an annual basis to help meet deficits involved in providing support services. Although voluntary housing organisations provide a range of on-site care and social support services in sheltered housing projects with communal welfare facilities, including services which are equivalent to home-help and domiciliary care, there is no defined funding scheme to assist them in planning to meet the annual budget costs of providing such services, including the staff costs.

5.8.4 *The encouragement of voluntary organisations in caring for older people*
It was recommended in *The Years Ahead* that:

- **(R11.17) health boards and local authorities should encourage by all possible means the involvement of voluntary organisations in caring for the elderly. Each board and local authority should agree with the voluntary organisations working with the elderly in their functional area their respective responsibilities in the delivery of services**.

Most (26 of 30) respondents to the local authority survey indicated that the authority encouraged voluntary organisations' involvement in caring for older people. Most (23) of these indicated the nature of the encouragement. In most cases it was clear from the nature of the encouragement that the organisations were housing organisations; thus for example, the nature of the encouragement in 17 cases related to capital grants, advice about sites or guidelines.

Four (of 30) respondents to the local authority survey indicated that their authority had made arrangements with voluntary organisations in regard to the delivery of services. Some of the arrangements indicated are vague and include financing of Meals-on-Wheels and cleaning of common areas, financing residents' associations and supporting 'elderly homeless persons' and 'tenants on waiting list'. Virtually all (28) respondents indicated that contracts had not been made with voluntary organisations in regard to the delivery of services. Most (8 of 14) voluntary housing organisations reported having had some contact with a local authority. Overall, the nature of the contact appeared to be quite limited: the largest organisation reported having 'telephone contact' with housing officers; three referred to a requirement to agree their tenancies with a housing authority; two had been in contact with a housing authority when seeking grants; one was 'in touch' with the local authority and one complained that contact only arose when the authority 'wanted something'.

Co-ordinators of Services for the Elderly were asked to describe their health board's arrangements for consultation with voluntary housing organisations; these are presented in Table 5.6. Four health boards, the Eastern, Mid-Western, North Western and Southern, according to the feedback obtained, have no formal relationships with voluntary housing organisations. They hardly arise in the North Eastern where no voluntary group has approached the health board. While it was clearly indicated in the South Eastern and Western that meetings take place, and that consultation is available, the impression received is that the arrangements are informal in nature.

Most (8 of 14) voluntary housing organisations reported having some contact with a health board. In six cases the contact was explained by the health board's

Table 5.6: Health boards' arrangements for consultation with voluntary housing organisations

Health board	Arrangements for consultation with voluntary housing organisations
Eastern	No specific formal relationship
Midland	Not applicable
Mid-Western	No formal links
North Eastern	No voluntary group has approached
North Western	Informal arrangements
Southern	None
South Eastern	Meetings and available for consultation
Western	CSE will consult with any organisation

Source: Interviews with CSEs

provision of an annual grant or rent subsidies. One organisation reported that the health board had funded the purchase of equipment and liaison with nursing and paramedical services. Seven of the eight organisations who had contact with a health board found the nature of the contact generally satisfactory. Two of the organisations without such contact gave no explanation for its absence and two others considered it unnecessary. Five of the 14 voluntary housing organisations reported having had contact with the health board's Co-ordinator of Services for the Elderly but the nature of the contact appears to have been quite limited.

5.9   Sheltered housing

In *The Years Ahead* (p. 74) reference is made to *sheltered housing* as the first choice which should be considered for older people who cannot be maintained in their own houses or local authority housing. *The Years Ahead* policy statement is not mentioned in the *1995 Social Housing - The Way Ahead* housing policy statement by the Department of the Environment and there is no reference to sheltered housing as the first choice which should be considered for certain older people.

Sheltered housing is defined in an advice note of the Irish Council for Social Housing (1993):

- sheltered housing comprises group schemes of dwellings with on-site communal facilities for assisted independent living
- the dwellings may be of a one to two person type in a suitably designed group scheme of houses or apartments, and or buildings suitable for conversion
- the project includes on-site communal facilities such as a catering kitchen for preparing congregate/group meals, dining/recreation areas, laundry and alarm system
- there is usually an on-site warden welfare/caretaker person with suitable accommodation
- care supports may include the provision of meals and assistance with cleaning, hygiene, bathing, requiring extra staff employed for this purpose subject to financial budgets
- the economically viable size for this type of sheltered housing project may be 30+ dwelling units.

5.9.1   The extent of sheltered housing

It was noted by the National Economic and Social Council (1988) that most of the purpose-built housing for older people in Ireland would not qualify as sheltered housing in the sense of providing special needs housing with communal facilities. Defining sheltered housing as 'schemes where the occupancy of dwellings is mainly restricted to elderly persons and the scheme has a resident warden and/or an alarm system connected to each dwelling', O'Connor and Ruddle (1989) estimated that the number of sheltered housing units in 1988 was 3,504 provided in 117 schemes. Most of these units (72 per cent) were in local authority schemes, 19 per cent were in schemes provided by voluntary organisations, 9 per cent were in schemes provided by private commercial organisations and a small number were provided by health boards.

Three (of 30) respondents to the local authority housing survey reported that sheltered housing was provided directly by the authority for older people and that voluntary organisations provided sheltered housing in their areas. Two others indicated that they had built schemes with some features of sheltered housing. However, most (17 of 27) of those who indicated that sheltered housing was not provided by the authority, reported that it was provided by a voluntary organisation. Explanations given by the ten respondents in the authorities where sheltered housing was not available included: no demand/need (4), no land, emphasis is on providing housing close to services, and sheltered housing was under discussion with a statutory or voluntary organisation (2). Where the authorities did not provide sheltered housing directly they were asked to indicate what housing choices were available to older people who were unable to stay in their own homes or in ordinary local authority housing. Most (17 of 27) respondents gave no answer, though eight of the 17 indicated in replies to other questions that voluntary housing was available. Of the ten who replied, four indicated that voluntary housing was available; two, in each case, indicated that voluntary sheltered housing or institutional accommodation was available; and one, in each case, referred to the private rented sector and local authority housing. Nine of these ten had also indicated in replies to other questions that sheltered housing was available.

5.9.2 Services provided in sheltered housing
It was recommended in The Years Ahead that:

- **(R5.32) the (health) board, for its part, should provide domiciliary services for the elderly residents and, where appropriate, associated day care centres**.

Two of the three local authorities providing sheltered housing gave details of the services provided by the health board for the residents. One, a large urban authority, listed public health and psychiatric nursing, Home Helps and meals provided by voluntary committees. The other, a medium sized urban authority, referred generally to community care services.

The services made available by health boards to residents of sheltered housing schemes, as described by the Community Care Programme Managers of the health board, are listed in Table 5.7. While only three reported that residents have full

Table 5.7: Services provided to residents of sheltered housing by health boards

Health board	Services provided by health boards
Eastern	Full access to health board services. Some schemes have in-built day centres. Wardens in voluntary schemes funded by EHB
Midland	Day centre, Meals-on-Wheels and laundry
Mid-Western	Full access to health board services
North Eastern	Home Helps, Care Assistants, nursing assistance, including full care
North Western	Full access to health board services, day facility attached to many housing complexes
South Eastern	GP, PHN, Home Helps, grant aid via section 65 and community welfare
Southern	No response
Western	PHN, Home Helps, Meals-on-Wheels, aids and appliances, laundry as required

Source: Interviews with Programme Managers of Community Care

access to health board services it is unlikely that residents in sheltered schemes in any health board are completely excluded from them. Day centres and other facilities are available in sheltered schemes in three health board areas: the Eastern, Midlands and North Western.

O'Connor and Ruddle (1989) reported that the move to sheltered housing had resulted in an increase in the availability of some statutory services to residents. Over half of the residents of such schemes were receiving an increased number of visits from their GP and more than three quarters were receiving more visits from chiropodists, Home Helps and PHNs than they had received in their previous dwellings. However, while the availability of services had increased, the level of provision was still low. Only one half of the residents had been visited by their GP and about one quarter had been visited by a PHN or chiropodist at least once during the previous six months.   Very few had received the services of a physiotherapist, social worker or Home Help or Meals-on-Wheels during the same period. O'Connor and Ruddle noted that older people cared for at home were more likely to receive visits from their GP and PHN than were residents of sheltered housing.

5.9.3   Liaison in the planning of sheltered schemes
It was recommended in *The Years Ahead* that:

- **(R5.32) there should be close liaison (by the local authority) with the health board in the planning of sheltered schemes**.

The arrangements described for liaison with local authorities in planning such schemes are presented in Table 5.8. The Eastern, South Eastern, and the Southern

Table 5.8: Liaison with local authorities in planning sheltered housing

Health board	Arrangements for liaison	Satisfaction with arrangements	Why less than satisfactory
Eastern	Liaise at area level with local authorities. Contribute to housing needs survey	Satisfactory	N/A
Midland	County Manager and Director of Community Care meet on issues. Environmental Health Officer is called on for housing assessment	Fair	Formal structures needed to ensure exchange of information
Mid-Western	None	N/A	N/A
North Eastern	Superintendent Public Health Nurse and Co-ordinator of Services for the Elderly liaise	Unsatisfactory	Housing for older people needs more structured approach. Co. Managers would support more structured approach. No liaison between Departments of Environment, Health and Social Welfare. Local authorities need to be given full responsibility and resources for housing
North Western	Health board and County Council Committee liaise on all aspects of housing	Satisfactory	N/A
South Eastern	Through community care at local level	Satisfactory	N/A
Southern	Determine need for sheltered housing. Public Health Nurses and Community Welfare Officers serve on local committees	Satisfactory	N/A
Western	Medical Officer of Health has close liaison with County Manager and County Secretary and other officers	Satisfactory	N/A

Source: Interviews with Programme Managers of Community Care

Health Boards reported that they have liaison procedures at local level - at community care area level in the case of the Eastern Health Board. In the Midland, North Eastern, North Western and Western Health Boards such procedures appear to operate at a higher level. No such procedures were reported in the Mid-Western Halth Board. In five cases the procedures were rated satisfactory. They were described as fair and unsatisfactory in the Midland and

North Eastern Health Boards respectively. In both of these cases a more structured approach for liaison was said to be required, and in the case of the latter, more liaison between the relevant government departments together with the allocation of full responsibility and resources to local authorities was recommended.

Two of the three local authorities providing sheltered housing directly indicated that they had arrangements for liaising with a health board in the planning of sheltered housing schemes. One of these described the arrangements as consisting of a joint working group with the health board to examine services for older people. Eight of the 17 respondents in authorities where only voluntary organisations provide sheltered housing indicated that they have arrangements for liaising with a health board. In three cases the voluntary organisation was referred to the health board fairly directly; in three cases there was discussion between the authority, health board and voluntary organisation; two respondents provided no details. Six respondents thought these arrangements were satisfactory and one described them as fairly satisfactory.

5.10   Prevention of isolation

It was recommended in *The Years Ahead* that**:**

- **(R5.34) wherever possible elderly people should be housed in their own area and to avoid the problem of isolation - dependent elderly in isolated rural areas should be encouraged to move to suitable accommodation in nearby villages and towns**.

Most (16 of 30) of the respondents to the local authority survey indicated that the majority or nearly all older people were re-housed as close as possible to where they lived previously or in the area of their choice. Four replied that this was not a factor, that all were within the urban district boundary, or that the (urban) authority consisted of a single area, and four stated that this information was unknown/not readily available Twelve respondents indicated that their authority usually encouraged dependent older people living in isolated areas to move to suitable accommodation in towns or villages. Ten indicated that this question was inapplicable as they were urban authorities and six respondents indicated that their authority did not attempt to do this. Eight of the twelve respondents who indicated this was their practice were county councils; the other four were urban district councils. Only two of the seven authorities without this practice were county councils, the other five were urban district councils. Most (8 of 12) respondents using this practice indicated that dependent older people generally agreed with it, while in three cases such agreement was not generally found.

In general this awareness by local authorities of the importance of location is supported by O'Connor and Ruddle (1989). They reported that more than three quarters of residents of sheltered schemes felt that they were close enough to such amenities as shops, chemists, post offices, banks, bus stops, public telephones, and to their families and friends. Moreover, most tenants were positive about the locality in which they were situated.

5.11   Homelessness

It was recommended in *The Years Ahead* that:

- **(R5.33) local authorities and health boards should co-operate to meet, in a flexible way, the accommodation needs of the small number of elderly who are homeless.**

5.11.1   *Defining homelessness*

The following definition of homelessness is given in Section 2 of the *1988 Housing Act*:

'A person shall be regarded by a housing authority as being homeless for the purposes of this Act if-

(a) there is no accommodation available which, in the opinion of the authority, he, together with any person who normally resides with him or who might reasonably be expected to reside with him, can reasonably occupy or remain in occupation of, or

(b) he is living in a hospital, county home, night shelter or other such institution, and is so living because he has no accommodation of the kind referred to in paragraph (a), and he is, in the opinion of the authority, unable to provide accommodation from his own resources'.

Fahey and Watson (1995) have commented on the difficulties in defining homelessness and on the variety of interpretations that can be made of it as defined in the *1988 Housing Act*. They acknowledged that estimates of homelessness in Ireland varied from the 2,667 homeless persons enumerated in the 1993 housing assessment, to 5,000 based on counts of the flows of homeless persons through voluntary agencies during 1993. Though unable to estimate the degree of undercount in the 1993 assessment of homelessness, they concluded that some had taken place. Reasons suggested by them for this undercount included a distinction made by some enumerators between the homeless and generally homeless people on housing lists and, in some cases, the exclusion of homeless persons with needs for special medical and social supports on the grounds that they were not seeking, or could not cope, in conventional local authority housing. Harvey (1995) reported considerable differences in the manner in which local authorities interpreted homelessness under the *1988 Housing Act*; for example 23 of 41 local authorities surveyed considered victims of male violence, discharged persons from hospitals or prisons and people in a temporary hostel to be homeless.

5.11.2   The extent of homelessness among older people

To illustrate the living arrangements of homeless persons Fahey and Watson (1995) constructed a profile of a sample consisting of 181 homeless 'household units'. Three per cent of their sample were 65 years or more, but it must be noted that the authors advised that the sample selected was not a nationally representative sample. If this proportion was applied to the total number of 2,459 homeless persons in 1996, approximately 74 older people were homeless at that point. The estimated 2,459 homeless persons in 1996 included 667 persons who, because they had no other accommodation were living in health board accommodation and 988 other persons who were living in hostel-type accommodation. As can be seen in Table 5.9 Programme Managers of Community Care indicated that few older people were homeless.

The information provided by local authorities on homelessness among older people is in agreement with this. Most (26) respondents to the local authority survey indicated that the authority had estimated the number of homeless older people in the region. Most (16) of these indicated there were no homeless older people and two indicated that the analysis was not yet complete. The number of older homeless persons indicated by the other eight respondents ranged from two to twenty. In some of these cases the numbers related to the number of older persons who had come to the attention of the authority over the course of a year rather than to the total number at any particular time.

A 1992 study of hostel residents in Dublin found that (over a three week period in March 1991) 152 of the residents were over 60 years of age. On examining the circumstances of older persons and other residents, especially long-term residents,

Table 5.9: Number of homeless older people by health board area

Health board	Number of homeless older people
Eastern	No older homeless; older occupants of hostels would have been offered housing
Midland	Up to 30 currently resident in institutions. Could be housed if suitable housing were available
Mid-Western	Very small problem in Mid-Western region
North Eastern	Very small problem. About 12 cases during 1995
North Western	Board staff work closely with County Council to provide accommodation
Southern	Not a major problem. Two couples in last month
South Eastern	Not a problem
Western	Three cases in 1995

Source: Interviews with Programme Managers of Community Care

it was concluded that standard local authority housing was unsuitable for many of them. However, it was concluded that long-term homelessness could be eliminated if adequate good quality sheltered housing with support were provided (Focus Point 1992). This recognition of the unsuitability of standard local authority housing in some cases may, as was suggested by Fahey and Watson (1995), account for some of the dispute concerning estimates of homelessness. Failure to take into account the homelessness of those people for whom standard local authority housing is unsuitable is less likely to arise in the future because of the innovations in estimating the circumstances of those in need introduced in the 1996 assessments. Some hostels in the Dublin area, notably the Iveagh Hostel and York House, have made substantial progress in the provision of high support social housing for people who previously had no alternative but hostel accommodation (Focus Point 1992).

5.11.3 Arrangements for liaison

It can be seen in Table 5.10 that Programme Managers of Community Care in the Midland and Mid-Western Health Boards, reported that they had no arrangements

Table 5.10: Arrangements for co-operation between health boards and local authorities in meeting the needs of homeless older people

Health board	Are arrangements for co-operation with local authorities satisfactory?	Arrangements for co-operating with local authorities to meet needs of homeless older people
Eastern	Satisfactory	Co-ordinator of Services for the Elderly would consult with housing authority
Midland	N/A	None
Mid-Western	N/A	None
North Eastern	Satisfactory	Would supply details of cases needing help to local authority. Contact with voluntary organisations.
North Western	Satisfactory	Health board and county council liaison committee
Southern	Satisfactory	Contact with Simon. Would discuss any problems with local authority
South Eastern	No answer	Director of Community Care/Medical Health Officer, Environmental Health Officer and Community Welfare Officer have close links with local authority
Western	Unsatisfactory*	Accommodation available in Shrone House

Source: Interviews with Programme Managers of Community Care
* The spokesperson for the Western Health Board was commenting on the facility available for housing homeless older people. Young homeless people share this facility with older homeless people and in his view these two groups do not always mix well together.

with local authorities to meet the housing needs of homeless older people. Details of arrangements were provided by the Programme Managers in the Eastern, North Eastern, North Western, Southern, South Eastern and Western Health Boards. The arrangements were described as unsatisfactory only by the Programme Manager of Community Care in the Western Health Board because of the unsuitability of the available facilities.

Most (20) respondents to the local authority survey indicated that their authority had arrangements for liaising with the health board with regard to housing homeless older people, seven indicated they had no such arrangements and three gave no answer. Six gave broad descriptions of the arrangements. These included 'health board arranges temporary accommodation', 'reporting and identification', 'referrals made by council to health board', 'details of elderly in institutions were established'. Twelve described arrangements in respect of the officers involved. The officers referred to included: the Community/Supplementary Welfare Officers, Environmental Health Officers, Medical Officers, social workers, PHNs and occupational therapists.

In a circular issued by the Department of the Environment (1991) local authorities were instructed to establish on-going liaison with the voluntary sector for the purpose of improving policy and programmes for the homeless. However, it was concluded by Focus Point (1992) that 'although negotiations had taken place with individual organisations, no mechanism had been instituted to allow the voluntary sector as a whole to have an impact into policy for homeless people'. The responses to the local authority survey give a similar impression. Most (18 of 30) respondents indicated that the authority had arrangements with voluntary organisations with regard to homeless older people. However, four gave no description of these arrangements, five described them only as regular/periodic contacts/liaisons, four only named the organisation(s) involved and only three identified the purpose of the arrangement.

In October 1996 an important development for the provision of services for the homeless in the Dublin Region, The Homeless Initiative, was launched. This initiative aims to improve the planning, delivery and co-ordination of services for homeless people. It is comprised of two elements, the Management Group and the Consultative Board. The Management Group is comprised, in each case, of two representatives from Dublin Corporation and the Eastern Health Board at senior management level. Certain statutory bodies and categories of voluntary /non-profit organisations, including the Irish Council for Social Housing, have the right to nominate ordinary members of the Consultative Board and it is open to any voluntary sector organisation providing services for the homeless to nominate itself.

5.12 Repairs and adaptations

It was recommended in *The Years Ahead* that:

- **(R5.37) the Department of the Environment should ensure as a matter of priority, adequate finance is allocated to operate the repairs and adaptations scheme... and pending the introduction of a comprehensive scheme to improve the accommodation of the elderly and disabled, ...that increased resources be allocated to the Task Force on Special Housing for the Elderly to allow more than minimal repairs to be carried out to the homes of vulnerable elderly people and to reduce the waiting list...that funding for the scheme of remedial works to older and substandard local authority houses be expanded to ensure that it achieves its potential to improve the accommodation of elderly, local authority tenants. ...and in the short-term that the Department of the Environment should consider ways in which the Essential Repairs Scheme and the Housing Improvement Grants for Disabled Persons could be better targeted to meet the needs of the more vulnerable elderly and disabled**.

The main repair/improvement schemes together with the out-turn for 1996 and the provision for 1997 are listed in Table 5.11.

Older people can benefit from any of the above schemes and from other schemes such as the Remedial Works Scheme and the bathrooms programmes under which improvements are made to local authority housing. The Special Housing Aid for the Elderly is however the only scheme exclusively addressed to older people. Over the period 1982-1994, 23,000 cases were dealt with under this scheme. Activity substantially increased in 1994 due to a special additional allocation of £2 million from the proceeds of the tax amnesty and this reduced the backlog of cases awaiting action. Amounts of £3 million and £4 million were allocated to the Task

Table 5.11: Repair/improvement schemes, out-turn for 1996 and provision for 1997

Scheme	1997 Provision £million	1996 Out-turn £million
Disabled Persons Grants Scheme	4.000	3.819
Essential Repairs Grants Scheme	0.500	0.508
Special Housing Aid for the Elderly (Task Force)	4.132	4.000
Improvement Works in Lieu	2.583	2.281
Extension to Local Authority Housing	1.500	1.061
Local Authority House Improvement Loans	6.000	2.900

Source: Department of the Environment, 1997

Force in 1995 and 1996 respectively compared with £1.5m in 1988 (Department of the Environment 1996b).

In *The Years Ahead* it was recommended that:

- **(R5.36) the Department of the Environment should replace the existing *ad hoc* grant schemes with a comprehensive and flexible repairs and adaptation scheme for the elderly and disabled which local authorities could administer either by the provision of a grant or by organising the work on behalf of the elderly person**.

The three grant schemes regarded in *The Years Ahead* as *ad hoc* schemes are still in operation. In the view of the Department of the Environment these schemes form an integral part of the social housing programme and provide a flexible response for essential type works (Department of the Environment 1996b).

It was recommended in *The Years Ahead* that:

- **(R5.29) in assessing housing needs, local authorities should assess the level of resources required for an effective repairs and adaptations scheme and to meet demand for public housing among the elderly**.

Only four respondents to the local authority survey indicated that a formal survey of the needs of older people for repairs and adaptations to their homes had been undertaken. Eight of the 26 respondents who indicated that such an assessment had not been made gave no explanation. Eight indicated that a lack of resources was the reason for not making an assessment, one indicated it was unnecessary and another was 'unaware of the scheme'. Three indicated that this was adequately dealt with by the statutory assessment of housing needs or by reports from the authority's elected members or officers. Seven others indicated various other reasons.

It was recommended in *The Years Ahead* that:

- **(R12.32) there should be a legal obligation on local authorities to provide for the repair and adaptation of the dwellings of elderly people, particularly those on low incomes**.

The Department of the Environment described the current position on this as follows: 'there is a long standing commitment in Irish housing policy to improve housing conditions and to secure adequate housing for all. The various schemes available under the social housing programme provide a broad framework in which local authorities can improve the quality of housing, especially for the elderly' (Department of the Environment 1996b).

5.13 Equity release and house exchange

It was recommended in *The Years Ahead* that:

- **(R5.39) the Departments of Finance and the Environment should explore with the financial institutions ways in which elderly people can be encouraged to make greater use of the financial asset that is their home.**

Equity release schemes, that is, where a mortgage lender advances an older person a loan secured on their house (which must be free of existing mortgages) have been considered by a number of mortgage lending agencies. However, mortgage lenders have indicated that without sufficient demand, they would be reluctant to incur the setting-up costs associated with the launching of any such scheme. The potential for these schemes may have been damaged by adverse experience in the United Kingdom (Department of the Environment 1996b).

It was recommended in *The Years Ahead* that:

- **(R5.40) the Department of the Environment should examine the possibility of introducing a scheme which would facilitate elderly people transferring their homes to a local authority in exchange for more suitable accommodation or for repairs and adaptations to their homes.**

The Department of the Environment takes the view that it is a matter for individual local authorities to consider such cases when they arise and deal with them in the manner which they consider most appropriate (Department of the Environment 1996b).

5.14 Summary of responses by local authorities and voluntary housing organisations to *The Years Ahead* and beyond

In general respondents to the local authority housing survey revealed a limited interest only in the recommendations made in *The Years Ahead*. Only six (of 30) identified significant influences on housing policy since *The Years Ahead*. Only three identified their authority's major achievements in implementing the recommendations of *The Years Ahead*. Only one indicated which recommendations of *The Years Ahead*, when implemented, had resulted in the most valuable outcomes. Seven referred to obstacles encountered in seeking to implement the recommendations of *The Years Ahead*; six indicated that lack of resources was the main obstacle and another identified fragmentation of responsibility between the health board and local authority for providing housing services as the main problem. Only one made any suggestions regarding which recommendations were unrealistic, ineffective or not feasible.

Less than half (12) of the respondents made suggestions concerning what the major emphasis should be in providing housing for older people in the future. They were as follows: safety and security (2); adaptability of housing; quality and proximity to services; contact between neighbours; a range of housing units; safety, security and community facilities; a strategic plan and resource availability; specific targeting of resources for older people; voluntary schemes with communal facilities; voluntary housing with plans for management, maintenance and provision of services by the health board; a co-ordinated approach between statutory bodies and voluntary organisations with responsibility for this assigned to one of the statutory bodies.

The degree to which the recommendations of *The Years Ahead* have been implemented is summarised in Table 5.12.

5.15   Summary and conclusions

The quality of the housing circumstances of older people has improved in recent years, as recommended in *The Years Ahead*, and these improvements are reflected in the increasing satisfaction of older people with their housing (Fahey and Murray 1994). As anticipated in *The Years Ahead*, despite the continuing need for housing for older people as indicated by the 1996 assessment, there has been a considerable reduction in the volume of housing provided directly by local authorities for older people since 1988. The most important development in the provision of housing for older people has been the strong growth in the contribution made by voluntary housing organisations.

Local authorities have not improved their planning of housing for older people by engaging in studies of their housing needs in the manner indicated in *The Years Ahead*. To further improve the housing circumstances of older people it is essential that the full range of housing options be made available to them. It is difficult to imagine how this can be done without more rigorous planning procedures. However, significant improvements have been made in the 1996 housing assessments.

While standard local authority old persons dwellings and indeed standard local authority housing and private housing is suitable for many older people, a substantial proportion of older people require more than this. In general houses built for older people by housing authorities are only different from other houses in that they are smaller. Lifetime adaptable housing and assistive technology for older people is low on the local authority agenda.

Improvements in design and assistive technology, though of considerable importance, will not in themselves address all the difficulties faced by those of diminished independence. It is in this context that sheltered housing as one of a

**Table 5.12: Summary of the implementation of *The Years Ahead*
recommendations**

Recommendations	Current situation
Housing provision (direct) by local authorities	Substantial reduction in local authority housing but big increase in voluntary housing provision
Improve existing housing of older people	Quality of housing of older people has improved
Include additional criteria for letting accommodation to older people	Criteria are taken into account
Department of the Environment to request local authorities to prepare a plan of action to implement recommendations of *The Years Ahead*	No plan of action reported by any local authority
Undertake comprehensive survey into housing conditions of older people	Not undertaken
Base housing provision for older people on factual assessment of need	Current procedures are short of this but assessment procedures have been improved
Increase provision of housing for older people by voluntary housing organisations	Done - 2,857 units of housing for older/disabled people approved under capital assistance scheme since 1988
Increase capital assistance to 95 per cent	Increased to max. of 90 per cent (95 per cent where tenants are homeless)
Department of the Environment to consider funding for maintenance of schemes	Funding can be provided by local authorities for *additional* costs incurred in providing aspects of sheltered accommodation for *homeless persons only*
Health board-local authority liaison, especially with CSEs, in planning sheltered schemes	Few *formal* procedures apparent; little involvement of CSEs
Health boards to provide domiciliary services to residents of sheltered schemes	Health boards rarely provide any *extra* services to residents - some provide day centres and wardens
Re-house older people in own areas	Most local authorities re-house older people either as close as possible to previous area or to area of choice
Encourage dependent older people living in isolation to move to villages/towns	Where relevant, most local authorities do and most older people concur
Flexible co-operation between local authorities and health boards to deal with homeless older people	Low incidence of homelessness among older people (though definition of same is contested) informal arrangements prevail
Increase funds for repairs/adaptations to homes of older people	Over period 1982-1994 about 2,000 cases dealt with annually by Task Force; 1994-1997 provision for Task Force much greater than in 1988
Replace existing *ad hoc* grant schemes with a comprehensive and flexible repairs and adaptations scheme	Not done. Schemes appear reactive - no formal survey of the need of the older people for housing repairs and adaptations and no programme of repairs planned by local authorities and health boards
Introduce equity release schemes	Not developed
Introduce house transfer schemes	No evidence of this practice. A matter for individual local authorities

range of housing/accommodation solutions is increasingly appreciated. However, as observed by the National Economic and Social Council (1988) and as indicated by the Irish Council for Social Housing's definition of social housing, most of the purpose-built housing for older Irish people does not address special needs or provide supportive communal facilities and services. O'Connor and Ruddle (1989) have shown that the design of sheltered housing and the provision of services for the residents of such housing is often unsatisfactory. More thought and resources need to be given to the design of buildings and support services for sheltered housing. In general, as concluded by Silke (1996), housing policy must anticipate people's long-term housing needs long before they become apparent. This conclusion is particularly relevant now when we are faced with the prospect of an ageing population and a greater reliance on community-based services.

It is clear that in a number of areas such as planning, responding to the recommendations of *The Years Ahead*, designing sheltered housing, dealing with homeless older people and providing services to residents of sheltered housing, there are deficiencies in co-operation between health boards and local authorities. Where co-ordination of policy and practice exists, it seems for the most part to be unstructured and *ad hoc*. Moreover, no local authority has made, or been involved in making, a plan for the implementation of the recommendations of *The Years Ahead*. They appear to have a limited knowledge of *The Years Ahead* report and few identified achievements in implementing its recommendations. The lack of co-ordination between regional authorities seems to reflect a lack of co-ordination between the Department of the Environment and the Department of Health. Greater co-ordination between these departments is required to provide a lead for the regional authorities.

As indicated above, the role of voluntary/non-profit housing associations in the provision of social housing, including sheltered housing, has increased substantially. This contribution, a product of locally-based concern and initiative, must be viewed as a very valuable resource and must be supported financially and otherwise. The capital funding of voluntary housing has been improved, but not to the degree recommended in *The Years Ahead*. Given recent developments in the housing market it is now urgent to re-examine the capital assistance levels made available. As previously indicated, the question of funding the maintenance of voluntary housing has not been adequately dealt with by the Department of the Environment as recommended in *The Years Ahead*.

To date there is little evidence of a co-ordinated approach to the assessment of sheltered housing needs between the Departments of the Environment and Health, the health boards, the voluntary housing sector and local authorities. Voluntary housing organisations must be viewed as a partner in the provision of social housing by local authorities and health boards and it is necessary for the

Departments of the Environment and Health to consider the implications of this in respect of funding and planning. Support for voluntary housing organisations might be best considered in the form of a partnership between voluntary organisations, health boards and local authorities at local level. The contributors to this partnership, who together would decide on its focus and status, would be likely to include voluntary housing organisations, their representative bodies, representatives of their tenants, local authorities and health boards.

Nearly all local authorities report that they take into account all the criteria for letting accommodation to older people recommended in *The Years Ahead*. Where local authorities revealed their main emphasis in housing policy for older people it was much in keeping with *The Years Ahead* with a focus on such issues as access to services and amenities, security and sheltered housing, and opportunities for social contact. While defining homelessness remains a contentious issue, the prevailing view throughout health boards and local authorities is that very few older people are homeless. However, Programme Managers of Community Care and local authorities reported rather informal arrangements, if any, in dealing with it.

Substantial funds have been allocated to The Task Force on Special Housing Needs for the Elderly and the Essential Repairs Grants Scheme as recommended in *The Years Ahead*. However, the operation of the schemes remains reactive, as local authorities have not undertaken formal surveys of the need for repairs and adaptations to older people's homes. Neither have these schemes been integrated as was recommended. Legislation has not been effected to oblige local authorities to repair and adapt the homes of older people, particularly those on low incomes, as was recommended in *The Years Ahead*. Equity release schemes, recommended in *The Years Ahead*, have not been developed in Ireland and the housing exchange schemes recommended in *The Years Ahead* have not attracted much interest in Ireland. The Department of the Environment takes the view that consideration of the latter schemes is a matter for individual local authorities

CHAPTER SIX

Care at Home

6.1 Introduction

The Years Ahead envisaged a continuum of care options ranging from care in the home, to special housing, to acute hospital care, to extended institutional care. The emphasis was on maintaining older people at the first point of the continuum for as long as possible. This chapter is concerned with the recommendations made by the Working Party for enabling older people who experience difficulty with the tasks of everyday living to continue living at home. Specifically, the chapter examines the implementation of recommendations with regard to home-based services such as general medical and nursing services, paramedical services including physiotherapy, occupational therapy, speech therapy and chiropody, social work services and home help services. Data on implementation was obtained from interviews and/or questionnaires from Programme Managers of Community Care in all health boards, CSEs (16), District Liaison Nurses (39), Superintendent PHNs (26), Senior PHNs (8), Home Help Organisers (22) and professional organisations representing GPs, physiotherapists, occupational therapists, speech therapists, dieticians, chiropodists and social workers.

The chapter begins by outlining the context within which the recommendations were made and the findings of some recent research since *The Years Ahead* was published.

6.2 Context of recommendations

6.2.1 *Profile of dependency of older people in the community*

A study conducted in the early 1990s provides an indication of the numbers of older people currently requiring some level of care in order to continue to live at home (Blackwell *et al.* 1992). Forty-five per cent of the study sample were found to be independent physically in the sense that they could either perform all the activities of daily living explored (15 per cent) or all except having a bath (30 per cent), without help. Twenty per cent were found to be dependent only with regard to mobility. Thirteen per cent of the sample were classed as dependent needing help with bathing, mobility, dressing, getting in and out of bed, sitting or standing and using the toilet. Fifteen per cent were classed as highly dependent with six per cent unable to perform any of the physical activities of daily living without help. As well as showing that there were highly dependent older people living in the community, this study showed that, on the other hand, there was a significant proportion of older people in hospitals who could be classed as being free of disability or as having only one disability. The authors of the study argued that low-dependency older people can end up in long-stay care if formal assessment and rigorous procedures for admission are not used, if there is an absence of rehabilitation programmes and an active policy on discharge and if the quantity and quality of community care support is inadequate.

Physical ability is, however, only one aspect of the independence of older people and, to be comprehensive, a community care service must also take account of the older person's psychological and social well-being. An older person may be physically independent but social factors such as isolation, geographical remoteness or poor housing may make institutional care inevitable.

6.2.2   *Providers of care in the community*

The provision of care in the community is typically envisaged as a four-way partnership between the family, neighbours and friends, voluntary organisations and statutory agencies. Research shows that informal family carers are key providers of community care. It has been estimated that around 66,000 older people are being looked after at home by informal carers (O'Connor *et al.* 1988). In principle, the policy of community care means that these informal family carers should be backed up by a variety of community care support services including domiciliary services, day services, accommodation, boarding out and assessment services (National Economic and Social Council 1987). However, with regard to home-based services, Ruddle and O'Connor (1993) found that 87 per cent of those caring at home for a dementia sufferer could be categorised as receiving a low level of domiciliary support. Studies carried out by O'Connor and Ruddle (1988) and Blackwell *et al.* (1992) on carers of older people in general also reported low levels of domiciliary support. Finucane *et al.* (1994) note not only low levels of domiciliary support but also point to the fact that the existing community care support services tend to focus on the physical/medical needs of older people and only partially on social and psychological needs. This lack of domiciliary support can spring not only from lack of provision of services, but also from lack of information and lack of accessibility to the services that do exist. *Shaping a Healthier Future* acknowledges that 'community-based services are not as yet developed to the extent that they can appropriately complement and substitute for institutional care, or provide adequately for those in the community who are dependent on support' (p. 10).

6.2.3   Cost of care in the community

The Care of the Aged report in 1968 supposed that community care of older people would not only be much better than care in hospitals and other institutions but also that it would probably be much cheaper. When the Working Party was convened, twenty years later, it noted that it did not have the information required to decide when it might be more cost effective to care for an older person at home and when it might be more effective to provide care in an institutional setting (pp. 182-183). A study carried out in 1992 by the Economic and Social Research Institute shows that the case for community care cannot be argued on the basis that it costs less and that its real cost is higher than generally thought (Blackwell *et al.* 1992). When all aspects of community care are quantified and given a value - cost of informal care hours, cost of acute care usage, cost of service usage - the cost of care in the community may be higher than in institutions at various levels of dependency. If community care services were to be provided at their optimal level rather than at the actual low level observed in the Economic and Social Research Institute study, then the estimated costs of community care would be even higher. The compelling argument for community care is not cost but that it is better for older people and it enables them to take up their preferred care option which is to 'stay put'.

6.3   Identification of older people at risk

The first element in the provision of an adequate system of care in the community is to be able to identify those older people in need of services. The Working Party considered that regular assessment of all older people was both impractical and unnecessary and that the system of identification should be primarily concerned with those older people who have a significant medical and/or social problem. Specifically, the Working Party recommended that:

- **(R6.4) the district liaison nurse maintain a register of elderly people at medical or social risk**.

As indicated in Chapter Three not all health boards have specifically designated District Liaison Nurses and, even where there are such nurses, they are not the people who maintain 'at risk' registers. However, in all health boards PHNs do maintain a register of older people. In the Eastern Health Board the register covers older people within a community care area rather than a district area.

The criteria used for identifying 'at risk' older people varies quite a lot between, and sometimes within, health boards. In seven of the eight boards, all older persons are automatically entered on the PHN's register once they reach a certain age but the particular age at which they are registered varies from over 65 years in the Eastern and North Western Health Boards, to over 70 years in the North

Eastern Health Board and over 75 in the South Eastern, Midland, Mid-Western and Southern Health Boards. Criteria other than age are also used to decide who should be on the register. The most detailed criteria for inclusion on the register were given by the Western Health Board where a particular 'at risk' screening tool was devised. This takes into account geographical isolation, social isolation, need for nursing care, financial circumstances, housing, impaired vision or hearing, need for help with activities of daily living, whether living with another older or dependent person, marital status and recent bereavement. At present all persons over 75 years in the Western Health Board are screened using this tool. The Southern Health Board has adopted the criteria noted in *The Years Ahead* - living alone or with dependent relative or an older person, whether aged 75 years or more, recent bereavement, recent discharge from hospital, need for nursing care - with the addition of isolation and recent re-housing. The South Eastern Health Board also uses a number of these criteria along with a Mental Test Score, an assessment of carers' ability to cope and access to support services. Among the other boards, medical condition is an important factor in identifying those 'at risk' but living alone and geographical isolation are also criteria that are used by most.

6.3.1   Compiling the 'at risk' register

In all health boards the compilation of the register is based on the PHN's assessment of the situation. In four of the boards (Western, Southern, South Eastern and North Western) the PHN appears to use a definite system for assessing risk but in the others no particular system is involved. Identification of those who may be potentially at risk is based on the nurse's local contacts and the information she picks up through her work. The PHNs use a variety of sources of information to acquire information on these people, including the medical card system, GPs, family members, neighbours, hospital discharge notices, self-referrals and voluntary organisations.

With the exception of two boards (Southern and North Western) PHNs typically perceive the current means of compiling the 'at risk' register as being ineffective or only fairly effective. According to these nurses different people have different ideas of what 'at risk' means and a more organised system needs to be developed where standardised criteria are formally set out. Many want national criteria to be developed so that there is uniformity across all regions. Three boards (Eastern, South Eastern and North Eastern) are currently reviewing the procedures used for identification of older people at risk. The Midland Health Board intends to pilot a formal 'at risk' register as part of its plan for future action. Several of the PHNs also note the importance of computerisation of information so that it can be easily accessed, updated and retrieved.

The Working Party acknowledged that the compilation of registers may be a complex issue and recommended that:

- **(R6.10) the best method of identifying the elderly at medical or social risk be one of the priority issues to be examined in the two model community care areas recommended**.

The model community care areas recommended by the Working Party have not been established and the need for research on the best means of identifying older people at medical or social risk is one that still has to be addressed.

6.3.2   *Perceptions of benefits of 'at risk' register*

In the experience of the PHNs, the presence of an 'at risk' register means that there is an alertness to need which allows for early intervention and the development of appropriate care plans. In some areas of the Western Health Board, for example, when an older person is put on the register an 'at risk management care plan' is immediately put in place. Many indicate that as a result of being put on the register, the older person is more closely monitored and receives more visits. A frequently noted benefit is that information on the register allows for more effective planning and prioritising of services. Some concerns about the register were also noted. To be useful it needs to be regularly updated, it can be time-consuming to maintain it and care needs to be taken with regard to the issues of confidentiality and privacy. Some nurses were concerned about the appropriate age at which someone should be monitored and expressed anxiety about the possibility of fostering dependency.

6.4   Medical care

The Years Ahead notes that the GP plays a critical role in domiciliary care. The GP tends to be the first professional who attends an older person when ill and his/her decisions are critical to subsequent care and the mobilisation of resources. The Working Party considered that an important element in the provision of a high quality GP care system is case finding, 'the early detection of established disease and assessment of the physical, mental and social function of the patient to achieve earlier diagnosis and better prospects of cure, alleviation and rehabilitation' (p. 85). The recommendation of the Working Party was that:

- **(R6.16) case finding among the elderly population considered to be at risk be developed as a normal part of general practitioner care of the elderly, and in particular as a normal part of the General Medical Service**.

Feedback from GPs (representing an ICGP faculty in each health board) suggests that case-finding is opportunistic. Most identification of 'at risk' older people occurs when they are examined during visits to the surgery. It is seen by the GPs that their day-to-day caseload precludes non-emergency domiciliary visits.

However, the GPs would usually be aware of older people 'at risk', with the PHN playing an important part in bringing such people to their attention. Some GPs note that they liaise regularly with PHNs about older 'at risk' patients and, where relevant, they also liaise with staff of the local rehabilitation unit and day hospital.

The Working Party also recommended that:

- **(R6.17) the system of remuneration in the general medical service should provide appropriate financial incentives to encourage anticipatory care of elderly patients deemed to be at risk**.

At present there is no specific provision in the GP contract for anticipatory care of older people. The current system is perceived by GPs as being consumer driven with no incentive to seek out those 'at risk'.

6.4.1   Issues related to screening

The feedback obtained from the GPs highlights some of the issues involved in screening older people. It is pointed out, for example, that in Britain - where the 1989 National Health System contract obliges the GP to carry out screening of older people - the value of such screening has been questioned. In this country, one of the problems identified by the ICGP is that the GP does not have a defined population to whom he or she gives care; especially among those not holding medical cards. Further problems are that there is no agreed scientific protocol for identifying the different problems of older people, the infrastructure to support anticipatory care is lacking (for example, more practice nurses would be needed) and the resources for effective treatment of some of the problems identified are limited.

According to the ICGP it must be taken into account that screening is a multi-factorial process. Furthermore, each disease screened for should meet the following criteria: be a relatively common disease, have a good test for its detection, have treatment available for it and a proven outcome and not be cost prohibitive. Given the wide range of problems that can arise for an older person and, consequently, the amount of time involved, the ICGP suggests that a non-medical but trained worker, rather than the GP, should do the screening backed up by an effective referral system.

6.4.2   Anticipatory care: the perspective of the Department of Health

From the perspective of the Department of Health, the General Medical Service has not been used to its fullest advantage with regard to anticipatory care of older people. This is an issue that is the subject of on-going discussion with the medical organisations. In June 1995, the Department requested the health boards to concentrate on Progressive Development in General Practice and to provide, *inter alia*, services for older people including physiotherapy, occupational therapy, chiropody, audiometry and eye assessment. Using savings from the Indicative Drug Target scheme, GPs can hire into the general practice setting paramedical services on a sessional basis.

6.4.3   Liaison between GP and community care professionals

The Working Party identified the separation of GPs from other professionals employed by the health board as one of the factors inhibiting a co-ordinated primary care service for older people. *Shaping a Healthier Future* also noted that although significant progress has been made in developing the General Medical Service in recent years, if it is to fulfil its functions adequately the service 'must be better organised and better integrated with other health services to enable it to function as an integral part of the work of the health care system in patient care' (1994, p. 52). In particular, the Working Party pointed to the importance of effective liaison between GPs and PHNs and between GPs and the district team. The recommendation of the Working Party was that:

- **(R6.19) it be the responsibility of the CSE to ensure good working relationships between the teams for the elderly and the general practitioners working in the respective districts**.

As indicated in Chapter Three, only two of the health boards have established district teams in the way the Working Party envisaged. In the Eastern Health Board GPs are represented in the multi-disciplinary area care teams that have been established in each community care area and through these teams have contact with other professionals. GPs are also actively involved with the community ward teams in each community care area which provide a community-based outreach service with multi-disciplinary support. The GP can refer older patients to the community ward team and retains clinical responsibility for the patient while in the care of the team. In most areas, the GP is invited to attend an initial case conference on the referred patient or, alternatively, the team leader or the CSE will liaise with the GP by letter or telephone. The GP is also informed when the patient is discharged from the community ward service. Arrangements in the North Western Health Board for liaison between the GP and the district team appear to be looser. The GP is not part of the team but there is contact with the District Co-ordinator by phone, letter and occasional visits.

The blueprint for developing general practice, which was agreed with the medical organisations in 1992, stressed the need for integration of GPs with the rest of the health system. *Shaping a Healthier Future* notes that the establishment of GP units in each health board has promoted GP links with other services. Because the GP units include general practice medical officers who are in active practice in their local areas, they are seen by the Department of Health as being in an ideal position to develop closer contact and better working relationships between GPs and the other health and social services.

6.4.4   Liaison between medical and nursing services

With regard to liaison between the medical and nursing services, the Working Party recommended that:

- **(R6.19) the Irish College of General Practitioners and the Institute of Community Nursing explore ways in which greater co-operation between general practitioners and public health nurses can be achieved in the interest of improved care of patients.**

To date no guidelines on co-ordination have been produced by either body. Feedback from the ICGP indicates that this is an issue they want to further explore. Position papers have been drawn up for the information of members and meetings between the ICGP and the Institute of Community Health Nursing have highlighted some of the issues but further joint consultation is needed.

The feedback from those nurses performing a liaison function almost always describes good co-operation and satisfactory working relationships with the GPs. This is particularly so in rural areas where the GPs and those in the public health nursing service are usually well known to one another. In most health boards there are no formal structures for liaison but there is frequent telephone contact and ready access when the need arises. Some of the liaison personnel in these boards call for a more formalised arrangement with regular meetings and a more definite team approach. It was also noted in one board that liaison can sometimes be one-way with the nurse calling regularly to the GP's surgery but the GP never calling to the nurse's place of work. In the two boards where there are district teams in operation (Eastern and North Western) feedback from liaison personnel indicates more definite means for co-operation. Case conferences, for example, are sometimes held in the GP's surgeries, meetings are arranged or the GPs visit the liaison nurse's place of work. Feedback from GPs with regard to co-operation with the District Liaison Nurses is more mixed. In some cases, the GP is not even aware whether there is such a nurse. Where there is contact it is almost always described as informal. While some find this works well there are others who find the level of contact unsatisfactory and call for a more formalised meeting schedule.

Within the public health nursing service generally, arrangements for co-operation with the GPs are much more likely to be described by nurses as fairly effective rather than effective. The typical picture is that co-operation is worked out at a personal level between the individual GP and the individual PHN and it depends on the personalities of the two people involved. Contact occurs but it is mostly by telephone and happens on an *ad hoc* basis. Contact is greater where the GP and the PHN share the same premises, for example, a health centre. It is often noted that this informal system for co-operation is easier to operate in rural areas where the GPs and nurses are known personally to one another. The most common suggestion for improvement from nurses is for formal structured meetings on a regular basis to allow a more effective flow of information and to enable the development of joint care plans. It is also noted that any structure must ensure that co-operation is two-way rather than, as is sometimes perceived, the nurse making most of the effort at liaison. A further suggestion is that there should be joint education so that GPs and PHNs can have a better understanding of each other's roles.

Feedback from GPs is similar to that obtained from the PHNs in that liaison arrangements are almost always described as informal and *ad hoc* and are often seen as less than satisfactory. It is also pointed out by the GPs that they do not share the same target population with the PHN and several nurses may be involved with the GP's patients. Like the nurses, the GPs call for more formalisation of liaison procedures with more face-to-face contact at regular intervals. Suggestions for improvement include the establishment of care teams which include the GP. In the case of large group practices another suggestion is the formal attachment of PHNs to the GP practice. It is noted that while close liaison brings many benefits, including free sharing of information and concerns, a co-ordinated approach and early intervention, it is not an easy process to work out. Among both GPs and nurses there may be some who perceive such links as a threat to their autonomy.

6.5   The nursing service
Alongside a good medical service, *The Years Ahead* identified a comprehensive nursing service as being vital to caring for older people at home. The Working Party made a number of recommendations for improvement of the home nursing service; in terms of levels of provision, back-up support services and greater attention to anticipatory care. The implementation of these recommendations is discussed below but it should be noted that the Department of Health has just completed a review of the public health nursing service - due to be published in Summer 1997 - which is likely to lead to significant changes in the role of the Public Health Nurse. A review is also about to be undertaken of the home help service which again is likely to have consequences for the role and particular emphasis of the public health nursing service.

6.5.1   Level of PHN provision
In 1987 the national ratio of PHNs to general population was 1:3,065 which was considerably below the target of 1:2,616 set in 1975 by the *Report of the Working Party on the Workload of Public Health Nurses. The Years Ahead* accepted that the large increase in the number of PHNs needed to bring the service up to the 1975 recommended level was not possible with the constraints at the time on public expenditure. Its recommendation was that:

• **(R6.29) additional public health nurses be appointed as resources permit**.

Table 6.1: Number of Public Health Nurse posts

Health board	1987	WTE 1995		WTE 1995 Excluding Superintendent PHN		WTE 1995 Excluding Superintendent PHN and Senior PHN		Population
		N	Ratio	N	Ratio	N	Ratio	
EHB	365	434.73	1: 2976	425.73	1: 3039	404.73	1: 3197	1,293,964
MHB	78	105.47	1: 1946	103.47	1: 1984	101.47	1: 2023	205,252
MWHB	103	125.42	1: 2527	123.42	1: 2567	109.42	1: 2896	316,875
NEHB	105	129.73	1: 2356	126.73	1: 2412	117.73	1: 2597	305,703
NWHB	97	106.33	1: 1976	104.33	1: 2014	101.33	1: 2074	210,112
SHB	129	180	1: 3034	176.00	1: 3103	161.03	1: 3391	546,209
SEHB	130	157.49	1: 2482	154.49	1: 2531	146.49	1: 2669	391,046
WHB	147	171.21	1: 2055	168.21	1: 2092	159.21	1: 2210	351,874
Total	1154	1410.38		1382.38		1301.41		3,621,035
Ratio	1:3065	1: 2567		1: 2619		1: 2782		

Source: Department of Health, 1995 Census of PHNs

A Census of PHNs conducted in 1995 by the Department of Health reveals that all of the health boards have increased nurse levels compared with 1987 (Table 6.1). Consideration of the total number in the public health nursing service in 1995 reveals that, with two exceptions (Eastern and Southern), each of the boards had exceeded the target set in 1975 of 1: 2,616. However, exclusion of Superintendent and Senior PHNs, who carry managerial roles, and consideration solely of those on district duties indicates a less positive picture with four of the boards (Eastern, Mid-Western, Southern and South Eastern) below the recommended level. It should be noted also that the 1995 Census figures are based on all nursing staff employed in the service in that year. Some of those included in the figures are Registered General Nurses rather than qualified PHNs and therefore are not able to undertake the full range of public health nursing duties. It must also be recognised that older people are but one of the care groups within the remit of the PHN.

6.5.2   Perceptions of adequacy of provision

The current number of PHNs is still perceived by Programme Managers as being only fairly adequate or inadequate and this is so even in those boards which note the contribution of Care Assistants and Registered General Nurses appointed since 1987. There is, for example, a need for more nurses to carry out liaison responsibilities and a need for more nurses dedicated to care of older people. Apart from additional numbers, the need is also identified for more back-up support for the nurses already in place. Several note that, within health boards, the adequacy of the public health nursing service can vary according to the spread and size of the population in different areas. The main issue for those boards wanting to increase their public health nursing service is lack of financial resources.

Feedback from PHNs reveals widespread dissatisfaction with current level of provision in every board with two exceptions (North Western and Western). Not only are more PHNs needed in certain areas to reach the recommended ratio of nurses to population, but it is also seen that many more Registered General Nurses need to be employed. It is seen that for the PHN to do her job, there needs to be effective back-up support in the form of trained Care Assistants and sufficient numbers of Home Helps. Many PHNs are also dissatisfied with the level of access to paramedical services such as occupational therapy and physiotherapy. PHNs in two of the boards (South Eastern and Southern) further highlight the need for support from district teams to enable their service to function as effectively as possible.

6.6   Employment of Care Assistants
The Working Party suggested that:

- **(R6.29) health boards should also explore the possibility of employing care assistants who would work under the supervision of the public health nurse**.

The Years Ahead does not specify what duties these Care Assistants might be expected to carry out nor does it specify what kind of background training or expertise they should have.

Four of the boards (Eastern, Midland, North Eastern and South Eastern) currently employ Care Assistants; most of whom are employed on a part-time basis (Table 6.2). These Care Assistants are given training for their work: for example, in the Eastern

Table 6.2: Employment of Care Assistants

Health board	Whether Care Assistants employed
Eastern	Yes
Midland	Yes
Mid-Western	No (Does have 'Home from Hospital scheme' with trained carers)
North Eastern	Yes
North Western	No
Southern	No
South Eastern	Yes
Western	No

Source: Interviews with Programme Managers of Community Care

Health Board formal training over a three-week period with practical placements is provided by the CSEs and PHNs, while in the Midland Health Board training is provided in areas such as lifting techniques, first-aid and safety in the home.

6.6.1   Perceptions of role of Care Assistant

Care Assistants are perceived by Programme Managers in those boards which employ them as playing a valuable role in the provision of a comprehensive community service. Their particular role is to provide care services rather than domestic services and they are seen as an important back-up to the nursing service. A note of caution is raised by one Programme Manager about the necessity of matching the Care Assistant with the older clients: the relationship has to be based on trust and needs to be carefully worked out.

The Care Assistants are perceived by PHNs as important in enabling older people to remain at home and to be rehabilitated on discharge from hospital. PHNs feel that the Care Assistants are also valuable because they relieve them of some of their workload. Care Assistants are intended to work under the direction of the PHNs but while PHNs in the Eastern Health Board are involved in the training of Care Assistants, nurses in other boards (such as the North Eastern) report that they have neither the time nor sufficient numbers to carry out training.

Among those boards not employing Care Assistants, the Western Health Board indicates that its preference is to extend the home help service and to provide further training in this area rather than add another layer to service provision. The Mid-Western Health Board is currently piloting a 'Home from Hospital' scheme where trained carers meet the older person before discharge and then give intensive care in the home for up to six weeks, with the amount of care given decided by the PHN.

There appears to be a lack of clarity about where the Care Assistant fits into the home and community care system. PHNs tend to see the Care Assistants as a complement to their service, but managers and those in the home help service seem to be uncertain about the specific role they play. For example, in a study of Home Helps (Lundstrπm and McKeown 1994), it was found that, in general, Home Helps and Home Help Organisers have not welcomed the introduction of Care Assistants which many of them see as an unnecessary partitioning of older people's needs into personal care and other types of care. Home Helps believe that they are already providing personal care and that the introduction of Care Assistants is wasteful and an encroachment on their territory.

6.7   Employment of panels of general nurses

In order to enable a nursing service to be provided quickly and flexibly for older people when they become ill at home or on discharge from hospital, the Working

Party recommended that:

- **(R6.30) a panel of general nurses willing to nurse elderly people at home on a part-time basis be established in each district**.

It was envisaged that these panel nurses would work under the supervision of the Superintendent PHN.

With one exception (Western) all of the health boards have established panels of general nurses (Table 6.3). (The Western Health Board has a limited service because the funding available does not allow for a full service). While some boards have a panel in each district (North Eastern, Southern) in other boards the service is spread over a community care area (Eastern, Mid-Western, South Eastern) or wider area (Midland). The provision of these part-time nurses is planned and managed by the Superintendent or Senior PHN and they work under the direction of the standard grade PHNs.

6.7.1   Perceptions of value of general nurse panels

Feedback from both Programme Managers and PHNs indicates that the panels of Registered General Nurses are highly effective - when sufficient resources are given to them - and play an essential role in care at home. From the PHN perspective the general nurses provide a useful locum service but their value is much wider than relief work. The nurses are seen to provide a high quality service which is particularly valuable for chronically or terminally ill older people. As well as the quality of the nursing care provided, the panels are valued because the delivery of the service is flexible: within budgetary constraints they can be called upon at short notice when needed, for as long as needed. The decision on their use is made at local level thereby avoiding delays in implementation of the service. The service is also flexible in that it provides for out-of-hours and weekend care.

Table 6.3: Establishment of panels of general nurses

Health board	Whether panels established
Eastern	Yes
Midland	Yes
Mid-Western	Yes
North Eastern	Yes
North Western	Yes
Southern	Yes
South Eastern	Yes
Western	Limited

Source: Interviews with Programme Managers of Community Care, Senior PHNs and Superintendent PHNs

By taking over some of the curative nursing workload of the PHN, the general nurse frees her to focus on the areas where her skills are best used such as anticipatory care, liaison and health promotion. The general nurse is also important in providing relief for carers and support for family members. The panels of general nurses are used continuously and the PHNs say they could not operate without them. The panels, however, can sometimes be difficult to manage because of turnover of participants and the need for continued recruitment.

6.7.2 *Funding of general nurse panels*

With regard to funding for the panels of Registered General Nurses and Care Assistants, the Working Party recommended that:

- **(R12.18) a sum of £2m be made available immediately to provide a panel of general nurses in every district and to employ home care assistants to help the elderly with dementia.**

The Department of Health indicates that the total additional figure for the period 1989-1997 is estimated to be £7.2m, making a yearly average of £800,000.

6.8   Management of incontinence

The Working Party recommended that:

- **(R6.32) in each community care area there should be at least one public health nurse with a special interest in the management of incontinence, who would act as an advisor to other nurses.**

In all of the health boards there are PHNs with special expertise in the management of incontinence. Nurses with special expertise provide an advisory service to other nurses, they enable appropriate assessment and they increase cost-effectiveness by reducing the need for incontinence supplies and by monitoring need on a regular basis. The Eastern board has established a Continence Promotion Unit which is designed to foster a greater awareness of incontinence among both staff and patients at in-patient and community level, and to enable the most effective treatment programme to be implemented. The functions of the unit include education, assessment and on-going monitoring of patients, implementation of care plans and cost effective use of incontinence supplies. In a pilot scheme carried out by the unit in 1994, the procedure for getting incontinence supplies was changed from granting of supplies on the basis of a letter from the GP to referral by the GP to the PHN for thorough assessment and identification of the exact supplies needed. Monitoring of the service in the year following the pilot project showed that while there was an increase in the number of people receiving the service, the cost per person decreased producing a saving of almost £16,000. Computerisation of the necessary client data was found to be a major factor in providing an effective and efficient service.

6.9   Anticipatory care by PHNs
On the basis of the provision of a comprehensive home nursing service, the Working Party recommended that:

- **(R6.31) public health nurses in their visits to the elderly place a greater emphasis on anticipatory care of the elderly and the promotion of their health.**

In order to support this, the Working Party further recommended that 'greater attention be paid in the training of nurses generally and public health nurses in particular, to anticipatory care of the elderly'. According to feedback from the PHNs, anticipatory care is a fundamental aspect of the public health nursing service. Anticipatory care is implemented through on-going surveillance of older people on the register. Through her surveillance visits the PHN not only can identify problems at an early stage, but she builds up a relationship with the older person and can use the opportunity for carrying out informal health education. The PHN carries out regular assessment of the needs of the older person so that problems can be identified at an early stage and care plans can be drawn up and services mobilised when necessary. Another element of anticipatory care involves building up support for carers and other family members at an early stage. There is general agreement among nurses that the current training of the PHN does equip her for anticipatory care. However, many noted that anticipatory care can be difficult to put into practice because of excessive workload. It is seen that if the PHN is to be able to devote herself to this essential aspect of her work, then there needs to be greater provision of other back-up services such as Care Assistants, Registered General Nurses and Home Helps.

6.10   Provision of medical appliances and aids
In the case of some older people experiencing difficulties with the activities of daily living, the provision of a medical appliance or an aid can be an essential element in being able to remain at home. In order to rectify the problems which the Working Party identified at the time of its deliberations, it made a number of suggestions (R6.34) with regard to both procedures for granting aids and appliances and practical arrangements for their provision and storage. In regard to the former, the suggestions were that:

- **in each community care area, an occupational therapist or public health nurse should develop a special expertise concerning appliances and aids for the elderly**
- **every elderly person requiring a medical appliance or aid be assessed by a public health nurse or occupational therapist with first hand knowledge of the individual circumstances**
- **when an elderly person is being discharged from hospital, and requires a medical appliance, the hospital personnel should inform the public**

> health nurse or occupational therapist in time for arrangements to be made for its supply prior to the patient's return home

- **the allocation of appliances and aids should be reviewed each year to ensure that they are still required by the elderly person. Computerisation of information concerning appliances and aids on loan in the community would make this task easier.**

With two exceptions (Mid-Western and Southern), each of the health boards has someone, usually an occupational therapist or physiotherapist, in each community care area who has special expertise in appliances and aids for older people (Table 6.4). In both the boards with lower than recommended levels of provision there are plans for an increase in the numbers with special expertise. While PHNs regard the occupational therapist as the primary source of expert knowledge, they also feel that they have expertise in this area particularly with regard to nursing aids. PHNs also point out that in the absence of adequate occupational therapy resources, they have taken on the remit in this area. Assessment of older persons for medical appliances or aids is usually carried out by the PHN; in consultation with the occupational therapist when specialist equipment may be needed. In all of the health boards, the PHNs indicate that they are informed when an older person requiring a medical appliance is discharged from hospital. This information is usually given through the liaison nurse or the ward sister and, in almost all cases, this communication system is seen to operate effectively.

Table 6.4: Management and administration of medical appliances and aids

Health board	Provision of special expertise	Review of provision each year	Computerisation
Eastern	Yes (in each community care area)	Yes	No
Midland	Yes (in each community care area)	No	No (in progress)
Mid-Western	Yes (approval for someone in each community care area)	No	No (planned)
North Eastern	Yes (in each community care area)	Yes	In some areas
North Western	Yes (in each community care area)	Yes	No
Southern	Yes (but not in each area)	No	No
South Eastern	Yes (in each community care area)	No	No
Western	Yes (in each community care area)	No	No

Source: Interviews with Programme Managers of Community Care, Senior PHNs, Superintendent PHNs, and board level CSEs

With regard to practical arrangements for the provision of appliances and aids, the Working Party made the following suggestions (R6.34):

- **within each community care area there should be a suitable premises with a person in charge of the purchase, storage, distribution, recovery, maintenance and cleansing of medical appliances and aids. An occupational therapist or public health nurse should advise on these aspects of the management of appliances and aids**

- **health boards should not be precluded by legislation from charging a deposit on medical appliances which would encourage their return in good repair when no longer needed**

- **health boards should consider charging for necessary aids, as they may do under section 61 of the Health Act 1970, rather than curtail the supply of aids completely**

- **the National Rehabilitation Board should continue to advise health boards on the latest advances in medical appliances and aids for the elderly and advise on the 'best buy' available.**

Apart from the Eastern Health Board which has a central premises for aids and appliances along with stores in each area, the health boards do not have special managed premises for aids and appliances.

Because of the more specialised range of appliances on the market and the often very high cost of such appliances, issues are now arising about how to decide who should get appliances and how priorities should be set. The Working Party recommended that the National Rehabilitation Board should advise the health boards on the latest advances in medical appliances and aids but, apart from the Eastern Health Board, the health boards do not report that they are getting such advice. Three of the health boards (Eastern, North Eastern and North Western) indicate that there is an annual review of the allocation of appliances and aids. In all of the boards the PHNs indicate that they carry out reviews but this appears to be more related to inventory-taking than to review of the need for appliances and aids. Many indicate that the task of reviewing is made considerably more difficult because of the lack of computerisation of the information. Information on aids and appliances is computerised in some areas of the North Eastern board. This is also in progress in the Midland board but does not occur in the other boards.

6.11   Provision of occupational therapy
The Working Party considered that the main contribution of occupational therapists to the care of older people was to advise on home adaptations to cope with increasing disability. The occupational therapist was also seen to have a role in advising on allocation of medical appliances and aids (see previous section).

Specifically, the Working Party recommended that:

- **(R6.35) occupational therapists should liaise with general practitioners and public health nurses to ensure that they are aware of the potential of adaptations and aids to improve the home conditions of the elderly**.

It appears from feedback from occupational therapists that liaison occurs more often with PHNs than with GPs. There is a suggestion that other professionals, particularly the GPs, need to be informed of the role of occupational therapists and the potential benefits of their intervention.

Feedback from PHNs indicates that in two of the health boards (North Eastern and North Western) there is a relatively formal, direct liaison system between nurses and occupational therapists. In the other boards liaison occurs as necessary mainly by phone and written referrals. PHNs generally describe the liaison with the occupational therapists as working satisfactorily. However, it is often noted that there are not enough community occupational therapists in place and, particularly in the Eastern and Southern Health Boards, it is perceived that workloads are too great, waiting lists are long and assessments are too slow. From the perspective of GPs, contact with the occupational therapists is almost always perceived as unsatisfactory. The main problem is that there are too few occupational therapists and, accordingly, there is little scope for liaison or dissemination of information.

6.11.1   Perceptions of deficits in occupational therapy provision
Several Programme Managers note that there is an increasing and unmet demand in recent years for occupational therapy services for older people. The occupational therapists, themselves, note the lack of resources for both equipment and personnel. The major gap in current service provision, in their view, is the lack of a community-based service, particularly in day care centres, but it is also noted that the service in long-stay facilities is also very lacking. There is a call also for continuity of service whereby one therapist continues care of the older person in the community on discharge from hospital. The occupational therapists emphasise their role in health promotion and call for greater resources for this aspect of their service through, for example, day care centres.

6.12   Provision of physiotherapy
The Working Party argued that a domiciliary physiotherapy service was both important in preserving the independence of older people and cost effective. The specific recommendation was that:

- **(R6.37) a physiotherapy service, based in the community hospital or health centre, should be available for elderly people at home when their medical condition justifies it**.

Few of the health boards (Eastern, Mid-Western and Southern) provide a domiciliary physiotherapy service for older people and even those which do

Table 6.5: Provision of domiciliary physiotherapy service

Health board	Whether provided
Eastern	Yes (but limited)
Midland	No
Mid-Western	Yes (new service)
North Eastern	No
North Western	No
Southern	Yes (but very limited)
South Eastern	No
Western	No (provided in exceptional cases only)

Source: Interviews with Programmes Managers of Community Care

provide the service emphasise that it is on a limited basis, particularly in the Southern Health Board (Table 6.5). Those who provide a domiciliary service see it as necessary but difficult to implement on a widespread basis because of a shortage of community physiotherapists and the cost and travel involved. In the Eastern and Mid-Western Health Boards in particular, the domiciliary service is seen as contributing enormously to the quality of life, mobility and independence of older people. It enables a 'seamless' service between the hospital and the community and ensures continuity of care. Among those boards not providing a domiciliary service neither the North Eastern nor Midland Health Boards sees the service as necessary. In the former board the policy is to provide a structured service in key locations that is easily accessible and available. Similarly, in the Midland Health Board the current view is that it is more feasible and appropriate to bring the older person to a local centre for the service, although the board's action plan does involve a pilot of the cost and feasibility of a domiciliary service. In the Western Health Board too, the physiotherapy service is provided in designated centres and a domiciliary service is regarded as only 'fairly necessary'. The service is also seen as only fairly necessary in the North Western Health Board where the priority is the provision of physiotherapy at centres such as district hospitals and day hospitals. The service is regarded as both necessary and feasible in the South Eastern Health Board but lack of funding prevents this from happening.

Physiotherapists point out that while location of the service in a centre rather than in the older person's home may be more efficient and less costly from a management point of view, it can reduce the autonomy of the service and is not necessarily the most effective way to meet the older person's needs. According to the physiotherapists a domiciliary service is feasible if organised properly and what is needed is a balance between community-based and home-based service delivery. An effective domiciliary service is seen to require the employment of more physiotherapists and back-up support such as provision of Care Assistants and provision of the training of carers. There is a perception that the development of a domiciliary service is hindered not just by a lack of resources but also by a lack of understanding of the required level of provision for an effective physiotherapy service.

6.12.1   Perceptions of deficits in physiotherapy provision
The physiotherapists highlight a number of gaps in the current physiotherapy service for older people. In their view the major problem is the gap between hospital care and care in the community, particularly where there is no geriatrician or geriatric unit. While rehabilitation facilities are seen to be well established in Dublin hospitals, in other areas it is very difficult to rehabilitate older patients where there is pressure on hospitals beds and no facilities at home. It is argued that rehabilitation cannot be delivered as part of the General Medical Service as it is a dedicated service with a completely different ethos. Rehabilitation must take place in an environment geared towards independent living (rather than in a general medical ward), there must be an adequately trained multi-disciplinary team led by a senior clinician with a special interest in rehabilitation and there must be an appropriate level of service with regard to nursing, physiotherapy, occupational therapy, speech therapy and nutrition. When patients have completed the first stage of rehabilitation, there then needs to be a 'step-down' facility which provides the same type, but less intense level, of multi-disciplinary input and the same holistic ethos of rehabilitation.

The physiotherapists perceive that, in future, the major emphasis should be on the development of a community physiotherapy service operating from health centres, day centres and social centres. The effectiveness of a community service is, however, influenced by transport facilities which, in the view of the physiotherapists, are at present very inadequate. Another recommendation from the physiotherapists is that they should be more involved in anticipatory care and health promotion and that greater use should be made of their ability to identify older people at risk.

6.12.2   Future demand for physiotherapists
The Working Party recommended that:

- **(6.37) the Department of Health review manpower requirements in physiotherapy as a matter of urgency in order to match the supply of graduates with the demand for physiotherapists.**

The physiotherapists note that the service is poised to grow, with increasing demand from older people and people with disability. Even now it can be difficult to fill vacancies in more remote areas and it is becoming urgent to examine personnel requirements. The Department of Health has indicated that it has the issue under consideration. Under the Programme for Competitiveness and Work, the physiotherapist's career structure and conditions are being examined and the Department suggests that these discussions should lead to a clearer sense of what action needs to be taken in relation to future requirements of the service. The question of matching supply of graduates with service needs is seen as a matter in the first instance for the Higher Education Authority and not the Department of Health, although the Department may enter discussions in due course.

The Working Party recommended that:

- **(R12.20) 50 physiotherapy assistants be employed to expand physiotherapy services for the elderly at an approximate cost of £0.5m annually.**

Information from the Department of Health indicates that the total amount of money provided since 1989 for the expansion of the physiotherapy service for older people amounts to only £0.5 million, or less than £60,000 per annum.

6.13   Provision of speech therapy
With regard to speech therapy, the Working Party also made a recommendation for a domiciliary service:

- **(R6.38) a domiciliary speech therapy service be provided to meet the needs of elderly people with impaired speech being cared for at home.**

Apart from the Eastern Health Board, none of the boards provide a domiciliary speech therapy service for older people (Table 6.6). Even in the Eastern Health Board it is noted that the service provided is limited. In this board stroke patients are referred to the community ward team where there is an input from a speech therapist. In the North Eastern Health Board there is a definite policy to focus on

Table 6.6: Provision of domiciliary speech therapy service

Health board	Whether provided
Eastern	Yes (limited)
Midland	No
Mid-Western	No
North Eastern	No
North Western	No
Southern	No
South Eastern	No
Western	No

Source: Interviews with Programme Managers of Community Care

the provision of a structured service in certain major locations. The Midland Health Board considers that, with scarce resources, it is more equitable to provide a community service, although its action plan does provide for a pilot test of the feasibility and cost of a domiciliary service. In the Mid-Western, Western and Southern Health Boards, a domiciliary speech therapy service is not regarded as being either necessary or feasible. The view in the North Western Health Board is that a domiciliary service is fairly necessary but it needs more resources than are currently available. In the South Eastern Health Board the service is seen as both necessary and feasible.

6.13.1   *Perceptions of deficits in speech therapy*

Several Programme Managers of Community Care report that speech therapy resources are already stretched and current resources are focused primarily on children. Feedback from speech and language therapists also highlights the huge demand on the current service from the child population. Inadequate staffing levels result in limited service provision for older people, with virtually no service in some areas. The speech and language therapists point out that they are not in a position to offer a comprehensive service to older people at any point, whether in the clinic, the day centre or in the home. Follow-up of older patients on discharge from hospital is limited and there is very little provision for on-site rehabilitation. Back-up services, such as dental services, are also perceived as being inadequate. Speech and language therapists feel that their service is regarded as less than important for older people and point out that patients can, for example, be discharged from hospital with a severe communication deficit although no viable means of communication has been established.

The view is expressed that health gain, such as return to mobility and safety in the home through occupational therapy and physiotherapy, is given greater emphasis than social gain which can be achieved through meeting communication needs. It is perceived by the speech and language therapists that communication disability following certain medical problems is often regarded as something older patients and their families have to live with and, accordingly, appropriate communication aids are not provided. It is noted that an important issue not mentioned in *The Years Ahead* is the management of dysphagia which has become a major part of the work of the speech and language therapists with older clients. From the point of view of the speech and language therapists, the development of an adequate speech therapy service for older people is seen to require funding, the promotion of speech and language therapy as a valuable service for older people, the creation of community speech and language therapy posts for adults, the inclusion of speech and language therapists on multi-disciplinary care teams for older people, the provision of speech and language therapy in day care centres and the provision of a domiciliary service.

6.14   Provision of chiropody

Many problems of mobility among older people arise from foot conditions and a good chiropody service can be an important element in maintaining independence.

The Working Party recommended that:

- **(R6.51) a chiropody service should be available in all areas to treat disorders of the feet in elderly persons on referral from the nurse or the general practitioner**.

Several models of delivery of the chiropody service are evident across the different health boards (Table 6.7).

Despite the fact that chiropody is often noted by board management as critical to the well-being of older people, it emerges that in most health boards the chiropody service is uneven and depends to a considerable extent on voluntary input. In several boards it is noted that the service is not standardised and it is hard to guarantee the quality of service provided by non-health board practitioners. PHNs in all boards typically note the service as inadequate. Apart from inadequate coverage, many PHNs note that the service is not equitably distributed, with some areas having practically no service at all. Feedback through the Irish Chiropodists Association suggests that, outside of the major cities, the chiropody service is extremely limited. Current levels of provision of the service are regarded as totally inadequate and it is seen that there is too much reliance on voluntary organisations to organise the service. It is seen that there needs to be greater recognition of the importance of the service and an appropriate level of funding

Table 6.7: Mode of delivery of chiropody service

Health board	Mode of delivery
Eastern	50 private chiropodists provide free service for older medical card holders
Midland	Chiropodists employed on sessional basis plus funding of provision by voluntary organisations
Mid-Western	1 chiropodist employed in one community care area. In other areas provided by voluntary organisations with health board funding
North Eastern	1 chiropodist paid on sessional basis plus funding of voluntary organisations
North Western	5 chiropodists provided through board and voluntary organisations
Southern	3.3 full-time equivalent chiropodists plus sessional chiropodists. In some areas service provided by voluntary organisations with funding from board
South Eastern	Chiropodists employed by board on sessional basis plus funding of service by voluntary organisations
Western	2 chiropodists on sessional basis equivalent to 5 full days per month

Source: Interviews with Programme Managers of Community Care and CSEs

devoted to it so that it is available in all districts with a co-ordinator at area level to oversee overall provision. It is also noted that most chiropodists cannot treat patients through medical cards.

6.14.1   Provision of a domiciliary chiropody service
The Working Party recommended that:

- **(R6.51) a domiciliary service should be provided for those elderly patients who are immobile**.

Four of the health boards say that they do provide a domiciliary service (Midland, Mid-Western, North Western and Western) but, except for one region in the Midland Health Board, the service appears to be only for exceptional cases (Table 6.8). Previous experience with a domiciliary service in the Southern Health Board showed that the conditions in which it was provided were often very unsuitable and the service was also often exploited. The board does not include a domiciliary service in its future plans for the chiropody service but rather wants to focus on expanding the community-based services already provided.

6.15   Funding of chiropody and speech therapy services
The Working Party recommended that:

- **(R12.24) £0.75m be allocated to improve dental services, chiropody and speech therapy for the elderly**.

Dental services are reviewed in the next chapter but, in respect of chiropody and speech therapy, the overall amount given for improvement of the services since 1989 is estimated by the Department of Health to be £300,000 and £200,000 respectively.

Table 6.8: Provision of domiciliary chiropody service

Health board	Whether provided
Eastern	No
Midland	Yes (one area)
Mid-Western	Yes (in special cases)
North Eastern	No
North Western	Yes (in special cases)
Southern	No
South Eastern	No
Western	Yes (limited basis)

Source: Interviews with Programme Managers of Community Care

6.16   Social work service

The Working Party recognised, for the first time, the personal and interpersonal tensions that can arise as a result of dependence in an older person. Since *The Years Ahead*, a number of studies have confirmed the emotional and social costs that can arise in the caring relationship (O'Connor and Ruddle 1988; Blackwell *et al.* 1992; Ruddle and O'Connor 1993; Finucane *et al.* 1994). Recognition of and attention to such issues can be an important factor in maintaining an older person at home. In the view of the Working Party, social workers are best equipped to address interpersonal problems arising in families with a dependent older person. Blackwell *et al.* also suggested that social workers have an important role in provision of advice and information and liaison between services. These authors argued that an increase in service provision by social workers could be one of the most effective ways of strengthening community care provision for older people (1992). The specific recommendation of the Working Party was that:

- **(R6.48) a domiciliary counselling service be available to dependent elderly people and their families and that the community care social work departments be gradually expanded for this purpose**.

Far from expansion of community care social work departments to accommodate the needs of older people, as the Working Party suggested, present community care social work services are overstretched and concentrate on families and children. Only in the North Western Health Board is there a community care social work service for older people (Table 6.9). With regard to provision of a domiciliary counselling service, the North Western Health Board provides such a service. Among the other boards (with the exception of the Mid-Western and South Eastern) the view is that a domiciliary service is not really necessary. In the Midland Health Board the emphasis is on developing a counselling service in care

Table 6.9: Provision of domiciliary social work counselling service

Health board	Whether provided
Eastern	No
Midland	No
Mid-Western	No
North Eastern	No
North Western	Yes
Southern	No
South Eastern	No
Western	No

Source: Interviews with Programme Managers of Community Care

centres rather than in the home. Management in several boards suggest that the responsibility to provide a counselling service can be met through the PHNs whom they perceive are already doing quite a lot of counselling. There is a view that while counselling support is required, it need not necessarily involve a special service but can be addressed by existing health professionals, such as the GP and the PHN, whose job description includes counselling.

6.16.1 *Perceptions of deficits in social work service*
Feedback from social workers suggests that, under current circumstances, the recommendation of the Working Party for a domiciliary service is not at all feasible. The development of an adequate community care social work service for older people requires, in the first instance, the commitment of health boards and the Department of Health and the deployment of extra resources. The social workers call for a pilot scheme to develop appropriate working models. Social workers, in interview, also noted that the term counselling is loosely defined in *The Years Ahead* and does not, by itself, encompass all that a social worker does. The narrow definition of their role, adopted in *The Years Ahead*, takes no account, for example, of their role with local authorities, their role in the area of occupational health and safety, and their role in boarding out schemes. One of their important functions could be support of carers and intervention and advocacy in families where conflict is adversely affecting the quality of life of the older person. Through such a service it is seen that many problems could be prevented and hospitalisation or institutionalisation reduced or delayed in many cases. Social workers in the North Western Health Board also point to a growing awareness of the existence of emotional and physical abuse and financial exploitation of older people.

Social workers point out that in virtually every other country in Europe and in North America, social workers are very much involved in work with older people and it is accepted that they have a unique contribution to make to care teams, case management, the assessment process, the resolution of family problems, protection from abuse and exploitation and advocacy for vulnerable older people. The narrow view of a social work service for older people put forward by the Working Party must be countered.

6.17   Help at home
The Working Party considered that the provision of help in the home with the tasks of everyday living is of vital importance to the success of the strategy to support older people at home. In addition to its role in helping older people living alone, the home help service also has a major contribution to make to the support of caring relatives and the provision of respite from caregiving. The Working Party

recommended that:

- **(R6.46) health boards should be legally obliged to provide or make arrangements to provide services to maintain persons at home who would otherwise require care in another setting**.

At present the health boards are empowered but not obliged to provide a home help service and, while all boards provide it, the service is optional. In reflection of its optional status, feedback from health board management and Home Help Organisers reveals variations across the boards in the organisation and scope of the service and the objectives which are set for it. A recent study (Lundstrπm and McKeown 1994) carried out for the National Council for the Elderly highlights the issue of the discretionary nature of the service and poses the question as to whether anomalies in assessing need and eligibility and wide variations in the level of provision might be due to the fact that the service is regarded as optional. The National Council for the Elderly study reveals the importance of the home help service from the point of view of the older consumers themselves: it is of note that 90 per cent of the older people surveyed declared themselves to be very to somewhat satisfied with the service.

The National Council for the Elderly regards home help as a core service, that is a service essential to maintain a quality of life and a level of functional autonomy which enables older people to live independently in the community and, consequently, to avoid unnecessary hospitalisation or admission to long-stay institutions. As a core service, the National Council for the Elderly has argued that home help should be underpinned by legislation and should be given appropriate statutory funding. *Shaping a Healthier Future* gives a commitment that national guidelines on eligibility and charges, which would be applied in a uniform manner in all areas, will be introduced in respect of services, such as home help, where legislative provisions are at present absent. The Department of Health also indicates that a fundamental review of the home help service is about to commence.

6.17.1   Models of delivery of home help service

The Working Party recommended that:

- **(R6.46) the flexibility and voluntary commitment, which form such an important part of the home help and meals service, be safeguarded and built upon in future**.

The 1994 National Council for the Elderly study of the home help service distinguishes six models of delivery of the service. The table below outlines these models and indicates the particular models used by each health board.

Table 6.10: Models of delivery of home help service

	Model of delivery	Health board
1	Overall responsibility with Superintendent PHN	·North Eastern and some areas of South Eastern and Southern
2	Overall responsibility with Superintendent PHN and Superintendent Community Welfare Officer	Areas of Eastern and South Eastern
3	Home Help Organiser employed by health board	Western and Midland and areas of Mid-Western, North Western, Southern and South Eastern
4	Overall responsibility with Superintendent PHN but with input from Home Help Organiser	Parts of North Western
5	Voluntary organisations have responsibility	Most of Eastern and areas of Mid-Western
6	Overall responsibility with Superintendent PHN but Home Help employed by voluntary organisation	Areas of North Western and part of Southern

Sources: Lundström and McKeown 1994
Interviews with Programme Managers of Community Care

The home help service is usually delivered directly by the health board but in the Eastern Health Board and in some areas of the Mid-Western and North Western Health Boards there is a large voluntary input. In the Southern Health Board there is a two-fold service operating in one of the community care areas. In addition to a personal home help service, which is the same as that operating in other community care areas, there is a second service called the 'district home help service'. The latter was evolved initially as a response to the needs of older people in isolated rural areas and involves, for example, collection of laundry, organisation of house repairs and once-off cleaning of houses and individual home help duties on a weekly basis.

6.17.2   Level of provision of home help service
The Working Party recommended the expansion of the home help service.

- **(R6.46) The immediate aim should be to develop the service to the extent of the whole time equivalent of 4.5 home helps per thousand elderly people.**

The 1994 National Council for the Elderly study noted that even in 1988 all but one of the health boards had exceeded the norm of provision recommended by the Working Party but despite this a considerable expansion in coverage was necessary. By 1995 all health boards had further expanded their home help service (Table 6.11). Although the home help service has expanded in recent times, the District Liaison Nurses (or those fulfilling this function) in all boards, with the exception of the Eastern, typically rate the service provided as inadequate or only fairly adequate. Usually the problem is not in the nature of the service provided,

Table 6.11: Level of provision of home help service

Health board	Full-time equivalent Home Helps 1995	Number per 1,000 older persons 1995
Eastern	950	8.1
Midland	260	10.6
Mid-Western	1,135 (full-time equivalent figures not available)	—
North Eastern	1,291 (full-time equivalent figure not available)	—
North Western	183	6.0
Southern	854	13.1
South Eastern	217	4.9
Western	333	6.7

Source: Interviews with Programme Managers of Community Care

although some District Liaison Nurses would like to see an expansion of night and weekend services. Rather, the problem is that the service is greatly underfunded. More Home Helps are needed and better payment has to be provided for those in the service. Several also call for less rigid criteria on eligibility for the service and standard guidelines on payment for the service.

6.17.3   Scope of home help service
With regard to the scope of the service, the Working Party recommended that:

- **(R6.46) an emergency home help service should be available within a day of request. A service should also be available outside of normal working hours and at weekends. The home help service should be expanded in scope to provide an evening and weekend relief service for persons caring for elderly relatives at home**.

With three exceptions (Mid-Western, South Eastern and Western) all of the health boards provide an emergency home help service (Table 6.12). The boards which do not provide the service pinpoint lack of resources as the reason for non-provision. The number of older people requiring an emergency service is noted as being quite small. The services can usually be implemented immediately on request. A home help service outside of normal working hours and at weekends is available in the Eastern, Midland, North Eastern and North Western Health Boards. The Southern and Western Health Boards do not provide this service, or provide it only in exceptional cases; primarily because they do not have adequate resources. The Mid-Western Health Board also says it does not have the resources for an out-of-hours service. Five of the boards (Eastern, Midland, Mid-Western, North Eastern and North Western) provide a limited home help respite service for carers. Among those not providing this respite service, the Southern Health Board

Table 6.12: Scope of home help service

Health board	Emergency service	Out-of-hours service	Weekend service	Relief service for carers
Eastern	Yes	Yes	Yes	Yes
Midland	Yes	Yes	Yes	Yes
Mid-Western	No	No	No	Yes
North Eastern	Yes	Yes	Yes	Yes
North Western	Yes	Yes	Yes	Yes
Southern	Yes	No	No	No
South Eastern	No	No	No	No
Western	No	No	No	No

Source: Interviews with Programme Managers of Community Care, Senior PHNs, Superintendent PHNs and Home Help Organisers

plans to redefine the home help function to include support of carers, with a priority being the provision of respite to carers of sufferers of Alzheimer's disease, stroke and other such disabling conditions.

6.17.4   Nature of home help service
With regard to the service offered by Home Helps, the Working Party recommended that:

- **(R6.46) the home help service should be comprehensive enough to assist elderly people with all the tasks of daily living**.

In essence this recommendation implied that Home Helps should be able to provide an element of personal care as well as carrying out practical home care tasks. In all of the health boards, Home Helps perform household chores (e.g. cleaning, cooking, washing), tasks outside the home (e.g. shopping, going to the bank or post office) and some elements of personal care (e.g. help with dressing, washing and giving medication). Many Home Helps also see part of their job as offering social and emotional support. To a lesser degree, Home Helps liaise with relatives and service providing agencies.

With regard to other types of personal care, there is variation between the health boards in the extent to which Home Helps carry out this function. In the North Eastern Health Board the management view is that Home Helps are employed primarily for domestic rather than care tasks. Several Home Help Organisers themselves note that if Home Helps are to provide personal care then it is essential that they get appropriate training. As indicated in a previous section, four of the boards also employ Care Assistants as part of the public health nursing service in an attempt to respond to the personal care needs of older people. Home Helps carry out some personal care tasks as part of their other duties but Care Assistants perform only personal care tasks. The National Council for the Elderly 1994 study on the home help service highlighted issues about the linkage between Care Assistants and Home Helps and the identification of the particular duties appropriate to each. The study also highlighted the negative reaction of many Home Helps and Home Help Organisers to the introduction of Care Assistants who saw it as wasteful and as an encroachment on their field of responsibility. With regard to the recommendation of the Working Party on the comprehensiveness of the home help service, the duties involved in 'assisting elderly people with all the tasks of daily living' and the tasks appropriate for Care Assistants and Home Helps need to be defined.

6.17.5   Future development of home help service

The National Council for the Elderly 1994 study asks whether the home help service should be a professional service which needs special training or simply a good neighbour service. There are differing views among the health boards with regard to the future development of the home help service. For example, in the North Eastern Health Board, the management view is that the Home Help is a good neighbour who performs domestic tasks and that further support and personal care is the domain of home support workers or Care Assistants who receive specific training. A very different view is expressed in the Southern Health Board where the aim is to expand home help services to include a greater provision for personal care and support of carers and families and, while maintaining the good neighbour philosophy, to provide Home Helps with appropriate training. In the Western Health Board also the aim is to extend the home help service and provide the necessary training rather than add another layer to the home care service. The Midland Health Board also seeks training for Home Helps. Almost all of the health boards call for more resources for the service and note that the pay rate is increasingly becoming an issue.

Home Help Organisers also call for more resources for the service. A further issue raised by the Organisers in every board is the difficulty in recruiting high quality personnel, given the low rate of pay for the service. When suitable people are recruited there can be a high rate of turnover with people moving on to other jobs offering more attractive pay. It is noted by several that the good neighbour philosophy is outdated. The service now requires a statutory basis with definite objectives. There is a perception among Home Help Organisers that the service has an unacceptably low profile. Failure to recognise its role leads to lack of standards for provision, scope, entitlements and eligibility. In most boards the Home Help Organisers perceive that, in addition to resources and pay issues, training of Home Helps is essential to the future development of the service.

6.17.6   Funding for home help service

In 1987, at the time of the Working Party's deliberations, expenditure on the home help service was £7.65 million. The Working Party recommended that:

- **(R12.19) an additional £6m be made available to expand the home help service**.

The Years Ahead significantly underestimated the future costs involved in running the home help service. The Department of Health indicates that expenditure on the home help service came to £16.4m in 1995, and is estimated at £17.6m for 1996.

6.18   Nutrition

Where a meals service is provided to older people, it is almost always provided by voluntary organisations. The Working Party recommended that:

- **(R6.46) catering officers in health boards should review the nutritional content of meals prepared for the elderly by voluntary organisations and advise on the maintenance of high quality**.

Feedback from health board dieticians and members of the Geriatric Interest Group of the Irish Nutrition and Dietetic Institute indicates that at present there is no system in place for reviewing the nutritional content of meals prepared by voluntary organisations. If meals are provided by a health board facility they are subject to monitoring and quality assurance, but voluntary organisations outside the control of health boards are not subject to these standards. The Eastern Health Board is developing an initiative involving one day seminars on Meals-on-Wheels in each of its community care areas. This board also has a Nutritional Advisor for the Elderly whose role is to advise on all aspects of the nutritional/dietary needs of older people in all settings and to provide a nutritional educational service to all staff dealing with older people and to older people themselves. The North Eastern Health Board's plan for future services includes a nutrition service designed to meet the needs of older people.

6.18.1   Perceptions of deficits in nutrition services

Dieticians draw attention to recent research on acute admissions in a geriatric unit in a Dublin hospital which showed an 84 per cent incidence of malnutrition on admission among those over 65 years of age (Charles *et al.*, 1997). It is pointed out that the staffing resources of nutritionists/dieticians specific for older people are grossly inadequate in community services, long-stay geriatric hospitals, special hospital and acute hospital services. With regard to community services, the dieticians call for adequate staffing to cover the following: dietetic input into Meals-on-Wheels and day care services, education of older people, carers, GPs, PHNs, Home Helps and meals services organisers on healthy eating and the specific requirements of certain groups; monitoring of those on enteral feeding in the community; domiciliary visits for the housebound; and rationalisation and standardisation of supplements and enteral feeding products.

6.19   Provision of alarm systems

Alarm systems play a role in the care of older people in relation both to medical emergency needs and security needs. With regard to the latter, a recent study carried out on behalf of the National Council for the Elderly found that crime against older people has increased in the recent past from an originally low base, particularly in urban areas (Fahey and Murray 1994). While older people are generally at a lower risk of crime than younger age groups, there are certain groups at high risk of burglary. These include those who are alone by day and night, those with impaired mobility and those who lack security equipment. Older people who become the victims of crime are particularly likely to experience physical and psychological after-effects. Crime victimisation may also lead to a sense of helplessness and a curbing of social participation. In recognition of the needs of older people living alone who may be suffering from long-term illness or who may feel isolated or feel apprehensive about their security, the Working Party recommended that in addition to the urban pilot project on alarm systems for older people taking place at the time:

- **(R6.54) a pilot scheme to assess the potential of radios and telephone based alarm systems to assist the elderly be initiated in a rural area as soon as possible.**

The Working Party also recommended that:

- **(R6.54) the long term goal should be to provide a telephone or radio based alarm to elderly persons living alone and assessed by the district team for the elderly as being at medical or social risk.**

All of the health boards have undertaken some initiative in relation to alarm systems for older people, whether for medical emergencies or security reasons (Table 6.13). The extent and nature of provision varies widely across boards. The extent of provision is typically limited and no board has as yet met the goal of the Working Party. It appears in some boards that there is uncertainty on how best to meet the emergency and security needs of older people and some concern that electronic alarm systems would require far more funding than is currently available. The most usual view is that the most effective approach for the board is to fund voluntary organisations who have an interest in this area.

A small number of voluntary national networks (such as Community Alert and Neighbourhood Watch) in conjunction with the Garda' are dedicated to addressing the issue of crime against older people. A Reach Out campaign operates in the greater Dublin Area involving local authorities, the health board, the Department of Health, the Garda' and a number of voluntary organisations. The National Council for the Elderly has advised that these efforts be co-ordinated to ensure the most effective community response and has recommended that the success of such programmes be evaluated (1996). The Council has also recommended that the

Table 6.13: Provision of alarm systems for older people

Health board	Provision
Eastern	Central monitoring alarm control unit established. Approximately 65 older people linked to the unit. 11 sheltered housing units and 12 units in local community linked to central monitoring unit in hospital in Athy
Midland	Medical alert systems installed for around 8 older people
Mid-Western	Paid for installation of around 10 Telecom Phone Watch Medi-System devices. Installed panic buttons for some older persons. Special allocation of £24,000 for alarm system in one area
North Eastern	Provided funds to a small number of older persons to purchase their own telephone or alarm system. 105 wireless intercoms installed
North Western	Pendant type alarms installed for 40 older people linked to a central monitoring unit. Assistance provided in setting up alarm contacts for those who wish to install their own alarm system
Southern	Financial assistance given in exceptional cases to install emergency communication system
South Eastern	Grant given to voluntary body for provision of alarms to older people. Assistance given to individuals to install alarms
Western	Funding given to voluntary organisation for provision of alarms to older people. Approximately 76 older people connected via the telephone to a central monitoring station. Emergency communication systems installed in five homes

Source: Task Force on Security for the Elderly, Department of Social Welfare 1996

experience of crime and its effect on older people should be examined in more detail in order to identify preventive measures which could be taken and the support needs of those who have been traumatised by victimisation.

6.19.1 Task Force on Security, 1996

The Department of Social Welfare, in early 1996, established a Task Force on Security for the Elderly. An outline of the main recommendations of the Task Force (1996) and the progress to date on their implementation is provided below:

- A renewed campaign to provide older people with information and advice on personal security would be undertaken by the Departments of Justice and Social Welfare. In late 1996, the Departments sent leaflets on security and welfare to 320,000 pensioners.

- Community-based initiatives should be evaluated to ensure equitable coverage and appropriate funding. Funding has been sought for this by the Department of Health and the Garda' but is not yet finalised.

- There should be regular co-operation and liaison between various service providers at local level. Meetings have been held between local groups and Assistant Garda Commissioners in five regions.

- FÁS should encourage statutory agencies and voluntary groups to put forward proposals for schemes aimed at enhancing the security of older people. Over 1,000 FÁS participants are employed in schemes designed to enhance the security of older people. Over 70 of the Student Summer Job Schemes in 1996 were directly related to the security of older people.

- Local authorities, when requested, should erect Community Alert and Neighbourhood Watch signs in their area. A circular was issued in March 1996 by the Department of the Environment asking local authorities to adopt a positive and uniform approach to erecting these signs.

- Consideration should be given to extension of tax relief measures for installation of security systems. Tax relief has been extended to enable a son or daughter of the older person to claim for installation of an alarm.

- Resources to be made available to voluntary groups to support the installation of security and alarm equipment in homes of 'at risk' older people. Grant aid has been provided, with £2m made available to voluntary and local groups for installation of security systems in 1996. A further £2m has been provided for 1997.

- The possibility of waiving or reducing the installation costs of telephones for older people unable to afford installation will be explored. Recipients of the living alone allowance were offered telephone installation at a reduced cost in 1996. The offer is being repeated in 1997.

In its submission to the Task Force, the National Council for the Elderly argued that the well-being of older people is threatened as much by their perception of how safe they are as by the level of crime which they actually experience. Accordingly, the National Council for the Elderly called for sensitive and considered handling of media coverage of crimes against older people and an emphasis on publicising measures to combat such crimes. The National Council for the Elderly also argued for a strategic approach to crimes against older people. For example, measures designed to meet security needs could be worked out in tandem with measures designed to ensure appropriate surveillance of frail and dependent older people in the community, particularly those living alone with significant medical problems. Registers of those at risk could play an important role in this context and accordingly, liaison with the health boards is essential to a co-ordinated and effective response to crime against older people. The National Council for the Elderly pointed out that most alarm and alert security systems rely on the telephone but 24 per cent of older people living alone and 20 per cent of all older people do not have a telephone. The Council recommended that no older person should be without a telephone on the grounds of cost and further recommended that older people be educated on the potential benefits of the telephone.

6.20   Summary and conclusions

The first step in the delivery of home care is to identify those older persons who may be in need. This review shows that while attempts are made in each health board to identify older people at risk, the current means of compiling registers is less than effective, with definitions of and criteria for 'risk' varying between and within health boards. The call by the Working Party for examination of the best method of identifying older people 'at risk' has yet to be addressed. National standardised guidelines and criteria for the development of an 'at risk' register are needed for uniformity across all areas and to ensure the most appropriate use of the information compiled. Computerisation of the data would facilitate easier access to the information collected, and would enable easier up-dating of the register and make it less time-consuming to maintain. A computerised system which would link the PHNs with GPs would facilitate more effective use of the information on the register.

In the initial period when an older person becomes in need of care, the GP plays a critical role in determining the kind of subsequent care which will be given and the resources which will be brought to bear on the problem. The Working Party had recommended that case finding should be a normal part of GP practice and of the General Medical Service, but the current GP contract makes no specific provision for anticipatory care and there are no particular incentives in it. Case finding occurs but it is opportunistic as resources are not available for a more proactive approach. The Department of Health is concerned that there should be more anticipatory care but from the GP perspective there are a number of issues to be addressed. For example, because of eligibility criteria and the choice of doctor scheme, GPs do not have a fixed patient population and not all older people have medical cards. In addition there is no infrastructure, at present, to support anticipatory care, there is no agreed protocol for identifying problems and there are limited resources for effective treatment of certain problems which may be identified. A major issue to be addressed is the lack of research into the effectiveness of screening procedures. If case finding does not occur then an investigation of alternative forms of anticipatory care must be undertaken.

It was noted in *The Years Ahead* and again in *Shaping a Healthier Future* that GPs need to be integrated into the overall health care system. It is apparent in this review that from the perspective of the GPs themselves, liaison with others such as District Liaison Nurses and PHNs is still less than satisfactory. It was envisaged by the Working Party that district teams would be one way of addressing this problem. However, most boards have not established such teams and, where there is a team, the GP is not always a participant. Feedback from GPs and PHNs highlights the need to establish more formal procedures for liaison. If the district team model has failed then it is imperative to discover other structures that would facilitate effective liaison. *Shaping a Healthier Future* envisaged the establishment of GP units in the health boards as an important contribution to integration but this awaits evaluation.

The Working Party made recommendations for the delivery of a variety of services to the home once an older person becomes in need of care. The extent of implementation of these recommendations is summarised in Table 6.14.

The public health nursing service is central to anticipatory care of older people and to enabling them to remain in their own homes. Three main issues arise here: the number of PHNs employed; the functions they perform; and the back-up services available. With regard to staff numbers, 1995 figures from the Department of Health indicate that all but two of the health boards have reached the recommended level of provision set down in 1975 for the service. However, the picture is less positive if those performing a managerial role (Superintendent and Senior PHNs) are excluded from the figures. The number of PHNs on district duties is below the recommended level in four of the eight health boards. It should also be noted that the figures include Registered General Nurses who are not qualified PHNs and therefore cannot undertake the full range of public health

Table 6.14: Summary of current provision of home care services

Recommendation	*Current situation*
Ratio of PHNs to population to be brought up to 1: 2,616	Overall ratio is 1: 2567. Below recommended level still in two boards
Panels of Registered General Nurses to be established in each district	Panels established in all boards but not in every district with the exception of two boards
Possibility of employing Care Assistants to be explored	Care Assistants employed in four boards
Domiciliary physiotherapy service to be provided	Limited service in three boards
Domiciliary speech therapy service to be provided	Limited service in one board
Chiropody service to be available in all areas	Not available in any area
Domiciliary chiropody service to be provided for immobile older people	Available in four boards but mostly for exceptional cases
Domiciliary counselling service to be provided	Community care social work service for older people available in one board. Domiciliary service provided by this board
Ratio of 4.5 Home Helps per 1,000 older person	Recommended level exceeded by all boards
Emergency home help service to be provided	Provided in five boards
Out of hours home help service to be provided	Provided in four boards
Home Helps to provide relief service to carers	Limited service in five boards

nursing duties. It must also be recognised that older people are but one of the client groups of the PHN. Programme Managers in all boards admit that current levels are less than adequate and there is widespread dissatisfaction among the nurses themselves about current ratios of PHNs to population.

With regard to the function of the PHN, one issue which arises is the increasing level of managerial work required, for example, in overseeing Care Assistants and Registered General Nurse panels. The nurses call attention to the danger of being distanced from their district nursing duties. A review of the service has recently been completed by the Department of Health which should spell out the appropriate functions of the service. The present study has found that PHNs consider that the most appropriate use of their skills is in anticipatory care, health promotion and liaison. A third issue is the need, identified by both management and nurses, for a greater level of back-up services such as nurse panels, Care Assistants and Home Helps. Unless such back-up is available, PHNs will be distracted from their more appropriate functions leading to ineffectiveness and wastage of resources in the service.

An important form of back-up to the PHN is the Registered General Nurse panel. All boards have established panels of nurses. This service is highly regarded both by Programme Managers and PHNs and is seen as playing an essential role in home care for older people. It is flexible, available out-of-hours and provides relief for carers. One of the more important benefits of the service is that it frees the PHN of curative nursing duties and allows her to focus on anticipatory care. There are problems to be addressed in relation to high turnover in panel participation and the consequent need for continued recruitment. More importantly, the service is very much underfunded and must be given greater resources if it is to fulfil its potential value.

Another potential form of back-up to the public health nursing service is the Care Assistant service. Four of the boards currently employ these assistants. Where they are employed, they are perceived as making a valuable contribution to the goal of enabling older people to remain at home. There appears, however, to be ambivalence about the place of Care Assistants vis-^-vis Home Helps. The specific roles, functions and focus of each service need to be more clearly delineated so that effective decisions can be made about the most appropriate service to put in place in particular circumstances.

The Working Party had envisaged that a range of paramedical services would be available in the home for older people. It emerges that domiciliary provision of paramedical services is extremely limited. Feedback from management and service providers alike highlights the fact that domiciliary provision of services is simply not possible with current limited resources. In addition, domiciliary delivery of services such as physiotherapy or speech therapy is not always regarded as necessary by health board management. This recommendation needs to be reviewed and its cost effectiveness *vis-^-vis* other services such as day hospitals and day care centres evaluated.

Apart from domiciliary provision, the different paramedical service providers raise other particular issues about their respective services. Physiotherapists, for example, highlight a number of other gaps in the current service such as the gap between hospital care and care in the community and the inadequacy of rehabilitation facilities. The major issue in relation to speech therapy services is the current focus on children who make a huge demand on the service. The service is perceived by speech therapists as being over-stretched and with current resources there is no possibility of offering a comprehensive service to older people. It is also perceived by the speech therapists that their service is not properly recognised as playing a valuable role in the well-being of older people. With regard to chiropody, a major issue is the extent to which the service depends on voluntary input and its uneven distribution across different parts of the country, with some older people having no access to the service.

The Working Party identified social workers as being best equipped to address the interpersonal problems that can arise in the caring relationship between an older person and a family member. A major gap in services for older people identified in this review is the lack of a community social work service, with only one health board currently providing such a service. The major problem is that community social work services are focused almost totally on families and children and are greatly overstretched in attempting to meet the demands of this group. There also appears to be an attitudinal problem whereby the full potential of a social community work service for older people is not recognised. The narrow view of the social work service must be countered and, as in most other European countries, social workers must be recognised as having a unique contribution to make in areas such as case management, resolution of family problems, assessment of needs and advocacy. The growing awareness of abuse of older people further underlines the need to provide a community social work service for older people. Development of a social work service for older people has been given little attention since *The Years Ahead* and requires much greater exploration and research to allow the development of appropriate working models.

The home help service is a key service for older people. Despite its central importance and the recommendation of the Working Party, there is no legal obligation on the health boards to provide a home help service. The fact that the service is not obligatory has been identified by the National Council for the Elderly as one of the problems with the service, leading to variations in levels of provision, eligibility for the service and the nature of the tasks carried out. While all of the health boards have attained the levels of provision recommended in *The Years Ahead*, it is clear from the National Council for the Elderly study and this review that the home help service still falls far short of what is required. With regard to the scope of the service, provision out-of-hours and at weekends is still limited and the service does not provide the extent of respite for carers envisaged in *The Years Ahead*. Not only did *The Years Ahead* underestimate the level of provision required but it also underestimated the amount of funding needed and, despite increases in funding, the service is still underfunded. One important issue is the perceived inadequate level of payment for Home Helps and the consequent difficulty in recruitment and in maintaining a quality service. A further issue that must be addressed is the respective duties and focus of Home Helps and of the Care Assistants employed by some health boards and the kind of linkages that occur between the two services.

The final element in care at home discussed in *The Years Ahead* is the provision of alarm systems. All of the health boards have introduced some initiatives in this regard but the level and nature of what has been done varies greatly across the boards. A major development in this area has been the establishment by the Department of Social Welfare of a Task Force on Security for the Elderly which has led to the identification of priority areas for action including: provision of information and advice to older people, tax relief for security systems, support of the work of voluntary organisations in this area, encouragement of inter-agency co-operation and the exploration of the possibility of waiving or reducing the costs of telephone installations among older people on low incomes.

CHAPTER SEVEN

Care in the Community

7.1   Introduction

In the previous chapter the focus was on community care services provided to older people in their own homes. The purpose of the present chapter is to examine those community care services provided on a communal basis within districts or community care areas. Specifically, the chapter assesses the implementation of the recommendations of the Working Party with regard to transport, day care services, dental, aural and ophthalmic services and boarding out. Sources of information on implementation include interviews and/or questionnaires from:

- Officers of Departments of Health, the Environment and Transport, Energy and Communications
- Co-ordinators of Services for the Elderly (16)
- Programme Managers of Community Care in all boards
- District Liaison Nurses (39).

7.2   Transport

A critical factor in the delivery of effective community-based services is the provision of appropriate transport. The ability of older people to meet many of their needs, such as medical care, social contact, shopping and recreation, is very much influenced by their access to transport facilities. Deteriorating mobility in later years increases this critical role. While all persons over 65 years of age and their spouses are entitled to free travel on public transport, studies have shown that in practice this concession is often of little use to older people. This is because regular services are not available or are scheduled at inconvenient times, or because the design of the vehicles is inappropriate for older people with restricted mobility (Daly and O'Connor 1984; O'Mahony, 1985). O'Connor *et al.* (1991) found that among older people the second most frequently mentioned unmet need was the provision of an adequate transport system. The older people in this study spoke of the worry caused by difficulties in getting to the GP's surgery or getting to hospital when admission is required. Some also noted that lack of attendance at day-care centres is often related to transport difficulties. Fahey and Murray

(1994) found that one quarter of older people living in the community had no public transport available to them. As would be expected, the problem was much greater in rural areas where the figure was 50 per cent compared with two per cent in urban areas. In recognition of the importance of transport in community care of older people, the Working Party made a number of recommendations covering adequate provision and co-ordination of services, the development of innovative schemes and attention to appropriate design.

7.2.1   Inter-departmental examination of transport
The working party recommended that:

- **(R7.6) the Departments of Tourism and Transport and the Environment examine ways in which transport in rural areas can be co-ordinated and how transport for the elderly can be improved. The law governing transport services and the use of subsidies should encourage greater flexibility in meeting the transport needs of the elderly in rural areas.**

With regard to inter-departmental examination of how transport in rural areas can be co-ordinated and how transport for older people can be improved, the Department of the Environment states that this is primarily a matter for the Department of Transport, Energy and Communications (previously the Department of Tourism and Transport). The latter Department indicates that it has carried out no examination of transport for older people. A second recommendation of the Working Party was that:

- **(R7.7) the Department of the Environment encourage greater attention to the design of public transport vehicles to ensure easier entry and exit for elderly people, to providing sufficient grab rails in the right places and to improved seating design.**

In the area of design of public transport vehicles, an initiative in 1992 by the Minister for the Environment authorised the granting of 50 new licences for wheelchair accessible taxis in the Dublin taximeter area on a pilot basis. Regulations were made in 1995 which included, *inter alia*, a new power to local authorities to grant wheelchair accessible taxi licences in all taximeter areas.

7.2.2   Review of transport resources in the community
The Working Party recommended that:

- **(R7.6) the Co-ordinator of Services for the Elderly should review transport resources in the community and encourage the transport services of statutory agencies and the resources of voluntary bodies to provide more adequate transport for elderly people in remote rural areas.**

Table 7.1: Review of transport resources in the community

Health board	Whether review carried out	Resulting initiatives
Eastern	Currently underway. Small scale review 6 years ago	Suggestion with regard to use of taxis for a small fee during the day in a confined area not taken up
Midland	No	N/A
Mid-Western	Informal review	Problems identified
North Eastern	No (Plan for review outlined in board's strategy)	N/A
North Western	No	N/A
Southern	Case study of one day centre	No new initiative. Problems identified
South Eastern	Yes	Minibuses provided for day centres. Voluntary transport financed. Ambulance services to clinics improved
Western	No	N/A

Source: Interviews with CSEs and Programme Managers of Community Care

With the exception of the South Eastern Health Board, the health boards have not undertaken a review of transport resources in the community (Table 7.1). The South Eastern Health Board's review identified a lack of transport in rural areas and difficulties with transport to health clinics. In particular the use of ambulances was not seen as 'user-friendly'. As a result of the review, minibuses were provided for day care centres, the ambulance service was improved and voluntary transport services were encouraged and given finance. In the Mid-Western, Southern and Eastern Health Boards small-scale reviews have been undertaken, but while problems have been identified, these reviews have not resulted in the establishment of any new initiatives. The latter board is currently carrying out a full-scale review of transport resources and there is also a plan for such a review in the North Eastern Health Board.

7.2.3   Nature of transport arrangements

The Working Party recommended that:

- **(R7.8) each health board ensure that adequate transport arrangements exist to give dependent elderly people access to day care, day hospitals and out-patient departments**.

Across the health boards very varied means of arranging transport for dependent older people are evident (Table 7.2).

With one exception, all health boards indicate that voluntary organisations are involved in transport arrangements usually by providing transport to day care centres. In just two of the boards (Eastern and Midland) transport arrangements

Table 7.2: Transport arrangements for dependent elderly people

Health board	Transport arrangements
Eastern	Board provides a minibus and ambulance service to out-patient departments, day hospitals and day centres. In addition to board vehicles, taxis are called upon to provide transport but reliance on taxis is unsatisfactory and is being reduced. Voluntary organisations and individual volunteers provide transport to some day care centres. Sometimes funding is given to voluntary groups for transport purposes
Midland	Board provides network of buses to day care centres and day hospitals. Funding of voluntary transport
Mid-Western	Co-operation with voluntary organisations to day care facilities. Board ambulances for out-patient services. Co-operation with voluntary organisations who provide services on request. Grants given to buy minibuses. Traded-in ambulances given to voluntary organisations
North Eastern	Specially adapted vehicles for day care centres and day hospitals. Co-operation with voluntary organisation for transport to day centre for Alzheimer's Disease sufferers
North Western	Board provides its own transport system for older people — ambulance service and private contracted service
Southern	Subsidise private transport in cases of hardship. Co-operation with voluntary organisations for transport to day care centres. Voluntary organisations sometimes raise funds for vehicles, or provide vehicles or drivers
South Eastern	Provides minibuses for day centres and ambulances for clinics. Co-operation with voluntary organisations to provide transport to some day care centres and some clinics and for recreational outings
Western	Provide transport to board premises. Co-operation with voluntary organisations for buses to day care centres and hospital visits

Source: Interviews with Programme Managers of Community Care and CSEs

are described by management as satisfactory. In the Eastern Health Board there is a Co-ordinator of Transport Services for the Elderly. In this person's experience there is an effective system for getting the older person to hospital, but problems then arise because of differences in the length of time for which different people are in hospital. In the Southern Health Board, arrangements are rated as unsatisfactory because they are seen to be *ad hoc* and unsystematic. In the North Eastern Health Board the sources of dissatisfaction are the lack of an integrated regional transport policy and the provision by the board of a service that should properly be delivered by the public transport authority. Among District Liaison Nurses (or those fulfilling this function) concerns about transport are widespread and current arrangements are described as, at best, fairly effective. It emerges that while some areas are well serviced, in other areas older people are virtually without any transport. It is noted by several nurses that while voluntary organisations 'do their best', what is required is an official transport system. In seven of the eight boards the District Liaison Nurses call for more financial support to ensure a properly run and equitable service.

7.2.4   *Current initiatives on transport*

Recent research by Fahey and Murray (1994) indicates that the extent of car ownership among older people has increased from 39 per cent in 1977 to 49 per cent in 1993. Alongside this there has been a reduction in the proportion of older people using public transport for most journeys from 46 per cent in 1977 to 36 per cent in 1993. Despite these changes, public transport still plays a major role in the lives of many older people. In the interest of improving the availability of, and access to, transport, Age Alliance recently formed an Action Group on Transport comprising representatives of a variety of local, regional and national groups. Problems surrounding the Free Travel Pass scheme have been identified by the Action Group. These include the lack of adequate transport preventing use of the pass, the restriction on purchasing return tickets forcing pass holders to queue twice for one journey and the lack of flexibility which would allow the pass to be used for taxis and private buses. The North West Connemara Community Transport Study published in 1995 also highlighted the problem of older people being unable to use their free travel pass because of inadequate transport (North West Connemara Community 1995). The study recommended that the free travel pass scheme should be extended to cover local transport initiatives.

The Rural Transport Initiative (RTI) launched in April 1996, in conjunction with the EU Sampo Project, aims to radically develop and expand transport services throughout rural Ireland. One of the main objectives of the RTI is to provide better mobility for citizens by removing barriers to travel especially among the disabled, older people and isolated communities through flexible, reliable and accessible transport services. It is planned that the first implementation of the RTI will be the Sampo Project (Systems for Advanced Management of Public Transport). The core of the Sampo Project is the provision of Public Passenger Transport Services on demand in rural areas to, among others, older and disabled people. Buses will run over flexible routes which will be determined by demand. Bookings will be made by phone, fax or by calling at travel and despatch centres located at different points in the region. Special booking facilities will be made available to facilitate people without phones. One of the areas being targeted by Sampo for advanced management of transport is health care. The Sampo Project is to operate a pilot scheme in the South Eastern part of the country. This is planned to commence in Summer 1997.

7.3   **Day centres**

The Working Party considered that day centres are an important element in the continuum of services needed to maintain older people at home. Such centres not only provide support and social contact for older people living alone, but also provide assistance and relief to those caring for older relatives and thereby can reduce unnecessary admission to institutional care. The main purpose of the day centre as identified by the Working Party is to:

- provide a service such as a mid-day meal, a bath and a variety of paramedical services
- promote social contact and prevent loneliness
- relieve caring relatives, particularly those who have to go to work
- provide social stimulation in a safe environment for older people with mild forms of dementia.

The Working Party identified a number of shortcomings in the day care service operating at the time and suggested that the absence of a statutory obligation for its provision inhibited the development of the service and made it vulnerable in times of scarce resources. Accordingly, the Working Party recommended that:

- **(R7.17) health boards be obliged by law to provide or support day care centres for the elderly, including transport to and from such centres.**

The National Council for the Elderly in 1993 again recommended that day care should be regarded as integral to the community care system and should be designated as a core service so that its provision is underpinned by legislation and appropriate statutory funding. To date such legislation has not been implemented.

The Working Party also recommended that:

- **(R7.17) the Department of Health prepare guidelines for the operation and management of day centres.**

To date such guidelines have not been produced.

7.3.1 *Level of provision of day care*
With regard to level of provision, the Working Party recommended that:

- **(R7.17) each Co-ordinator of Services for the Elderly estimate the number of day care places needed for the elderly to be incorporated in the plan for the development of services for the elderly in that area.**

Apart from the Western Health Board, all boards indicate that they have carried out a review of day care places. The Western Health Board is currently undertaking such a review. Some reviews, however, have not covered the whole board region (Eastern and South Eastern) and generally reviews are not systematic in the way recommended by the Working Party. With regard to the number of places provided, it was noted in all boards that it is difficult to estimate places and the numbers supplied are only approximations (Table 7.3). The number of places required for the future are also approximate. The figures supplied reveal that the

Table 7.3: Provision of day care places for older people

Health board	Estimated number of places required	Places provided	Centres provided
Eastern	250 more in next three years	200 board places	Approx. 1,600 voluntary places in 68 centres
Midland	Figures not provided	248 (approx)	17
Mid-Western	340 (at minimum)	280 (approx)	14
North Eastern	585 (approx)	315-420 (approx)	21
North Western	Figures not provided	410	13
Southern	600 (approx)	250 (approx)	17
South Eastern	Figures not provided	10-25 in each centre	43
Western	560 (approx)	153 (approx)	12

Source: Interviews with Programme Managers of Community Care and CSEs

number of day care places currently provided falls far short of the number required to meet estimated need. The plan for most boards for the future is to have a centre in each district or centre of population. The fact that accurate information on numbers of places was difficult to obtain, that there are wide variations in level of provision and that some areas have no day care facilities at all, highlights the need to designate day care facilities as a core service, whose provision is not discretionary but instead is provided to a certain standard throughout the country.

7.3.2   Perceptions of deficits in day care service

Feedback from management in some boards highlights a number of problems with current day care services. For example, transport is often a limiting factor in respect of attendance. The older people in towns can attend daily but those in rural areas depend on transport and schedules. A question is also raised about the meaningfulness of the activities programmes at day care centres. It is felt that more innovative approaches to occupying clients' time are required as otherwise there is a danger that persons attending may become more dependent by virtue of attendance. The need for day care for those suffering mental illness is a further issue which needs to be addressed (this issue is discussed in a later chapter). One board suggests the use of local halls, GAA centres and health centres to make the service more accessible.

District Liaison Nurses (or those fulfilling this function) in all health boards apart from the North Western typically describe the day care service available as, at best, fairly adequate. These nurses note that despite the major importance of the service, there are still many areas, especially rural areas, without a day care centre. In addition to an inadequate level of provision, some nurses point out that at weekends many older people in need are left without a service because of the closure of the day centre at weekends.

7.3.3   Voluntary involvement in day care

From the information available, it appears that voluntary organisations play a major role in the provision of day care services. Exact figures are not available but in the Eastern and South Eastern Health Boards, for example, the great majority of day care places are provided by voluntary organisations, while the figure is around 63 per cent in the Southern Health Board and around 50 per cent in the Western Health Board. The Working Party recommended that:

- **(R7.17) a model contract be drawn up by the Department of Health for use by health boards and voluntary bodies where voluntary organisations provide a day service on behalf of a health board**.

Such a model contract has not been developed. From the perspective of the Department of Health, present arrangements between health boards and voluntary organisations in respect of day centres are operating satisfactorily with certain criteria and standards having been developed over the years. However, if the argument is accepted that day care facilities are a core service is accepted, then it is essential that much more is done to regulate the provision of the service by voluntary organisations, so that the service is provided to a certain standard in all areas of the country. Contracts of service must be drawn up which set out the obligations of both the health board and the voluntary organisation providing the day care service. Funding procedures must be formalised and standardised across the country and must be based on accepted criteria. Previous research (Convery 1987) suggests that there can be wide variations in the activities undertaken in day care centres and, in this review, some Programme Managers express concern about the meaningfulness of what is done in day care. Research is needed to discover the scope and nature of the day care service around the country, to evaluate the effectiveness of the service and to decide on standards and principles of good practice.

Where voluntary organisations are providing day care services, the Working Party recommended that:

- **(R7.17) health boards provide opportunities for staff to develop their expertise**.

Only the North Eastern and Midland Health Boards indicate that they provide any training for staff working for voluntary day care centres. In the North Eastern Health Board PHNs give training in areas such as diet and hygiene while the Midland Health Board gives a training course in caregiving. A previous study of day centres (Convery 1987) drew attention to the importance of training for voluntary staff in order to ensure compatibility between local centre activities and national day centre standards and objectives, to improve the quality of services and to offer support and direction.

7.3.4   Perceptions of value of day care

Among both CSEs and District Liaison Nurses there is agreement that day care centres make an invaluable contribution to maintaining older people in the community. The benefits identified may be categorised as respite for carers, social contact, relief of loneliness and isolation, access to services such as chiropody, occupational therapy and physiotherapy, provision of personal care (baths, hairdressing, nutritious meals), provision of medical and nursing care, monitoring of health status and provision of a forum for structured health education programmes.

Of course this is but one perspective on the value of day care services. Comprehensive evaluation which includes the perspective of the older users themselves is a vital research area which has yet to be addressed.

7.3.5   Funding of day care

With regard to funding of day care facilities, the Working Party recommended that:

- **(R12.11) in each of the next five years, a total of £0.5m be allocated by the Department of Health for the purpose of establishing day centres**.

Figures from the Department of Health reveal that the average capital expenditure on day centres for older people in each of the years from 1989 to 1995 was in the region of £200,000, a figure far short of the amount recommended. The figures for 1996 and 1997 are £400,000 and £700,000 however, and should remain at the latter level for a number of years.

7.4   Dental health

In the area of dental health, the Working Party identified two main issues: the provision of dentures for the present generation of older people and, for the future, the prevention of dental decay and gum disease. One of the concerns of the Working Party was the cost of fitting dentures. In order to make dentures affordable for older people, the recommendation was that:

- **(R7.20) the Dental Council introduce a scheme to permit dental technicians to fit dentures**.

The Dental Council points out that this proposal has been superseded by the 1994 Dental Health Action Plan whereby older people on medical cards can obtain dentures through their chosen dentist. A second recommendation was that:

- **(R7.20) in the interest of providing elderly people with dentures, section 67 of the Act be amended to allow health boards make charges up to half the cost of fitting and supplying dentures**.

The Department of Health states that this recommendation has been superseded by recent developments in dental services. Dental services are currently being developed in accordance with the 1994 Dental Health Action Plan. Under the first phase of the Dental Treatment Services Scheme the priority was full denture treatment for edentulous persons aged 65 years and over. At the end of 1995 all waiting lists for denture treatment under this scheme were cleared. There was also provision for dentures for older people who were not edentulous under a separate element of the Dental Treatment Services Scheme. According to the Department of Health, £9.8m has been made available annually since 1994 under this Scheme, with approximately £6m per annum spent on older people.

In the interest of prevention, the Working Party recommended that:

- **(R7.21) all elderly people be entitled to an annual dental check-up free of charge. Elderly people with medical cards should be offered treatment without charge for necessary dental care identified at the annual check-up. Health boards should also be able to contribute towards the cost of treatment.**

At present, not all older people are entitled to free dental check-ups. Dental benefit forms part of the wider Treatment Benefit Scheme and is available to insured persons and their dependent spouses who satisfy certain statutory qualifying conditions related to income and to social insurance contributions. Persons who satisfy the qualifying conditions on reaching 66 years of age remain qualified for life. Dental benefit provides for free dental examination, free diagnosis and free scaling and polishing. Bi-annual rather than annual check-ups are offered but there is an emergency service which older people can avail of at any time.

As a basis for the future planning and costing of services, the Working Party recommended that:

- **(R7.21) comprehensive information be collected on the dental health of the elderly and middle-aged.**

In 1991, a national survey on the oral health of all Irish adults was carried out. It is planned to follow-up this survey on a ten-year basis but, in the meantime, information is collected from the health boards on a regular basis.

7.5 Aural and ophthalmic services

In the area of aural services, the major issues identified by the Working Party were the long waiting period for fitting of a hearing aid and the eligibility criteria for the service. The Working Party recommended that:

- **(R7.22) the National Rehabilitation Board should reduce the waiting period for hearing aid clinics so that no elderly person has to wait longer than three months for an appointment.**

In addition, the Working Party recommended that:

- **(7.22) the regulations governing the service be changed to permit the National Rehabilitation Board to provide a service to those with Category II and Category III eligibility at a charge**.

According to the National Rehabilitation Board, it is only on very rare occasions that an older person would now have to wait three months for an appointment at a hearing aid clinic. The Board's services are available only to medical card holders.

At the time of its deliberations, the Working Party considered that ophthalmic services were reasonably satisfactory but were concerned that economic constraints would adversely affect the service. The recommendation was that:

- **(R7.23) the present ophthalmic service be developed to meet the needs of the increasing population of elderly people**.

From the perspective of the Department of Health, the present situation with regard to ophthalmic services is unsatisfactory, with significant waiting lists in many health board areas. There has been renewed investment, largely in 1995 and 1996, in the Adult Sight Testing Scheme under which health boards issue authorisations to eligible adults to obtain eye-tests and spectacles. The health boards themselves determine priorities for the issue of authorisations. Management in most boards report some improvements in ophthalmic services such as the appointment of Community Ophthalmic Physicians and improved diagnosis of certain eye diseases. The Mid-Western and Eastern Health Boards also note that the increased funding available in 1995 and 1996 has enabled waiting lists to be reduced. However, most boards still report that lack of resources has prevented development of an adequate ophthalmic service.

The Working Party recommended that:

- **(R7.23) more information should be available locally to elderly people about coping with the disability of visual impairment through the use of better lighting, large print books and the lay-out of facilities at home**.

The Eastern, North Eastern, South Eastern and Western Health Boards indicate that information on coping with visual impairment is made available to older people. This information is provided primarily through GPs, PHNs and out-patients clinics. The Eastern Health Board also operates a customer service department with a free phone service and the North Eastern Health Board is pioneering the use of pharmacists as an information source.

7.6   Boarding out
The term 'boarding out' refers to the placement of an older person in another private household, usually with a non-relative, with the carer receiving some

reward for caring for the person placed. The Working Party considered that boarding out provides an attractive alternative to long-term care in an institution. It is particularly suited to older people who can no longer live on their own but also offers possibilities for the relief of carers. At the time the Working Party was sitting, a small number of boarding out schemes were in operation and their recommendation was that:

- **(R7.28) much greater use be made of boarding out in the care of frail elderly people who can no longer live at home.**

It was also recommended that:

- **(R7.29) the Co-ordinator of Services for the Elderly in each area be responsible for developing boarding out arrangements.**

At present, six of the boards (Midland, Mid-Western, North Eastern, North Western, South Eastern and Western) operate a boarding out scheme for older people (Table 7.4). In two of these boards (Mid-Western and South Eastern) the number of places provided is very limited. In the Mid-Western Health Board, the service is described as having been *ad hoc* up to now but serious consideration is being given to an expansion of the service.

7.6.1   Experiences of boarding out service
Feedback from boards providing the service suggest that it can be difficult to establish. Management in the Western Health Board report that the extent of the service on offer is due to financial constraints and the fact that homes are not available because of the low payment for boarding out. The CSE in this board reports that there has been little or no response to advertisements inviting participation in the scheme. The perception is that owners of bed and breakfast establishments would find the work too onerous and that boarding out is less financially rewarding than bed and breakfast services. The Midland Health Board

Table 7.4: Use of boarding out in care of older people

Health board	Whether boarding out scheme provided
Eastern	No (other welfare options preferred)
Midland	Yes (41 places)
Mid-Western	Yes (limited; 6 places)
North Eastern	Yes (34 places)
North Western	Yes (35 places)
Southern	No (future service is planned)
South Eastern	Yes (limited; 5 places to date)
Western	Yes (60 places)

Source: Interviews with CSEs and Programme Managers of Community Care

notes that the number of placements declined from 72 in 1994 to 41 in 1995 and, while the board would like to increase the number of places available to 120, it seems the service may not have great appeal in certain areas. In this board it is also pointed out that the matching process between the older person and the householder with whom he or she is placed, is crucial to the success of the service. In the North Western Health Board, some CSEs report that it is difficult to develop the service in some areas because people do not want boarding out. Similarly, in the North Eastern Health Board, while there is one area in which the service has been established for a considerable number of years, attempts to introduce the service to other areas have had either minor or no success. CSEs in this board perceive that inadequate finance is a major deterrent to the development of the service because the reimbursement given is not commensurate for the work involved.

7.6.2   *Perceptions of benefits and drawbacks of boarding out*
Management in the boards which provide a boarding out service perceive it as being important in maintaining older people in the community with the supports they need and a high quality of life. In rural areas, particularly, boarding out can enable older people to stay among neighbours and social networks with whom they are familiar. Boarding out is seen to encourage independence and self-reliance and prevent the decay of social skills. It is also seen to be cost-effective and a cheaper alternative to other forms of care outside the home.

Among the two boards which do not provide the service, the Eastern Health Board reports that it did try a boarding out scheme in one area but it failed to take off and there are no plans at present to develop the service. It has been the experience of this board that there was no great demand for the service. The less dependent older people for whom this kind of bed and breakfast type accommodation is suitable preferred to stay at home or felt too proud to take up the service. Another factor was that the boarding out scheme became less relevant with new developments in the area such as greater provision of sheltered housing and extra provision of day care and respite places. It was also perceived that boarding out did not meet the need for company that older people expressed. By contrast, the Southern Health Board indicates that it is committed to the development of a boarding out scheme and it has a committee currently working on how this should be done.

7.6.3   *Guidelines on boarding out*
The Working Party had recommended that:

- **(R7.29) health boards be given statutory authority to board-out elderly persons under certain circumstances and that the Department of Health prepare guidelines on boarding-out based on the experience of successful schemes to date**.

Section 10 of the *Health (Nursing Homes) Act, 1990* provides the health boards with the power to make and carry out an arrangement for the boarding out of older people. Under the Act there are guidelines laid down regarding the choice of householder, the inspection of dwellings, the maintenance, care and welfare of the older person, the privacy of the older person, the number to be accommodated, the nature, cleanliness and safety of the accommodation, the personal possessions of the older person and visits to the older person. Guidelines are also provided with regard to record-keeping, complaints procedures, insurance, termination of placement and boarding out payments (See *Boarding Out Regulations* 1993).

7.6.4   Funding of boarding out
The Working Party recommended that:

- **(R12.25) £0.5m be made available initially to encourage boarding out as a way of meeting the welfare needs of elderly people who can no longer live at home**.

The Department of Health estimates that the total additional funding for boarding out in the period 1989-1995 amounted to £0.25m. The amount given reflects the low take-up of the service.

7.7   Summary and conclusions
This chapter has examined that aspect of community care where the point of delivery of services is in the community rather than in the home. A summary of current provision of services in the community is provided in the table below.

Over and above the actual services provided, the availability of transport is a major influence on the effectiveness of community care. For over a decade, researchers have been calling attention to the transport problems experienced by older people; particularly in rural areas. Older people themselves identify the lack of an adequate transport system as one of their major unmet needs. This review shows that managers and service providers in most health boards are agreed that transport services are still unsatisfactory. At Government level, no department appears to be taking clear responsibility for addressing the problem. None of the recommendations of the Working Party for action at departmental level has been implemented. At health board level, few attempts have been made to carry out the kind of review of transport resources recommended by the Working Party; a review which could facilitate identification of options and possible solutions. All of the health boards have, however, implemented some initiatives to try to address transport needs; the nature of these initiatives varying across boards. In all boards, with one exception, voluntary organisations have a considerable input into attempts to meet transport needs, particularly with regard to transport to day care centres. There is an indication from managers and service providers that

Table 7.5: Summary of current provision of services in the community

Recommendation	Current situation
Health boards be obliged to provide or support day care centres	Boards not obliged but do provide or support day care centres. In the boards where figures are available, the number of places provided falls far short of the number of estimated places needed
Dentures to be provided to older people on low incomes	Older people with medical cards can obtain dentures through their choice of dentist. Waiting lists have all been cleared
Annual free dental check-up to be provided to all older people	Bi-annual rather than annual check-ups provided and only to those entitled to dental benefit
Waiting lists for hearing aid clinics to be no longer than three months	Waiting time of three months now rare
National Rehabilitation Board hearing aid services to be provided to those with Category II and Category III eligibility at a charge	National Rehabilitation Board services available only to medical card holders
Development of ophthalmic service to meet needs of increasing older population	Some improvement of the service in most boards but still regarded as inadequate; Department of Health considers current situation unsatisfactory
Much greater use to be made of boarding out	Boarding out schemes provided in 6 boards; number of places very limited in 2 of these boards

responsibility for transport should not belong to the health boards but should rest with the public transport authority.

Despite the importance of transport, a recent study has shown that a quarter of older people have no public transport available to them. This figure rises to 50 per cent when older people in rural areas are considered separately. The issue of deficiencies of public transport for older people has recently been taken up by a voluntary organisation, Age Alliance, and it has also been highlighted in the North West Connemara Community Transport Study. Another recent initiative of potential significance for the transport problems of older people is the Rural Transport Initiative launched in 1996 in conjunction with the EU Sampo project. A pilot project to assess possible solutions is due to begin in Summer 1997.

An integral element in community care for older persons, and their carers, is the provision of day care centres. Because of their importance, the Working Party recommended that health boards should be obliged by law to provide them. The National Council for the Elderly also has recommended that day care facilities should be considered a 'core service' that is underpinned by legislation and appropriate statutory funding. This recommendation has not been implemented and the provision of day care facilities is still at the discretion of the health boards. Precise information on the number of centres and places available, and the level of provision required to meet future need, was difficult to obtain. This may be due to the absence of a statutory basis for the service.

This review also highlights the inadequacy of current levels of provision and the unevenness in provision across different areas, with some areas having no day care at all. Legislation must be enacted to ensure that such an essential service is provided to a certain standard throughout the country and is available to any older person who requires such care. Further issues arise around the major role of voluntary organisations in day care provision. The Working Party recommended that the Department of Health should draw up a model contract for use where voluntary organisations provide day care on behalf of a health board. Failure to implement this recommendation makes it very difficult to ensure standards of provision and quality of service. Contracts of service should be drawn up which set out the obligations of both the health board and the voluntary organisation providing the service, and funding procedures should be formalised and standardised across the country. The recommendation that health boards provide training for voluntary staff in day care centres has not been implemented to any great extent. A further source of concern is the lack of transport which makes the day care centre inaccessible for older people in some areas.

Both CSEs and District Liaison Nurses describe day care as making an invaluable contribution to the care of older people. Research is needed, however, to systematically evaluate what actually happens in day care facilities around the country, to find out what benefits older people themselves identify from their use, and to determine standards and principles of good practice. Despite many attestations to the value of the service, the funding given to it has been less than half that recommended by the Working Party in the years up to 1995, although it has to be acknowledged that the amounts provided in 1996 and 1997 are significantly higher.

With regard to improvement of dental services the recommendations of the Working Party have been largely superseded by the 1994 Dental Health Action Plan. Persons over the age of 65 years were given priority in the first phase of implementation of the plan leading to improvements such as the clearing of waiting lists for denture treatment for edentulous people by the end of 1995. Improvements have also been implemented with regard to aural services so that the long waiting period for hearing aid clinics, which was a source of concern for the Working Party, is no longer a problem. Some improvements have occurred in the ophthalmic service but the Department of Health still regards the current situation as unsatisfactory. There has, however, been renewed investment in 1995 and 1996 in the Adult Sight Testing Scheme.

The Working Party considered boarding out to be an attractive community alternative to institutional care and recommended that much greater use be made of it and that funding be made available to encourage the service. The amount of finance provided in the period 1989-1995 was around half that recommended because of the low take-up of the service. At present, six of the boards provide a boarding out scheme but the level of provision is very limited in two cases. The scheme is perceived to have many positive outcomes but a number of difficulties are also noted. The scheme appears not to have much appeal either for the older people themselves or for those providing the home from home. In the latter case, one of the main problems appears to be the low level of remuneration involved. Research is needed to determine first how older people themselves view the option of boarding out, and second what conditions are required to ensure a quality service that is satisfactory for both the user and the provider of the service.

CHAPTER EIGHT

Care in General Hospitals

8.1 Introduction

In *The Years Ahead*, the Working Party noted that older people make greater proportionate use of acute hospital services than other groups. In addition to their special hospital needs for medical problems which are associated with age, they are also associated with greater bed use with the result that pressure on beds can mean that older people are regarded with some reluctance on the part of health board personnel because they may be viewed as 'blocking' bed places. Throughput of patients in hospitals, including older patients, has become an issue which the hospital services have addressed in a number of ways but, as the literature has indicated, this is closely related to planned admissions and discharges (Blackwell *et al.* 1992). One important development is the fall in the average acute in-patient length of stay by older people. Between 1985 and 1996 the average length of stay for people aged 65 years or more fell from 15.3 days to 10.5 days (Hospital In-Patient Enquiry, unpublished). This makes it critical that discharges are carefully planned so that unnecessary re-admissions do not occur.

This chapter examines acute care of older people in general hospitals in the country, covering admission and discharge policies, bed provision, day hospitals, geriatricians and geriatric departments. Data sources used for this chapter were the following: Programme Managers of General Hospitals (all); Co-ordinators of Services for the Elderly (17); District Liaison Nurses (39); Superintendent Public Health Nurses (26); Senior Public Health Nurses (8); Geriatricians (14); Hospital Liaison Officers (7); GPs (7); Consultant Ophthalmologists (2); and Consultant Orthopaedic Surgeons (1).

8.2 Policies on the admission and discharge of older patients in general hospitals

The Working Party noted in 1988 that planned admissions and discharges were not occurring in general hospitals throughout the country, and as a result recommended that:

- **(R8.10) every general hospital develop a policy on the admission and discharge of elderly patients in consultation with the Co-ordinators of Services for the Elderly in the catchment area of the hospital**.

Table 8.1 below gives details of the current situation across all health boards.

Table 8.1: Admission and discharge policies in health boards and involvement of Co-ordinators of Services for the Elderly

Health Board	Policy	Coverage	Contents of policy/comments, if no policy	CSE
Eastern	Yes	All hospitals with Depts of Medicine for Elderly	Planned admission which involves plans for discharge and multi-disciplinary teams. Existing policy is focused primarily on patients in Departments of Medicine for Elderly	No
Midland	Yes	All hospitals	Assistance before admission to long-stay. Planned discharge with Liaison Nurse, PHN and GP informed	No
Mid-Western	No	N/A	Discharge Policy Committee working on this. Geriatrician, Director of Public Health Medicine and CSE on committee. There is a policy for Elder Care Units, but these deal with a smaller number of older people than general hospitals	Yes
North Eastern	Yes	Few hospitals	Monaghan and Cavan General Hospitals have a policy. Navan is currently working on it and will complete it once geriatrician takes up duty. Drogheda has no policy. Policy in Cavan/ Monaghan covers admission, treatment, assessment, placement, discharge and, in Cavan, involves referral to Liaison Nurse for all patients over the age of 65	Some
North Western	Yes	All hospitals	Communication between GPs, PHNs and Carers; for frail and dependent older people it also includes social workers who provide vital link between hospital and carers	Yes
Southern	No	N/A	Policy being developed and guidelines have been drawn up, protocols being worked on	No
South Eastern	Yes	Some hospitals	Discharge policy is in place throughout board, but only some hospitals have a written admissions policy. Discharge policy involves liaison with geriatric liaison nurse, one of whom is in each community care area. For admissions different procedures apply: in some hospitals the geriatrician sees the patient, in others the Registrar sees patients	No
Western	Yes	Most hospitals	Social reports; multi-disciplinary assessments; discharge liaison with GP and PHN	Yes

Source: Interviews with Programme Managers of General Hospital Care, CSEs and geriatricians

As can be seen from Table 8.1, six of the eight health boards have developed a policy on admissions and discharge of older patients in their general hospitals. In four of these boards, the policy covers most or all general hospitals in the health board area, while for the remaining two boards (the North Eastern and South Eastern) only some hospitals are involved. In the North Eastern Health Board the remaining hospital is awaiting the appointment of a geriatrician. In the South Eastern Health Board, all hospitals have a discharge policy, which is standardised throughout the board area and involves liaison with Liaison Nurses in each community care area. Only some hospitals, however, have a written formal admissions policy, and admissions involve either the geriatricians or the Registrar.

8.2.1   Perceived effectiveness of policies

For boards with a planned admission and discharge policy, the CSEs and Liaison Nurses involved state that in most cases the policy operates effectively (see Table 8.2 below). In those boards where there is a policy in place and procedures are planned, but the operation of the policy is reported as being only fairly effective, several possible explanations are available. In the Western Health Board, for example, social reports and multi-disciplinary assessments are given with discharge liaison occurring between GPs and PHNs. As coverage of the policy does not extend to all hospitals in that board, however, this may explain why the policy is perceived as only fairly effective. A similar explanation may also account for the South Eastern Health Board where only some hospitals have a written admissions policy.

8.2.2   Health boards with no admissions and discharge policies

Consultants in the Southern Health Board, which has no formal admissions and discharge policy, said that it is difficult to plan for discharge because of the pressures exerted by a shortage of beds. In the Mid-Western Health Board, a committee is working on drawing up a discharge policy, and current admissions of older patients over the age of 80 in most of the general hospitals take place under the care of the geriatrician. In Ennis, for example, the geriatrician participates in case conferences for admission to all other units in the general hospital. She is also involved in weekly discharge meetings to discuss the follow-up care services that are required. From there, PHNs and nursing staff take over liaison and the organisation of support services (see below). In Nenagh, however, admissions are arranged between the GPs and the Matron's office, but the geriatrician is responsible for the discharge of older patients under her care in the general hospital.

8.2.3   Involvement of CSEs in policies

Contrary to recommendations laid out in *The Years Ahead*, there are only two boards (Western and North Western) where CSEs are involved in drawing up

Table 8.2: Liaison person for discharge of older patients

Health Board	City hospitals	Non-city hospitals	Effectiveness of procedure	Comments
Eastern	Patient Services Officer, hospital manager, matron, social worker	Patient Services Officer, nursing administration	Effective	Liaison groups as outlined have been set up in both city and non-city hospitals
Midland	N/A	Ward Sister (Laois/Offaly); Liaison Nurse in hospital (Longford/ Westmeath)	Effective	Multi-disciplinary weekly meetings are held to plan discharges. These involve physiotherapists, occupational therapists, speech therapists, nursing and medical staff and, in Longford/ Westmeath, the Liaison Nurse
Mid-Western	Senior PHN, geriatrician or nursing staff	Consultant, Matron and ward staff	Fairly	Liaison with Community Care services and nursing homes. The Elder Care Units run very smoothly. Outside of these not enough use made of Liaison Nurse
North Eastern	N/A	Liaison Nurse in hospital	Effective	N/A
North Western	Ward Sister	Ward Sister	Fairly	This board ruled out arrangement for general liaison officer as liaison part of CSE's responsibility
Southern	Nurse Liason Officer	Nurse Liason Officer	Effective	Good structure; Nurse Liaison Officer 'reaching out' into community, arranging transport, notifying medical social workers; some weak links with GP, however
South Eastern	Ward Sister, Nursing Officer	Ward Sister, Nursing Officer	Fairly	Liaises with PHN or Liaison Nurse. Hospital Liaison Officers may be appointed in future when Departments of Medicine for Elderly are established in hospitals
Western	Community Care Liason PHN	Ward Sister and nursing administration	Fairly	N/A

Source: Interviews with Programme Managers of General Hospital Care, CSEs, Superintendent PHNs, Senior PHNs, District Liaison Nurses, GPs, geriatricians and hospital liaison personnel

admissions and discharge policies. In the North Eastern Health Board, the CSE was not in post when the policy for Cavan/Monaghan General Hospital was drawn up. Furthermore, in those boards where policy is currently being drafted, CSEs are generally not involved.

8.3   Appointment of liaison person in hospitals

The Working Party recommended that:

- **(R8.11) in city hospitals, a member of the staff of the hospital with sufficient authority be responsible for liaising with departments of the hospital, general practitioners and District Liaison Nurses to arrange support for vulnerable elderly people on discharge**.

Calling this person the Hospital Liaison Officer, the Working Party recommended that she or he should be a member of the specialist department of geriatric medicine. In non-city hospitals, the liaison person should be the ward sister who would take responsibility for notifying the appropriate District Liaison Nurse who would mobilise and organise support services for the older patient.

In city hospitals the liaison role has usually been undertaken by nursing staff. In the Southern Health Board a designated liaison person for older patients has been appointed, to ensure they are returned quickly and comfortably to the community. In the Eastern Health Board, despite having a specific title, the liaison role is taken on by other personnel, such as hospital managers or matrons, who combine this function with other responsibilities. In non-city hospitals most health boards appear to have followed the recommendations laid down by the Working Party, although there are some distinctions. In both the North Eastern and North Western Health Boards, the liaison personnel operate at both hospital and community levels.

8.3.1   Benefits of liaison

In general the designation of liaison personnel is seen as beneficial. In the Southern Health Board, for example, the Nurse Liaison Officer is perceived as 'reaching out' into the community. Indeed, liaison personnel may also serve to develop the service by pointing to discharge procedures which may need to be streamlined. For example, a Hospital Liaison Officer in the Eastern Health Board stated that a paging system for Liaison Nurses and fax machines in GPs' offices would further streamline operations and make them more efficient for quicker communication.

Most CSEs, District Liaison Nurses and PHNs believe that discharges worked effectively. The District Liaison Nurses and PHNs were less positive than the CSEs, however, with a perception that hospitals need to commit more resources (time and personnel) to liaison. This was pronounced among superintendent PHNs in five boards (Eastern, Mid-Western, North Western, South Eastern and Southern). The need for more formal arrangements, better communication structures and the inclusion of PHNs in the discharge plans for older patients, was also noted.

Table 8.3: Follow-up on discharge

Health Board	Follow-up arrangements	Satisfaction rating	Comments
Eastern	GP, community services and ward teams are alerted. Note is taken by hospital people about future respite or day care. Note goes to GP, and the Liaison Nurse or PHN makes necessary arrangements	Fair	System does not work effectively every time and efforts are ongoing to improve this at the moment
Midland	Liaison Nurse contacts PHN and GP	Fair	Letters of discharge not reaching GPs quickly enough. The board is in the process of proposing formal letters
Mid-Western	Ward Sister contacts PHN, Liaison PHN, Home Help supervisor (if necessary), and GP to discuss plan. Consultant writes to GP	Fair	A system of feedback on discharge is needed as hospital loses touch with patient on discharge; this would guard against unnecessary re-admission
North Eastern	Liaison Nurse notifies PHN and GP; ensures post-discharge accomm-odation, rehabilitation, home help and occupational therapy. Review clinics at the hospital	Satisfactory	N/A
North Western	Day hospital, Out Patients Depart-ment inform district co-ordinator, GP, PHN and social worker who arrange social supports as required	Satisfactory	N/A
Southern	Liaison Senior PHN visits hospital twice weekly for discharge slips and distributes them to the PHNs. Nurse Liaison Officers involved if further care needed	Fairly Unsatis-factory	Weak link with GP. Senior PHNs and nurse liaison officers do not have enough time to discuss individual cases with each other. More communication, more formal links to ensure better planning for admission and discharge
South Eastern	In Waterford geriatrician follows up and maintains interest in patient. Elsewhere Community Care programme takes charge with GP. Liaison Nurse informed pending discharge and she confers with Senior PHN about what is required	Fair	Lack of resources in community is a factor
Western	Out-Patients Department Assessment and PHN follow-up. Written letter of discharge to GP. Liaison PHN for older people is informed	Fair	Day hospital required to improve situation and more day care places. Problem with lack of resources in Community Care. Better liaison with housing authorities needed

Source: Interviews with Programme Managers of General Hospitals, GPs, geriatricians, hospital liaison personnel, carers, Directors of Community Care, District Liaison Nurses, Superintendent PHNs and Senior PHNs

8.4   Follow-up on discharge

Follow-up procedures can include socio-economic assessments to identify need on discharge, counselling, negotiations about the availability and supply of equipment and aids, assignment of Meals-on-Wheels and Home Helps, liaison with local authorities with regard to housing adaptations and repairs, and an evaluation of the patient's domestic arrangements.

Table 8.3 outlines the situation with regard to follow-up procedures across the health boards and, as can be seen, all GPs and PHNs are supposed to be notified. As PHNs note, however, GPs are advised in writing, whereas PHNs are informed by the GP, District Liaison Nurse or Hospital Liaison Officer. For the majority of health boards, follow-up was stated to work in a fairly satisfactory manner with CSEs being more positive, overall, than Superintendent and Senior PHNs. In the Southern Health Board, it was noted that there are weak links with GPs and that more liaison personnel with a formal liaison role would be beneficial. In the Midland Health Board letters to GPs were sometimes delayed. In the Mid-Western Health Board a system of feedback on discharge was recommended which would guard against unnecessary re-admission.

8.4.1   Problems with follow-up

As the above table shows, follow-up needs to be more effective. Liaison problems appear to be more of a problem in the general hospital sector than in the community. Some respondents note that once older patients have left the hospital, the hospital-based professionals may lose touch with them because they now come within the remit of the Community Care programme. This again raises the issue of co-ordination and liaison (see Chapter Three above), which is not happening as was envisaged in *The Years Ahead*. It also implies the existence of a boundary around the hospital which is only breached on admission and discharge. The Eastern Health Board has commenced a system of home nursing observation and care with hospital nursing staff, to deal with this problem. Staff nurses in attendance at the out-patients department supervise arrangements for out-patients attendance, admission, transport, post-discharge observation and rehabilitation. Very frail older patients benefit from extra attention and day hospital care, and re-admission, where necessary, can be arranged with minimum delay.

The case for stronger liaison was made by several Superintendent PHNs in the Mid-Western, South Eastern and North Western Health Boards. It was noted that liaison was dependent upon the co-operation of the personnel involved and that it was not formal in many instances. Note was taken of the time spent on liaison by PHNs and personnel in the community with the feeling that this should be 'matched' in some way by hospitals, with committed full-time liaison posts, or, at the very least a greater awareness among hospital staff of the role of community care and its limitations.

The majority of District Liaison Nurses and PHNs said that they were informed about the discharge of older patients, but several suggestions for improvement were made. Given the primacy of PHNs in community care, it was felt that more information was needed on patients and the types of treatment required. Said to be of most benefit were discharge letters sent directly to the PHNs. In the South Eastern Health Board this was found to have been very useful, enabling ease of access to the older patient's home and leading to greater confidence in the PHN by the older patient. The sending of discharge letters to PHNs would also help them in their liaison role and might reduce the time spent chasing up older patients.

8.5 Discharge from Accident and Emergency departments

It was noted in *The Years Ahead* that many admissions of older patients occur from Accident and Emergency departments. For those older patients who were discharged from Accident and Emergency, the Working Party made the following recommendation:

- **(R8.12) that the hospital liaison officer be responsible for informing GPs and District Liaison Nurses about elderly patients discharged from**

Table 8.4: Discharge from Accident and Emergency departments

Health Board	Procedure	Personnel
Eastern	Yes	The onus is on the Senior Medical Officer in Accident and Emergency to contact community care services if the older person is considered at risk
Midland	Yes	Sister or nurse informs accompanying family member, relative, GP, or Liaison Nurse. If unaccompanied, domestic circumstances are investigated and patient admitted overnight if the GP cannot be contacted. Older patients are required to have someone accompanying them
Mid-Western	Yes	Doctor in Accident and Emergency sends note to GP
North Eastern	Yes	Nursing staff inform family, GP, PHN or Liaison Nurse where appropriate
North Western	Yes	In Sligo the Accident and Emergency Consultant informs Registrar, GP, nursing officer and PHN by formal written communication. Elsewhere nursing administration performs this task
Southern	No	Accident and Emergency Department may tell patient to contact GP depending on treatment required
South Eastern	Yes	Doctor or medical team in Accident and Emergency contacts GP; information is usually limited
Western	Yes	Nursing administration informs PHN where person living alone. Patient given letter for GP

Source: Interviews with Programme Managers of General Hospital Care, GPs, hospital liaison personnel, District Liaison Nurses, Superintendent PHNs and Senior PHNs

the Accident and Emergency department of the hospital. Elderly persons seen in Accident and Emergency departments in the night-time should not be discharged at night unless they are accompanied by a relative or friend.

Hospital liaison personnel do not have a role to play in the majority of discharges from Accident and Emergency as this function is directly performed by Accident and Emergency personnel. GPs are informed in writing but, with the exception of three boards (the Midland, North Eastern and North Western), District Liaison Nurses or PHNs are not informed by Accident and Emergency. GPs stated that they were not informed directly as written notes are given to the patients. Liaison Nurses who are informed on discharge remarked on the effectiveness of the procedure. GPs and PHNs who reported that they are not informed felt that a better communication system would be beneficial.

8.6   Specialist geriatric departments

According to the Working Party, the development of geriatric departments is one of the most significant advances in the care of older people. Consequently, *The Years Ahead* made the following recommendation:

- **(R8.26) that additional geriatric departments be provided as a matter of urgency, priority being given to the establishment of departments in the three health boards which currently have no geriatric departments — the Midland, the North Eastern and the South Eastern. In Dublin, geriatric departments are recommended at the Mater and in the hospitals which form the nucleus of the new Tallaght Hospital and an expanded department should be developed at Beaumont Hospital. The units should be called 'specialist geriatric departments' to distinguish them from the assessment unit in community hospitals.**

Table 8.5 gives the current situation in relation to specialist geriatric departments across all health boards.

Before examining the present situation as outlined in Table 8.5 below, it should be noted that Comhairle na nOspidéal recommended a minimum general population of 80,000 as viable for the appointment of physicians in geriatric medicine. The Working Party used this as the basis for its recommendation on geriatric departments, and consequently recommended the establishment of 11 new geriatric departments and the expansion of some existing departments. Table 8.5 shows that 10 new geriatric departments have been established since 1988 in the Midland, Mid-Western, South Eastern and Eastern Health Boards. Two of these boards did not have geriatric departments before 1988. Furthermore, the Department of Health indicates that an average of £0.1m, as was recommended in *The Years Ahead*, has been allocated annually since 1988 for the provision of geriatric departments in general hospitals.

Table 8.5: Specialist geriatric department in health boards

Health Board	Geriatric departments 1996	Geriatric departments 1998	Number of beds	Benefits and comments
Eastern	Eight	Three	187	These are acute assessment beds. Anticipatory care is the major benefit; team draws up early plan avoids need for long-term institutional care
Midland	Two geriatricians in the board, but only one specialist geriatric department in Laois/Offaly	None	49 dedicated beds in Laois/ Offaly. (In Longford/ Westmeath 12 dedicated beds in St Mary's across road from general hospital)	Better attitude to medicine of old age. More positive perceptions of older people. Older people get better assessment and treatment
Mid-Western	Three	One	32	Ensuring patients receive appropriate rehabilitation services. Specialised streaming of older patients. Access to rehabilitation when needed. Numbers going home increased. Reduction in admissions to long-stay hospitals
North Eastern	None	None	N/A	Specialist geriatric departments not seen as appropriate concept in county hospitals. Six beds are designated for assessment in Cavan. Recent appointment of geriatrician in Dundalk will result in redesignation of beds. This will also be the case in Navan once geriatrician is in post.
North Western	One	One	20	More focused care and treatment of older patients; equal treatment with other patients
Southern	One	One	25	N/A
South Eastern	One	None	25	Provides focused care. Allows for better preventive medical care. Patients can be admitted without having an acute episode
Western	Two	Two	28 in Merlin Park	Specialisation in care of older people. Development of better expertise and centres of excellence. Mayo General Hospital Phase II development starting 1997

Source: Interviews with Department of Health, CEOs, Programme Managers of General Hospital Care and geriatricians

In the Midland Health Board there are two geriatricians and a new specialist department of geriatric medicine (in Tullamore). This department provides 49 dedicated beds which are used for assessment and rehabilitation, under the guidance of a geriatrician who deals with all older patients in the Laois/Offaly area. In the Longford/Westmeath community care area, on the other hand, the geriatrician is based in a general medical rather than a specialist geriatric department. He deals with older patients in the general hospital and also provides outreach and outpatients services in the community care area. This takes the form of twice monthly visits to St Joseph's Hospital in Longford and monthly visits to the district hospital in Athlone. Feedback suggests that this arrangement results in an effective and satisfactory service for older patients as the consultant is travelling to where they are based, rather than in Laois/Offaly where there has been some dispute about the consultant having only one base. In addition, the geriatrician in Longford/Westmeath has access to 12 dedicated rehabilitation beds in St Mary's hospital, which is located across the road from the general hospital.

In the Western Health Board, while there are two geriatric departments, only one of these has designated beds for acute assessment (Merlin Park). In the Southern Health Board the geriatric department is split on two campuses, St Finbarr's and Cork University Hospital. Twenty-five acute beds are provided in the latter, with the former acting as a long-stay unit. In the Eastern Health Board, the Mater and Beaumont Hospitals, as recommended in *The Years Ahead*, both have specialist geriatric departments providing 21 and 22 beds, respectively. The Meath Hospital, a constituent hospital of the new Tallaght hospital, presently provides 17 beds in its Department of Medicine for the Elderly, and the Tallaght Regional Hospital will have a department once it opens in 1997. According to the Department of Health, the expansion in Beaumont was delayed because of logistical problems, with space earmarked for that department being awarded to another department. The problem has now been addressed following negotiations with the hospital authorities, and although expansion within the geriatric department is small the plans also include a day hospital which is proposed to become a five-day unit.

The only board with no specialist geriatric department is the North Eastern, as it was not felt to be appropriate in county hospitals. There is a unit for older people on the campus of Cavan General Hospital, providing a total of 69 beds which are used on the basis of need, the majority being taken up in extended care. In addition, six beds are designated for assessment in Cavan General Hospital. The recent appointment of a geriatrician in Dundalk will result in the redesignation of beds. This will also be the case in Navan once a geriatrician is in post.

8.6.1   Benefits associated with specialist geriatric departments
The benefits of having specialist geriatric departments were noted by geriatricians and most Programme Managers, with advantages for the health care of older

people being cited. Indeed, the benefits noted correspond with those made by the Working Party which emphasised the increased efficiency of hospitals and increased throughput of older patients.

8.7 Geriatricians

The benefits of having specialist geriatric departments are closely associated with the benefits of having geriatricians in post. The Working Party had recommended in 1988:

- **(R8.30) the re-allocation of beds and facilities in general hospitals for assessment and rehabilitation of the elderly in tandem with the appointment of additional geriatricians**.

Table 8.6 below outlines the current situation with regard to the number of geriatricians in post around the country.

As can be seen, all except the Southern Health Board have increased their number of geriatricians, in some cases quite substantially (Eastern and North Eastern Health Boards). As the Southern Health Board's extra geriatrician was also due by early 1997, it appears that all the health boards have made some commitment to the appointment of geriatricians.

8.7.1 *Lack of full-time dedication to older patients*

In many cases geriatricians do not spend all of their time dedicated exclusively to older patients. One of the geriatricians in the Mid-Western Health Board, for

Table 8.6: Geriatricians in health boards in 1996 and 1988

Health Board	1996	1988	Future plans and comments
Eastern	Ten	Six	Health board is involved with eight appointments; these are joint appointments all with community responsibility The other two appointments are in co-operation with voluntary hospitals. There are plans to employ another geriatrician on the northside of Dublin city
Midland	Two	None	—
Mid-Western	Three	One	One being recruited
North Eastern	Two	None	One more will be in post by November 1997
North Western	1.5	None	Would like 0.5 in Sligo to become one full-time post
Southern	Two	Two	One due soon in Kerry. Would like two more
South Eastern	One	None	Three more — resulting in one in each of four community care areas
Western	Three	Two	One in Galway

Source: Interviews with CEOs and Programme Managers of General Hospital Care

example, has no dedicated sessions with older patients despite her official title. This is the case too in the Western and Eastern Health Boards; in the latter, geriatricians feel that more posts need to be filled because of the number of older people in the board area and the demand on resources.

8.8   Provision of assessment beds
The Working Party recommended that:

- **(R8.29) a norm of 2.5 beds per 1,000 elderly persons in geriatric departments in general hospitals be provided for assessment.**

As can be seen all health boards fall below the recommended norm of 2.5 beds for assessment per 1,000 older people although Programme Managers in both the Eastern and Mid-Western Health Boards felt that the present number was adequate. Most Programme Managers thought the norms were adequate and feasible although some thought the norms may need to be adjusted in future, for

Table 8.7: Designated geriatric beds per 1,000 older people for assessment

Health Board	Designated beds for assessment	Norm adequate	Norm feasible	Future adequacy of norm	If below norm, why
Eastern	1.65	Yes	Yes	Norms may be too high	Level will be 1.72 soon when extra beds in St Michael's become available. Level sufficient
Midland	2.0	Yes	No	Yes	Lack of timetable
Mid-Western	1.15	Yes	Yes	Yes	Access to additional beds and present number is adequate
North Eastern	0.2	No	No	No	Being addressed in context of recent recruitment of geriatricians
North Western	1.5	Yes	Yes	Yes	Approx. 20 extra available and working towards norm
Southern	0.4	No	No	No	Lack of resources
South Eastern	0.6	Yes, provided used for assessment	Yes	By 2011 would need an extra 13 beds	Problem with impact on general medical beds
Western	0.6	Yes	Yes, but not in short term	Yes	Lack of resources for capital development. Lack of adequate community care leads to increased requirement for hospital beds

Source: Interviews with Programme Managers of General Hospital Care and geriatricians

example, upwards in the case of the South Eastern Health Board, but downwards in the case of the Eastern Health Board.

8.9   Provision of rehabilitation beds

The Years Ahead had recommended that:

- **(R8.29) a norm of 3.0 beds per 1,000 elderly persons for rehabilitation beds be adopted for planning purposes.**

Table 8.8: Designated beds per 1,000 older people for rehabilitation

Health Board	Number	Norm adequate	Norm feasible	Future adequacy of norm	If below norm, reason
Eastern	2.1	Fairly	Yes	Board to provide 100 secondary rehabilitation places in proposed nine Community Units for the Elderly (see Chapter Nine)	Lack of resources; also no timetable laid out in *The Years Ahead*
Midland	4	No	No	Above norm now	N/A
Mid-Western	1.71	No	Yes	N/A	N/A
North Eastern	None	Yes in Cavan/ Monaghan and Meath. No in Louth	Yes in Cavan/ Monaghan and Meath. No in Louth	Only in Meath	Norms may have to be revised now geriatricians are in post. In Louth, for example, demand on resources is anticipated to increase
North Western	2	Yes	Yes	Yes	Other rehabilitation beds available in community hospitals; 20-bed rehabilitation unit due Letterkenny
Southern	3	Yes	Yes	No	None given
South Eastern	2.16	Fairly	Yes, if additional resources made available	By 2011, 78 extra beds would be needed based on current morbidity patterns	Lack of resources
Western	2	Fairly	Yes	Yes	Extra district hospital beds available; lack of resources reason below norm

Source: Interviews with Programme Managers of Community Care, Programme Managers of General Hospital Care and geriatricians

This norm applies to both general and community hospitals (see Chapter Nine), yet, as can be seen, only two health boards (Midland and Southern) have reached the recommended norm for rehabilitation beds. Indeed, while most health board respondents thought the norm was feasible to attain, they did not think it was very adequate. The North Western Health Board is awaiting the construction of another rehabilitation unit with 20 beds. In the North Eastern Health Board the situation will be addressed shortly with the recent appointment of geriatricians. The lack of a timetable for reaching the norms was mentioned by the Midland and Eastern Health Boards.

8.10   Integration of rehabilitation facilities on campus of general hospital
In *The Years Ahead* it was recommended that:

• **(R8.31) in order to facilitate greater integration of general hospital and rehabilitation facilities for the elderly, rehabilitation beds should be designated on the campus of the general hospital.**

Table 8.9: Integration of general hospital and rehabilitation facilities for older people

Health Board	Designated rehabilitation beds on general hospital campus	Arrangements for greater integration
Eastern	307 out of 448	Consultant geriatricians attend site
Midland	12 dedicated across road from Longford/Westmeath general hospital (in St Mary's, Mullingar); 17 rehabilitation beds in St Joseph's, Longford, which geriatrician visits twice monthly	In future each Care Centre for the Elderly will have assessment and rehabilitation beds, up to 20 in each sector. GPs will be designated with these beds along guidelines set by geriatricians
Mid-Western	None	Co-ordination by geriatrician. Limerick and Ennis close, so easy for integration there. Some problems have been experienced in Nenagh, but there are plans for rehabilitation beds there
North Eastern	None	Rehabilitation beds available in community hospitals. No arrangements stated for integration of general hospitals and rehabilitation facilities
North Western	14 designated out of 60 beds	Visits by geriatrician
Southern	80	Rehabilitation beds are available in district hospitals which are due to be upgraded to community hospitals
South Eastern	None; all in geriatric hospitals	Geriatrician takes clinical responsibility
Western	None; all in geriatric hospitals	Geriatrician and team care for older patients. Long stay committees; weekly case conferences

Source: Interviews with Programme Managers of General Hospital Care and geriatricians

Apart from the fact that the integration of general hospital and rehabilitation facilities has not occurred to any great extent, the geriatrician is also the key to this integration. Where her or his time is taken up with general patient care, the integration envisaged in *The Years Ahead* cannot happen.

8.11 Day hospital provision

Day hospitals are a facility on the campus of the hospital, providing secondary level health care. They enable the investigation, treatment and rehabilitation of older patients without the need to stay overnight. The Working Party noted that the development of day hospitals in general hospitals had been slow with six day hospitals in 1988. On the basis of that, the Working Party recommended that:

- **(R8.33) every hospital with or associated with a specialist geriatric department provide a day hospital to facilitate diagnosis, treatment and rehabilitation of elderly patients**.

It should be noted in the above that, as stated in *The Years Ahead* recommendation, only those hospitals with or associated with a specialist geriatric department were deemed to be appropriate for this question. While some health boards do not have day hospitals in association with geriatric departments, therefore, this does not mean that there are no day hospital facilities available in the board area. In the North Eastern Health Board, for example, there are eight day hospitals in the board area which are part of the community hospital service. Furthermore, in the Southern Health Board, day hospitals will be provided in community hospitals in future, not in the general hospitals.

8.11.1 Availability of capital funds to expand day hospitals
The Years Ahead recommended that:

- **(R8.13) capital funds be made available to hospitals for expansion of their day hospitals**.

According to the Department of Health, capital funds have been made available to expand day care facilities, but this funding has only been running at an average of £0.2m annually, rather than the recommended £0.5m. Only in 1996 and 1997 was this allocation increased, to £0.4m and £0.7m respectively. Expansion has occurred, however, in other hospitals in the board areas (such as community hospitals) and, as already stated, the Southern Health Board plans to expand day hospitals associated with community rather than general hospitals, although geriatricians in that board would like a day hospital on the site of Cork University Hospital.

8.11.2 Transport to day hospitals
Coinciding with the provision of day hospitals is the very necessary provision of transport to avail of such facilities. The Working Party recommended that:

- **(R8.33) transport be provided to and from day hospitals**.

Table 8.10: Day hospitals in general hospitals

Health Board	Number	Places	Contribution	Reason why none	Future plans
Eastern	Five	153	Facilitates assessment and earlier discharges and obviates need for overnight admission	N/A	St Michael's Dun Laoghaire, St Vincent's Elm Park and Naas to open day hospitals late 1997. Tallaght to have a day hospital when it opens. Beaumont being expanded to five-day service
Midland	None	None	N/A	Lack of resources	One planned in Longford/ Westmeath General Hospital
Mid-Western	None	None	N/A	Four day hospitals run under the Community Care Programme	N/A
North Eastern	N/A	N/A	N/A	Day hospitals under Community Care in Cavan and Dundalk	Plans for Monaghan and Navan, to open 1997
North Western	One	Not designated specifically for older people	Older people do not have to be admitted to hospital. Little disruption to their lives	Being examined by planning group	Would like to develop day hospital in Sligo General
Southern	One	15	Aids care of older people in community	N/A	Day hospitals to be attached to Community Care rather than General Hospital Programme
South Eastern	None	N/A	N/A	Only one geriatrician in board	Once more geriatricians in post would like to develop day hospitals
Western	None	None	Facilitates care of older people in community and less traumatic for them	Day hospitals are provided in some community hospitals	One planned in community hospital, Roscommon

Source: Interviews with Programme Managers of General Hospital Care

Table 8.11: Transport to day hospitals

Health board	Transport	Provider
Eastern	Yes	Health board provides more than 90 per cent contract taxis; families of patients
Midland	N/A	N/A
Mid-Western	Yes	Health board
North Eastern	Yes	Health board
North Western	Yes	Contract for services with private companies, car hire, taxi and minibus
Southern	Yes	Health board arrangements with taxi companies
South Eastern	N/A	N/A
Western	Yes	Health board

Source: Interviews with Programme Managers of General Hospital Care

Where day hospitals are in existence the health board provides transport or has made arrangements for transport with taxi and minibus companies. Chapter Seven has dealt with the issue of transport in greater detail.

8.11.3   Day hospital provision in remote areas

The Working Party called for day hospital provision in remote areas to be addressed with the example given of a mobile day hospital facility in the Eastern Health Board. It recommended that:

- **(R8.34) health boards explore different ways of bringing the benefits of day hospitals to elderly patients remote from general hospitals**.

As can be seen, health boards had different methods for dealing with day hospital facilities in remote areas. These ranged from the provision of a mobile day hospital facility in the Eastern Health Board, which is also being examined by the Midland Health Board, to the provision of day hospitals in community hospitals (North Western, Southern and Western Health Boards).

8.12   Special hospital needs of older people

The Years Ahead noted the benefits of developments in orthopaedic and cataract surgery for older people and made the following recommendations:

- **(R8.40) that the Department of Health undertake a review of the present organisation of elective orthopaedic surgery and joint replacement surgery in particular, to ensure that elderly people have access to a service of high quality, that they receive the same priority as younger age groups, and that the service expands to cope with the increasing numbers of elderly people.**

Table 8.12: Health boards' plans for day hospital services in remote areas

Health Board	Scheme/plan	Details
Eastern	Yes	Mobile day hospital facility introduced in 1988. Visits areas remote from general hospitals. Custom-built vehicle with examination, bathing and reception facilities. Mobile team includes geriatrician, nursing and paramedical staff. Close liaison with local GPs and PHNs. Quite similar to assessment unit team. Also, geriatrician visits hospitals and homes in Wicklow and Kildare
Midland	Yes	Examining getting mobile day hospital at sector level; do not have day hospitals, in any case, and have only just appointed geriatricians
Mid-Western	Yes	Outreach services provided around Limerick City. Extension of facility depends on resources
North Eastern	Yes	Plans for a new geriatric service in Ballyconnell and Virginia with day hospitals there. There are also long-term plans for a new development in Dunshaughlin which will house a day hospital
North Western	Yes	14 day hospitals in the community hospitals providing services to remote patients
Southern	Yes	Day hospitals in community hospitals
South Eastern	No	There are no day hospitals in this board. Transport identified as an issue
Western	Yes	Day hospital in several community hospitals, for example Swinford and Castlebar

Source: Interviews with Programme Managers of General Hospital Care

- **(R8.41) that the Department of Health review present arrangements for cataract surgery in the elderly to ensure that those requiring treatment receive it in reasonable time and that the service is expanded to deal with increasing numbers of elderly people.**

The Department of Health indicates that there have been no formal specific reviews of elective orthopaedic surgery, joint replacement surgery and cataract surgery, but suggests that older people have been beneficiaries of recent initiatives on waiting lists. Under the Waiting List Initiatives since 1993, a total of £50m has been provided to reduce hospital waiting lists and priority has been given to areas such as Ear Nose and Throat, ophthalmology, orthopaedics, vascular/cardiac surgery and plastic surgery. The number of hip replacement operations undertaken in 1995, for example, was 2,567, almost 80 per cent of which were performed on older people. A total of 2,373 operations for the removal of cataracts were also undertaken in 1995, almost 90 per cent of which were performed on people aged 60 and over.

Response from the Irish College of Ophthalmologists suggests that waiting lists for surgery, however, are still too long and better day surgery facilities are required in general hospitals. According to the Department of Health, there is no data on average waiting times for operations, as they vary between health boards, hospitals and consultants. Recent figures suggest, however, that waiting lists in three health boards (Eastern, Mid-Western and Western) for cataract operations are still significantly high (*Irish Medical Times* 1996), and Consultant Ophthalmologists suggest that inadequate staffing levels have contributed to an increase in waiting lists in out-patients departments. In addition, they felt that dedicated 'eye' beds, as well as more rehabilitation, intermediate and long-term care beds were required.

8.13 Summary and conclusions

Table 8.13 provides a summary of the relevant recommendations. Most health boards have an admissions and discharge policy, and while some reduction has occurred in waiting lists, follow-up procedures on discharge are problematic as the

Table 8.13: Summary of provision of acute hospital care

Recommendation	Current situation
Admission and discharge policies in each general hospital in consultation with CSE	Most boards. CSE involvement in only three boards
Eleven new specialist geriatric departments in general hospitals	Ten new geriatric departments in four boards; however system also reliant upon provision of geriatrician posts
Appointment of additional geriatricians	13.5 new posts since 1988, but problem where geriatricians not full-time dedicated to older people
Day hospitals in general hospitals	Only provided in three hospitals (although day hospitals are provided in community hospitals also). Only £0.2m provided annually up to 1996 rather than recommended £0.5m. £0.4m allocated for 1997.
Expansion of day hospitals	Apart from above, expansion in day hospitals located in community hospitals
Day hospitals provision in remote areas	Schemes in most boards
Review of arrangements for elective orthopaedic, joint replacement and cataract surgery	No review, and although older patients have benefited from recent Waiting Lists Initiatives, greater improvement still needed
Norm of 2.5 beds per 1,000 older people for assessment in geriatric departments	No board has reached norm
Norm of 3.0 beds per 1,000 older people for rehabilitation	Two boards have reached and surpassed norm
Designated rehabilitation beds on general hospital campus	Four boards have made provision

method of dissemination of information (whether by letter directly to the GP or via the patient or patient's family) can entail delays in follow-up. This is worrying given that the average length of stay by older people in acute hospitals is falling. Dedicated liaison personnel in some health boards, for example, appear to be effective in 'reaching out' into the community, but in all health boards follow-up procedures need to be systematised and tightened up, so that the older patient does not get lost, once she or he has left hospital, and does not have to re-enter hospital unnecessarily. Regular assessment of older people is required, with a flexible care package offering a range of options, to guard against this.

There has been an increase in the number of specialist geriatric departments and the number of geriatricians since 1988, but this has not happened in all health boards. There has been a large investment in specialist geriatric departments in the Eastern Health Board, for example, and very little or none in the Southern and North Eastern. Similarly, while the number of geriatricians has increased since 1988, not all geriatricians work full-time on the care of older people. This leads to differences in the types of care available across the health boards. Geriatricians have a powerful role in influencing policy-makers and in lobbying for older people, and this voice needs to be heard undiluted.

It should be noted that in some geographical locations, however, there may not be a need for a full-time dedicated geriatrician, or that several physicians with a mixed role may provide the best solution. This points to the need for a thorough review of the role of geriatricians which examines their workloads, their population catchment areas, the outreach services they provide and the support services available. The individual requirements of particular geographical areas and hospitals could then be matched more efficiently with geriatrician provision. At present, older people attend specialist geriatric departments, or geriatricians, in a hospital within their catchment areas. In emergency cases, where older people require specialist treatment or if there is a shortage of beds in the hospital within their own catchment area, individuals may be referred to hospitals in another catchment area. What is clear about current provision, therefore, is that the question of geographical differences needs to be addressed. While there may be an argument for not providing specialist geriatric departments in a hospital where there is a geriatrician with specialised support staff and equipment who can provide an effective outreach service (as happens in Longford/Westmeath), there is a need to match requirements with provision so that older people are not disadvantaged as a result of their geographical location.

As well as specialised support teams and equipment, geriatricians need designated beds. None of the health boards has reached the recommended norm for assessment beds, and only two have reached the recommended norm in *The Years Ahead* for rehabilitation beds. There is also an argument to be made for the availability of step-down beds, so that general hospitals can act as medium-term recovery facilities as well as acute units.

As a step along the continuum of care, general hospitals obviously play a very important part. It is interesting, however, that when thinking about older people in hospitals, there was an assumption apparent in *The Years Ahead*, that the complete medical rehabilitation of older people will not occur and that they need ongoing care. This will be taken up again in Chapter Thirteen, in general, while attention now turns to long-term care options.

CHAPTER NINE

The Community Hospital

9.1   Introduction

As part of a continuum of care long-term options play a major role in the health care of older people. *The Years Ahead* envisaged the development of community hospitals which would cater for both acute and long-stay needs at local level. In recent times, nursing homes have become increasingly important in the provision of long-stay care. This chapter examines both of these long-stay care options. The chapter is based on responses received from: Programme Managers of Community Care and General Hospitals (15); Directors of Community Care (19); Co-ordinators of Services for the Elderly (17); District Liaison Nurses (39); Superintendent PHNs (26); Senior PHNs (8); Geriatricians (14); GPs (7); Nursing Home matrons/directors (30).

9.2   The Community hospital service
9.2.1   Development of community hospitals
The Years Ahead recommended that:

- **(R9.14) existing geriatric hospitals and homes, long-stay district hospitals and welfare homes, be developed as community hospitals, where appropriate, providing a wide range of acute and long-stay services for older patients and their carers.**

The purpose of the community hospital as envisaged by the Working Party was the provision of quality care at community level, so that older patients could remain within their communities. The proposed new facilities could also reduce demand on general hospitals. It was anticipated that where facilities were not already in place which could be developed as community hospitals, purpose-built facilities would be constructed. Table 9.1 details the situation in relation to the development of community hospitals across the eight health boards.

As shown in the table below, the development of community hospitals has not occurred in the way the Working Party recommended. Some health boards have

233

Table 9.1: Development of community hospitals

Health board	Number of units	Comments on current provision	Future plans
Eastern	14	N/A	Plans to build nine small-scale units for older people
Midland	3	Funding a problem	Each district (six) will have at least one Community Care Centre for Elderly
Mid-Western	2	N/A	Currently being upgraded; no new hospitals planned
North Eastern	12	Lack of investment in beginning; has become easier recently	Four new hospitals and one replacement (Drogheda)
North Western	12	From 1977 to 1986 used EU and DoH funding. Problem with lack of capital since	Two new hospitals and arrangements with private nursing homes to provide beds in areas not covered
Southern	17 (district hospitals)	Problems with funding	Under Community Hospitals Development Plan 1996, each district will have a hospital
South Eastern	1	Voluntary organisation re-opened a district hospital as a community hospital	No plans
Western	4	District hospitals used for direct referrals from the community and transfers from acute general hospitals	Programme to provide further homes for the aged but funding is a problem

Source: Interviews with Chief Executive Officers, Programme Managers of Community Care and Directors of Community Care

provided purpose-built community hospitals or units (Eastern and North Eastern). Six health boards have developed existing geriatric homes and hospitals as community hospitals (Eastern, Midland, Mid-Western, North Eastern, North Western and Western), but this has happened only on a small scale and the community hospital model has not replaced the old district hospital model. Two health boards have not developed community hospitals (South Eastern and Southern). In the South Eastern Health Board, a former district hospital has been taken over by a voluntary organisation and it is being run as a community hospital. The Southern Health Board has plans to develop all of its district hospitals as community hospitals from 1997.

The main reason for these different approaches would appear to be funding. Financial allocation for the development of community hospitals has been far below the level recommended by the Working Party, with only £1m being allocated over the period 1989-1994 rather than the £10m recommended for the

Table 9.2: Geographical distribution of community hospitals by community care area

Health board	No. of units	Community care areas with community hospitals	Community care areas with no community hospital provision
Eastern	14	Area 2 (2), Area 3 (1), Area 5 (4), Area 6 (1), Area 7 (1), Area 9 (2), Area 10 (3)	Areas 1, 4 and 8
Midland	3	Laois/Offaly (2) Longford/ Westmeath (1)	N/A
Mid-Western	2	Clare (1), Limerick (1)	Tipperary North Riding
North Eastern	12	Cavan/Monaghan (5), Meath (2), Louth (5)	N/A
North Western	12	Donegal (8), Sligo/Leitrim (4)	N/A
Southern	17 (district hospitals)	Cork City and South Cork (1), North Cork (5), West Cork (6), Kerry (5)	N/A
South Eastern	1	Waterford (1)	Carlow/Kilkenny, Wexford, Tipperary South Riding
Western	4	Galway (2), Roscommon (1), Mayo (1)	None

Source: Health boards

period 1989-1993. In the period 1995-1997, however, £8m was allocated, and the Department of Health foresees continuing growth in the capital amounts allocated.

Community hospitals are unevenly distributed throughout the country as can be seen in Table 9.2. This is particularly noticeable in the South Eastern Health Board, where three of its community care areas have no community hospitals, although all of these community care areas have health board geriatric hospitals and welfare homes (Department of Health 1995b). Furthermore, provision in some community care areas is better than in others. Again, funding was cited as the main problem and was mentioned specifically in the Midland, North Eastern, North Western and Western Health Boards.

Future plans for the further development of community hospitals or long-stay community solutions to health care of older people include purpose-built units (Eastern, North Eastern, North Western and Midland boards). In the Midland, these will be called Community Care Centres for the Elderly. Plans also envisage the development of existing geriatric hospitals and homes and district hospitals (North Eastern, Southern, Western), as well as arrangements with nursing homes to provide long-stay beds in those districts without community hospitals (North Western).

9.2.2   Service provision in community hospitals

The Working Party recommended that community hospitals provide a range of services including:

- **(R9.14) assessment, rehabilitation and convalescent care, day hospital and/or day care services, respite care, terminal care facilities, information and support for carers**.

Table 9.3 outlines the services currently being provided in community hospitals across the different health boards.

The Years Ahead envisaged community hospitals contributing to the continuum of care by being accessible and providing a high quality comprehensive range of treatment in the community. The range of services available across the various boards includes respite, day care, long-stay, convalescence, day hospitals and day care but no indication was given by CEOs or Programme Managers of the adequacy of these or of their coverage within the various health boards. While the table above may refer to what is available board-wide, it does not refer to what is available within an individual community hospital. Furthermore, current provision includes services supplied by health board geriatric hospitals and welfare homes in some boards. This becomes even clearer when the number of community hospitals providing assessment and rehabilitation are examined (see Table 9.4).

Table 9.3: Services provided in community hospitals

Health board	Services provided
Eastern	Respite, welfare, day care, long-stay, convalescence, day hospitals; some provide assessment and rehabilitation
Midland	Respite, terminal care, convalescence, dementia care, behavioural dementia care, day care, some assessment and rehabilitation
Mid-Western	Long-stay care, respite, physiotherapy, chiropody, day hospital, day care, terminal care, assessment and rehabilitation
North Eastern	Convalescent, respite, long-stay continuing care, day care, day hospitals; most provide assessment and rehabilitation
North Western	Home support, day care, respite, convalescence, assessment and rehabilitation, terminal care, social workers, aids and appliances, regional consultant clinics
Southern	District hospitals currently provide range including convalescent, respite, terminal care and limited physiotherapy
South Eastern	Voluntary community hospital provides residential nursing care
Western	Day care, assessment and rehabilitation, respite

Source: Interviews with CEOs, Programme Managers of Community Care and District Liaison Nurses

Table 9.4: Assessment and rehabilitation facilities in community hospitals

Health board	Number of community hospitals	Number providing assessment and rehabilitation
Eastern	14	1
Midland	3	1
Mid-Western	2	2
North Eastern	12	12
North Western	12	12
Southern	17 (district hospitals)	11
South Eastern	1	None
Western	4	4

Source: Interviews with CEOs and Programme Managers of Community Care

9.2.3   Assessment and rehabilitation

As part of the range of services provided by community hospitals, the Working Party recommended that:

- **(R9.14) assessment and rehabilitation facilities should be provided in each community hospital**.

As Table 9.4 shows, not all community hospitals in each board provide assessment and rehabilitation. Of the 65 units in the table above, 43 provide assessment and rehabilitation facilities. In the Eastern Health Board, for example, most do not have assessment units and it is believed that this is best undertaken in geriatric departments in the general hospitals. In the South Eastern Health Board, assessment and rehabilitation are not provided in the voluntary-run community hospital, but are provided in Waterford General Hospital. In the North Eastern Health Board, the hospitals are categorised according to the provision of extended, respite, and convalescent care. Within these categories all hospitals provide some degree of assessment and rehabilitation. Future plans in the Midland Health Board will provide for more assessment and rehabilitation, as will the planned developments in both the Mid-Western and Southern Health Boards. Clearly, there is scope for the improvement of current assessment and rehabilitation provision at community level, but many see this service as appropriate for the general hospital.

9.2.4   Geriatrician support to the community hospital

Critical to the provision of assessment and rehabilitation services is the input of the geriatrician. In *The Years Ahead* it was recommended that:

- **(R9.20) where possible a physician in geriatric medicine should provide specialist advice to the assessment and rehabilitation unit of the**

community hospital by means of regular visits, seeing patients on referral from the unit to the general hospital, and by providing training opportunities for staff from the unit in the specialist geriatric department.

As Chapter Eight has shown, all health boards were to have geriatricians in post by the end of 1996 and seven of the eight boards have increased their complement of geriatricians since 1988. The input from geriatricians to assessment and rehabilitation at community hospital level involves regular visits for the provision of consultation and advice. In many cases, however, geriatricians are not spending all of their time exclusively on older patients and may not have the time to visit all community hospitals. Table 9.5 outlines the position with regard to the provision of support to the assessment and rehabilitation units across the health boards.

9.2.5   Medical direction of assessment and rehabilitation units
The Years Ahead report recommended that:

- **(R9.28) medical direction of the assessment and rehabilitation unit of the community hospital should be the responsibility of one general practitioner with an interest in the elderly who would be appointed as**

Table 9.5: Geriatrician support in community hospitals

Health Board	Number of geriatricians	Comments
Eastern	10	Geriatrician available for consultation
Midland	2	Available in Longford/Westmeath community care area only. Monthly visits to Athlone coupled with fortnightly visits to St Joseph's Geriatric Hospital in Longford. Unit in Athlone is staffed by GPs, with guidelines for assessment and rehabilitation provided by geriatrician
Mid-Western	3	Fortnightly visits made by geriatrician
North Eastern	3	At present, GPs, nurses and medical officers provide high quality assessment and rehabilitation. It is envisaged that geriatricians will be more important in the acute rather than long-stay sector
North Western	1.5	Geriatricians visit community hospitals
Southern	2	No community hospitals; geriatricians do not provide support to the district hospitals
South Eastern	1	Geriatrician does not provide assessment and rehabilitation support to voluntary-run community hospital, only in Waterford General Hospital
Western	3	Weekly visits by geriatrician as part of assessment and rehabilitation service

Source: Interviews with Programme Managers of Community Care and geriatricians

part-time medical officer to the hospital. The medical officer of the community hospital would also be responsible for the implementation of the medical policy of the hospital generally ...appointment as medical officer to a community hospital should be for a period of five years and the post should be filled by open competition ...the consultant physical in geriatric medicine, where appointed, would provide specialist medical advice to the staff of the community hospital and assist in the monitoring of the agreed policies of a hospital in relation to admissions, discharges and standards of care.

The Working Party further envisaged that the medical officer who takes responsibility for the assessment and rehabilitation unit would be supported by a geriatrician as stated already (see 9.2.4 above). Table 9.6 gives details of current arrangements across the health boards. As can be seen, all health boards except the South Eastern have appointed someone to take responsibility for the assessment and rehabilitation units in their community hospitals. In four health boards (Eastern, Midland, North Western and Southern) GPs play a significant role, whether as appointed part-time medical officers or under a GP Access Scheme (North Western Health Board). In two health boards the geriatricians play an advisory role as part of the responsibilities to the community hospitals (Mid-Western and Western Health Boards). In the North Eastern Health Board, however, this responsibility is taken by the CSE with support from GPs. Different arrangements, therefore, are in place across the health boards and the recommendation made by the Working Party has not been implemented along the lines envisaged in *The Years Ahead*. The intention behind this recommendation

Table 9.6: Medical direction of assessment and rehabilitation unit of the community hospital

Health board	Details
Eastern	Medical officer on part-time basis. Support also provided by consultant geriatrician
Midland	GP operates according to guidelines laid down by geriatrician
Mid-Western	Geriatrician plays advisory role and makes fortnightly visits to community hospitals.
North Eastern	Co-Ordinator of Services for the Elderly (full-time) supported by GPs
North Western	GPs as a group by contract under GP Access Scheme. Trying to have a greater role for geriatrician
Southern	No community hospitals, but in those district hospitals which have assessment and rehabilitation units GPs, appointed as part-time medical officers, take responsibility for medical direction
South Eastern	N/A
Western	Geriatrician on a part-time permanent basis

Source: Interviews with Programme Managers of Community Care and geriatricians

was to facilitate access by GPs to patients admitted for assessment and rehabilitation and as will be seen in the following section, despite the differing arrangements, all health boards have addressed this issue in some way.

9.2.6   GPs' care of own patients in community hospitals
The Working Party recommended that:

- **(R9.28) once an elderly patient has been accepted for extended, including respite, care in the community hospital, his or her own general practitioner should provide medical care while in hospital.**

Table 9.7 outlines current arrangements in place across health boards.

Table 9.7: Arrangements for GPs to provide medical care to their own older patients in community hospitals

Health board	Details
Eastern	Designated GPs have responsibility for patients in most community hospitals
Midland	Designated GPs have responsibility for patients in care centres for older people
Mid-Western	Medical Officers in Ennistymon and Raheen with locum cover from local GP services when required
North Eastern	Medical Officers encourage close liaison with older patients' own GPs. In some hospitals older patients are managed by own GPs
North Western	GP Access Schemes: two-tier service 1. GPs living within five-mile radius provide emergency cover and look after own older patients 2. GPs outside five-mile radius provide care to own older patients. GPs generally serve population of 120-200 older people
Southern	While there are no community hospitals, GPs act as part-time Medical Officers in district hospitals
South Eastern	In health board geriatric homes and hospitals, GPs have access to own patients
Western	Rota of local GPs who take on role of part-time medical officers

Source: Interviews with Programme Managers of Community Care and GPs

As can be seen from Table 9.7 the GPs of older patients provide care in two health boards with the most comprehensive service being provided by the North Western Health Board under its GP Access Scheme. In four other health boards (Eastern, Midland, Mid-Western and Western) GPs living in the vicinity of the community hospital provide cover. This arrangement has also been adopted by the Southern Health Board in its district hospitals. In the South Eastern Health Board GPs have access to their own patients in geriatric homes and hospitals. While, therefore, all health boards appear to have addressed the issue of GP access, the most comprehensive scheme which facilitates GPs' access to own patients is that operated by the North Western Health Board and would appear to come closer to that recommended by the Working Party.

9.2.7   Support facilities in community hospitals
The Working Party also recognised the need for patients in community hospitals to:

- **(R9.27) have access to necessary support facilities and professional expertise**.

These support facilities included x-ray, laboratory and rehabilitation, as well as access to physiotherapy, chiropody, dental and occupational therapy.

Programme Managers from the different health boards indicated that a variety of services was available to the community hospitals. It has already been noted that there are problems with the availability of certain paramedical services at community care level (see Chapter Seven). There are also problems in providing these services in community hospitals (for example, in the Midland and Mid-Western boards). The level, extent and adequacy of provision differ across health boards, and across community care areas within health boards and are linked to the absence of adequate funding for the development of the community hospital service.

Table 9.8: Support facilities in community hospitals

Health board	Facilities
Eastern	Occupational therapy, physiotherapy, chiropody, speech therapy
Midland	All have access to pathology, some have access to occupational therapy, physiotherapy, chiropody, speech therapy
Mid-Western	Speech therapy, hygienist, sessional physiotherapy and hoping to get occupational therapy
North Eastern	Paramedical support, including occupational therapy and physiotherapy
North Western	Physiotherapy, occupational therapy, chiropody, counselling, social work
Southern	Limited physiotherapy, chiropody in district hospitals
South Eastern	Physiotherapy, occupational therapy, speech therapy provided in health board geriatric hospitals and homes and also to voluntary-run community hospital
Western	Physiotherapy, occupational therapy and social work

Source: Interviews with Programme Managers of Community Care and geriatricians

9.2.8   Nursing care in community hospitals

Of crucial importance to the success of the community hospital, as noted by the Working Party, is the provision of high quality nursing care. Accordingly it was recommended that:

- **(R9.29) a scheme of retraining for nursing staff be initiated in the proposed community hospitals, based in the specialist geriatric departments of general hospitals and in existing geriatric hospitals which have developed an active approach to the assessment and support of elderly people at home**.

A retraining scheme is provided in four boards (Eastern, North Eastern, North Western and Western), the most comprehensive of which appears to be that provided by the North Western Health Board. The Southern Health Board also provides some training on long-stay care. According to the Department of Health no formal training programme has been developed for community hospital staff. Programme Managers state, however, that they aim to ensure that community hospital staff are adequately trained.

9.2.9   Long-term care beds

For long-term care beds the Working Party recommended:

- **(R9.22) a norm of 10 beds for extended care per 1,000 elderly, in the context of a norm of 2.5 beds per 1,000 elderly in the specialist department of geriatric medicine in the general hospital and 3 beds per 1,000 elderly for rehabilitation in general and community hospitals**.

Table 9.9: Retraining scheme for nursing staff

Health board	Scheme	Details
Eastern	Yes	On-going training courses available in patient handling, lifting techniques, continence advice, health and safety, nutrition
Midland	No	Training only as part of general training programme, none specifically for community hospital staff
Mid-Western	No	No specific study leave for nursing staff
North Eastern	Yes	Staff selected for re-training
North Western	Yes	All nurses underwent two to three year programmes. Developed skills in relation to older people in long-stay care. Projects were encouraged between various departments
Southern	N/A	N/A
South Eastern	N/A	N/A
Western	Yes	Ongoing training provided; at present under review of Matrons and Personnel Department

Source: Interviews with CEOs and Programme Managers of Community Care

Table 9.10: Long-term care beds
(Recommended norm: 10 per 1,000 older people)

Health board	Level	Is norm appropriate	Is norm feasible
Eastern	26.2	No	No
Midland	33.5	No	No
Mid-Western	34.8	No	No
North Eastern	27.6	No	No
North Western	35.3	No	No
Southern	26.1	Fairly	Yes
South Eastern	28.2	No	No
Western	20.1	Fairly	Yes

Source: Department of Health (1995b): Survey of Long-Stay Units 1994; interviews with Programme Managers of Community Care

> **These norms (should) be reviewed by the Department of Health to ensure their adequacy. Beds for assessment and respite care in community hospitals should be met from the norm of 10 beds per 1,000 elderly for extended care.**

Table 9.10 outlines the provision of beds in all long-stay units, apart from nursing and welfare homes, as returned to the Department of Health for 1994 (Department of Health, 1995b).

All health boards provide above the norm recommended in *The Years Ahead* and given the general concurrence among Programme Managers that the norms are neither appropriate nor feasible, a review would seem timely. Programme Managers feel, furthermore, that demand on beds will be greater in future because of increasing numbers of older people and changes in the social support structure.

9.2.10   Review of norms
The Working Party also recommended that:

- **(R9.22) these norms be reviewed by the Department of Health to ensure their adequacy**.

According to the Department of Health, no such review has taken place. While the norms have been the subject of discussion between the Department and the health boards, it has been accepted at Department level that the norms are correct and feasible. Most long-stay beds are generic in nature, however, and they can be used for different needs including welfare, respite and terminal care. If beds are dedicated to different needs then norms for long-term care beds may not be too low, but their current use for different needs means that such use and their dedication must be examined.

9.2.11   Welfare accommodation

The Working Party had recommended that:

- **(R9.32) the need for welfare accommodation for frail elderly persons be met in a flexible way, in sheltered housing with support from day care and voluntary organisations, in boarding-out arrangements, in accommodation associated with the community hospital and in hostels for the elderly mentally infirm.**

Most boards have adopted flexible approaches to welfare accommodation and these operate in tandem with welfare homes. While different approaches are being taken, the response to the issue of welfare accommodation has been mostly *ad hoc* with very few places designated. As was made clear in previous sections on housing and boarding out schemes, information on the number of welfare places is poor. The issue of flexibility in the type of welfare accommodation as recommended in *The Years Ahead*, particularly in the light of the current phasing out of welfare homes, must be addressed adequately. As will be argued in Chapter Ten, confusion over terms such as welfare places, welfare accommodation and welfare homes must be sorted out (this confusion was also apparent in *The Years Ahead*) so that the issue of welfare accommodation is adequately and efficiently addressed by health boards.

Thinking on welfare accommodation has changed since 1988 and many Programme Managers were explicit about the need to find a community solution as well as the need to move away from the traditional welfare homes. In the North Western Health Board, for example, there are plans to convert existing welfare

Table 9.11: Type of welfare accommodation provided by health boards

Health board	Welfare accommodation
Eastern	Hospitals, geriatric homes and dedicated welfare homes
Midland	Welfare homes, boarding out, bed and breakfast
Mid-Western	Geriatric hospitals
North Eastern	Sheltered housing, reshaping own housing, boarding out, own family
North Western	Sheltered housing, working with St Vincent de Paul (most preferred option). Boarding out schemes, trying to develop these with Programme Managers of community care meeting Superintendent PHN and CSEs. There are three welfare homes which health board wants to convert to nursing homes to become satellites of community hospitals
Southern	Welfare homes (two) and welfare places in other homes
South Eastern	Statutory or voluntary welfare homes
Western	Within long-stay facilities and geriatric homes. Placements made by long-stay committee following assessment. Limited boarding out scheme also in operation

Source: Interviews with CEOs, Programme Managers of Community Care and geriatricians

homes to nursing homes in order to provide a back-up to the community hospital sector. In the Eastern Health Board, services such as the community ward teams, improved day care and the proposed community units for long-term care for older people are seen as catering for the demand for welfare accommodation. Yet, as will be seen in the next section, a lack of dedicated welfare places characterises the situation in relation to welfare accommodation.

9.2.12   Welfare place provision

With regard to the provision of welfare places the Working Party stated:

- **(R9.32) the need for welfare accommodation for frail elderly persons be met in a flexible way in sheltered housing with support from day care and voluntary organisations, in boarding-out arrangements, in accommodation association with the community hospital and in hostels for the elderly mentally infirm. We recommend a norm of 20-25 places per 1,000 elderly for this kind of welfare accommodation.**

Since *The Years Ahead* the number of beds in welfare homes has been falling (Keogh and Roche 1996). Figures for dedicated beds were not available from most health boards, so the following table gives the number of places in welfare homes in 1994 using Department of Health returns (Department of Health 1995b).

As can be seen, the provision of places in welfare homes is well below the norm recommended in *The Years Ahead*. This is because of the decline in welfare home bed provision. Welfare places in other kinds of accommodation are not dedicated (except in the Midland Health Board). The slack arising from the decrease in the number of places in welfare homes therefore is not being taken up elsewhere in a structured manner. To summarise briefly at this stage, there are a number of issues

Table 9.12: Beds in welfare homes
(*Years Ahead* norm of 20-25 per 1,000 older people)

Health Board	Number of welfare beds 1994	Ratio per 1,000 older people
Eastern	181	1.54
Midland*	161	6.58
Mid-Western	121	3.30
North Eastern	111	3.28
North Western	114	3.76
South Eastern	172	3.91
Southern	124	1.89
Western	370	7.44

includes proportion designated in the community hospitals in Birr and Edenderry
Source: Department of Health (1995b): Survey of Long-Stay Units 1994

which need to be addressed in relation to welfare accommodation. While information is poor and there is a definitional problem that needs to be examined, feedback shows that different models exist across the health boards. A range of flexible accommodation is being provided, but the dedication of places as welfare accommodation needs to be addressed urgently.

9.3   Nursing homes

9.3.1   The Health (Nursing Homes) Act 1990
Private nursing home bed provision has increased significantly, particularly in the Eastern Health Board area, over the last decade (O'Shea *et al.* 1991; Department of Health 1995b). It is envisaged that provision will increase further as a result of the ageing population, changes in the social structure, such as the greater numbers of women who might formerly have been available for caring now entering paid employment and falls in the number of public long-stay beds. *The Years Ahead* noted the increase in the private nursing home sector and made the recommendation that:

- **(R9.38) the Health (Homes for Incapacitated Persons) Act 1964 be amended to include the operation of nursing homes run by voluntary bodies and include an annual licensing system for nursing homes**.

Prior to *The Years Ahead*, nursing homes were covered under the *Health (Homes for Incapacitated Persons) Act, 1964*, and the *Health Act (1970)*. In the former, while standards, inspections and the notification of all new establishments were provided for, it was confined to the profit-making sector. The latter provided for the granting of ministerial approval which ceased in 1980 as a result of budgetary constraints. Difficulties had also been experienced by that time with the funding of 'approved' homes as the means or dependency of the residents were not taken into consideration. *The Health (Nursing Homes) Act* was passed in 1990 and extended regulation and inspection of nursing homes to include those run by voluntary organisations. The Act was influenced by *The Years Ahead*, particularly in relation to subvention arrangements and the assessment of older people before being admitted to long-stay beds (O'Shea *et al.* 1991). The Act tightened quality controls through compulsory registration of nursing homes. Nursing homes apply for registration upon payment of a declaration fee. Having been entered on a register maintained by health boards, a prescribed fee of £10 per bed must be paid by nursing homes which is offset against the declaration fee. The period of registration lasts three years and each nursing home receives a certificate of registration from the health board concerned. Rather than an annual licensing system, therefore, as recommended under *The Years Ahead*, the Act allows for registration which is updated every three years. The Act also allows for stricter enforcement of standards of design, nursing care, nutrition, general management, greater accountability of proprietors, stiffer penalties for offences, and more powers for health boards to deal with offenders.

9.3.2   The views of nursing homes on the 1990 Nursing Homes Act

The Irish Registered Nursing Homes Association represents more than 200 private nursing homes, while the Catholic Voluntary Nursing Homes Association represents voluntary nursing homes run by Catholic religious orders. Sixty-one nursing homes from both organisations were sampled across all the health boards, and 30 responses were received across all health boards except the Midland as can be seen in Table 9.13.

Table 9.13: Nursing homes' responses to Act

Health board	Response
Eastern	Overall satisfactory (9) although noted that there is a lack of uniformity across health boards in how regulations are applied and inspections carried out.
Mid-Western	Fairly satisfactory (3)
North Eastern	Fairly satisfactory (3)
North Western	Satisfactory (2)
South Eastern	Satisfactory (2)
Southern	Overall only fairly satisfactory (6) as problems were cited with inadequate funding, unsatisfactory assessments and the need for independent assessments.
Western	Fairly satisfactory (5). Huge difference in interpretation of regulations across health boards; should be independent body of inspection under direction of health boards

Source: Interviews with Nursing homes' proprietors and matrons

The response of nursing home proprietors and managers to the *1990 Nursing Homes Act* was positive in general. Problems experienced included a lack of uniformity across health boards in the implementation of the regulations and in conducting inspections. In the Southern Health Board, respondents were the least positive with difficulties over funding and assessments cited.

9.3.3   Subvention of nursing home patients

The Working Party recommended that:

- **(R9.41) Section 54 of the Health Act 1970 be amended to enable health boards to subvent the care of eligible elderly patients, after assessment, in nursing homes licensed by the board and to enable health boards to vary the level of subvention according to the patient's needs**.

Section 54 of the *1970 Health Act* was problematic because it took no account of the means or dependency of residents and it was subsequently addressed in the *1990 Health (Nursing Homes) Act*. Assessments are carried out at three levels: medical, economic and social. The economic assessment includes income and assets and also takes into consideration the means of an individual's adult children

Table 9.14: Subvention of care of older patients in licensed nursing homes

Health board	Nursing homes' responses
Eastern	Unsatisfactory. Subvention too low and system of who is accepted or not is unfair. Taking savings into consideration is unfair
Mid-Western	Unsatisfactory. Money granted should be index linked and there should be subventions for mobile isolated people unable to live alone
North Eastern	Fairly satisfactory. Assessments inconsistent and means testing unfair
North Western	Satisfactory
South Eastern	Medical assessment satisfactory. Financial assessment unsatisfactory. Subvention is too low and means testing is not satisfactory
Southern	Unsatisfactory. Insufficient funding. Method of means testing unfair and no account taken of older patients' social needs
Western	Unsatisfactory. Methods of means testing unsatisfactory and delays in payment. Also need for fourth category to cover 'very poor'. Consistent criteria should be put in place across all health boards

Source: Interviews with Nursing homes' proprietors and matrons

who are resident within the jurisdiction. It is this regulation which has raised most objections as the Table 9.14 shows.

It is noteworthy that respondents from nursing homes only objected to assessments to ascertain financial and social dependency, which were considered to be inadequate and unfair. Medical assessments, carried out by GPs, PHNs and the matrons of nursing homes were regarded as satisfactory.

It is important to note that the 1990 Nursing Homes Act has resulted in a large increase in spending on private nursing home care by the Department of Health. Over the period 1993-1997 inclusive, over £65m has been spent on the implementation of the Act, a huge amount when compared, for example, to the £2.5m spent on the development of day care facilities.

9.3.4 Support services in nursing homes
The Working Party recommended that:

- **(R9.42) private and voluntary nursing homes arrange to provide medical, nursing, dental, physiotherapy and chiropody services directly or on a contract basis with the health board**.

Under the *1990 Nursing Homes Act*, older patients receiving subventions should receive services necessary for their maintenance and the Act cites the provision of bed, board, nursing care, incontinence wear, bedding, laundry services, aids and appliances. Subvented patients requiring special services or equipment are covered under the contract of care which each resident receives within two months of taking up residence in the home. For residents not subvented, services provided are covered under the fees paid, although extra services are charged separately (as laid down in the Code of Practice, Department of Health 1995d).

According to nursing home proprietors and matrons, older patients on medical cards, or in receipt of subvention, are provided with support services, but these are dependent upon provision within a particular health board. Problems have been cited with the provision of support services on a sessional basis only and this has been noted in connection with services such as chiropody and physiotherapy. Older patients not in receipt of subvention are financially responsible for services they require.

9.3.5   Liaison between health boards and nursing homes
The Working Party noted that there was scope for better liaison between health boards and private and voluntary nursing homes. Accordingly, the recommendation was made that:

- **(R9.42) the Co-ordinator of Services for the Elderly establish liaison arrangements with the nursing homes operating in the community care area**.

Tables 9.15 summarises feedback from CSEs, District Liaison Nurses and PHNs with regard to liaison arrangements.

Health board staff perceive that liaison appears to be working well. CSEs liaise with nursing homes in all health boards in respect of inspections. In addition, CSEs make regular contact by telephone and/or visiting nursing homes in their areas. CSEs are also involved with the processing and payment of subvention. All CSEs reported liaison arrangements to be satisfactory, although CSEs in the North Eastern board said that they would like more formal contact and more control of the beds which the health board subvents.

Table 9.15: Liaison arrangements

Health Board	CSE (17)	District Liaison Nurse (39)	PHN (34)	Rating
Eastern	Yes	Yes	Yes	Satisfactory
Midland	N/A	Yes	Yes	Satisfactory
Mid-Western	Yes	N/A	Yes	Satisfactory
North Eastern	Yes	Yes	Yes	Satisfactory
North Western	Yes	Yes	Yes	Satisfactory
South Eastern	Yes	Yes	Yes	Satisfactory
Southern	Yes	Yes	Yes	Satisfactory
Western	Yes	Yes	Yes	Satisfactory

Source: Interviews with CSEs, District Liaison Nurses, Superintendent PHNs, and Senior PHNs

Table 9.16: Nursing home proprietors' perception of liaison and relationship

Health Board	Nursing homes' relationship with health board	Overall rating re liaison arrangements
Eastern	Good	Satisfactory
Mid-Western	Good	Satisfactory
North Eastern	Good	Satisfactory
North Western	Good	Satisfactory
South Eastern	Good	Satisfactory
Southern	Good	Fairly satisfactory
Western	Good	Satisfactory

Source: Interviews with Nursing homes' proprietors and matrons

District Liaison Nurses and some PHNs are also involved in liaison with nursing homes over subvention and the assessment of patients. According to District Liaison Nurses liaison works satisfactorily overall. Superintendent PHNs, while generally positive, were less optimistic than the District Liaison Nurses about the arrangements, and proposed solutions which included better liaison on the part of nursing homes, particularly in relation to the notification of vacancies.

Nursing home respondents, while giving satisfactory ratings overall in relation to liaison arrangements, were not as positive as health board personnel and some felt that liaison needed to be more formal (Eastern, Western and Mid-Western Health Boards). Members of the Irish Registered Nursing Homes Association felt that their representative body made more effort with regard to liaison than the health boards. Several District Liaison Nurses from those boards felt however that the onus lay on the nursing homes to improve liaison. The relationship that nursing homes have with the health boards has to be viewed therefore in the context of inspections which may influence the perceptions of the nursing home personnel. Nursing Homes in the North Eastern Health Board reported a good relationship with the board for example but one nursing home respondent objected to unannounced inspections and felt, in addition, that complaints by health board personnel were unreasonable.

9.3.6 Inspections of nursing homes

In relation to the inspection of nursing homes, the Working Party recommended that:

- **(R9.48) an independent inspectorate of extended care facilities for the elderly be established within the Department of Health comprised of people with first-hand experience of providing high standards of care for the elderly**.

According to the Department of Health, this inspectorate has not been established. It is felt by the Department that health boards have adequate powers to inspect nursing homes. Furthermore, as standards are felt to be at an acceptable level, the Department has no plan to change this arrangement. O'Shea *et al.* argued in 1991 that inspection needs to be the same in all health board regions and it interesting to note that several nursing home respondents (in the Eastern, North Eastern, Southern and Western Health Boards) felt that there were differences in the interpretation of regulations across the health boards. Inspections of nursing homes are carried out on a six month basis by teams comprising a GP, a nurse and an Environmental Health Officer. Visits are unannounced and the team uses the guidelines set out by the *1990 Health (Nursing Homes) Act* and the *Care and Welfare Regulations 1993*.

9.3.7   Training of nursing home staff

Not only would the recommended inspectorate be involved in standardising regulations for inspections, but the Working Party also recommended that:

- **(R9.48) the Department of Health, through the inspectorate of extended care facilities, in consultation with the health boards and the Private Hospitals and Nursing Homes Association, draw up and implement a code of good practice suitable to this country's needs and a training programme for nursing home and community hospital staff.**

A Code of Practice for Nursing Homes was drawn up and published in 1995 by a group of people specialised and interested in the care of older people. This group included proprietors of nursing homes, health boards, the National Council for the Elderly and carers. The Code of Practice, which is voluntary, but monitored by the health boards, covers the philosophy of care, introductory visits, trial stays, written contracts of care, involvement of residents in decision making, medication and activities for nursing home residents. The vast majority of respondents from nursing homes were in favour of the Code (18 out of 30 stated it was 'good' and a further two said it was 'excellent'). The majority of those who were less than positive did not know about its existence.

As far as the provision of training for nurses in nursing homes is concerned, the Department of Health indicated that there were no formal training programmes for either nursing home or community hospital staff. While there was no statutory programme available, however, there was a range of training provided through the Vocational Education Committees and private institutions. The Irish Registered Nursing Homes Association is presently involved in discussions with the Department of Health and various statutory bodies about education programmes for nurses.

As Table 9.17 shows, 60 per cent (18) of nursing home respondents provide training for their staff. The training ranges from patient care and handling to safety

Table 9.17: Training programmes for nursing home staff

Health board	Availability of training programmes
Eastern	5/9 provide courses for staff. 1/9 sends staff on VEC pre-nursing course
Mid-Western	2/3 nursing homes provide or fund
North Eastern	1/3 nursing homes provide
North Western	1/1 nursing homes provide
Southern	5/6 nursing homes provide or fund
South Eastern	1/3 provide or fund
Western	2/5 provide or fund

Source: Interviews with Nursing homes' proprietors and matrons

and evacuation procedures. Nursing home respondents felt that funding should be available for training, and in the case of respondents from the Mid-Western Health Board, thought that this was a gap that could be filled by the hospitals. The lack of a statutory programme was noted by the Department of Health, but the range of other programmes available was cited as filling the demand.

9.3.8 Brochure

Finally, the Working Party recommended:

- **(R9.44) it should be a condition of a nursing home licence that a nursing home makes available to prospective clients and their families a brochure detailing the services it provides, the charges, the qualifications of its staff and other information about the home**.

Respondents from all nursing homes said that they provide brochures for prospective clients.

9.4 Summary and conclusions

The following table summarises the implementation of the recommendations made in *The Years Ahead* in relation to long-stay care facilities.

The development of community hospitals has been very slow and *ad hoc* and has not happened as envisaged in *The Years Ahead*. While some former district hospitals, geriatric hospitals and homes have been developed as community hospitals in some boards, and new purpose-built units have been or will be established in other boards, it is uncertain that these provide the range of services recommended by the Working Party in 1988, or that future development will occur along the lines envisaged. This is most evident in the lack of provision of assessment and rehabilitation facilities in community hospitals, with the Southern, Eastern and South Eastern Health Boards most noticeably deficient in this regard. In both the Eastern and the South Eastern Health Boards, feedback indicates that

Table 9.18: Summary of extent of provision of long-stay care

Recommendation	Current situation
Development of geriatric hospitals, homes, district hospitals, welfare homes as community hospitals	Not available in all districts in all boards; *ad hoc*
Provision of assessment and rehabilitation facilities in all community hospitals	Of 65 community and district hospitals, over half provide assessment and rehabilitation, but in two boards (EHB and SEHB) very little assessment and rehabilitation facilities and there are no plans for the community hospital sector to provide these in the future
Geriatrician support in community hospitals	Available in five boards, but not in all community hospitals. Also affected by lack of full-time dedication to older patients among geriatricians
Medical direction of assessment and rehabilitation unit of community hospital	Geriatricians, GPs or CSEs in all boards
Arrangements for patients' own GP to provide care	All boards
10 beds per 1,000 older people for extended care	All boards provide over norm
20-25 welfare places per 1,000 older people	No board has come near to norm

these facilities do not come under the remit of the community hospital and are considered more appropriate for the general hospital.

For community hospitals to be effective, there is a need for support services and facilities to be comprehensive. Yet this review indicates that the range of services provided in community hospitals is inadequate. Furthermore, the support currently provided by geriatricians to community hospitals may not be as great as it should be because of other demands on their time and resources. Where geriatricians also spend time on general patient care, the development of an effective geriatric service at community level cannot happen as it should. The provision of geriatricians influences the effective operation of community hospitals. For example, day hospitals will be provided in community hospitals in the Southern Health Board in the future, yet a greater number of geriatricians are needed in that board in order to ensure that these day hospital facilities will operate effectively.

This chapter has also questioned the role of the community hospital in providing long-stay care. The impact of community hospitals on long-stay bed provision has not been significant, and questions must be asked about the impact the community hospital makes at present to the long-stay sector.

The chapter has shown too that the lack of dedicated beds, whether long-stay or welfare, must be addressed in a meaningful way by the boards. As the older population increases, the demand on the health care services, particularly by the 'old old', is set to rise. The increase in the number of private nursing home beds (Department of Health 1995b), and the seemingly disproportionate sum spent on subventing private nursing home care (£65m), is one indication of the way in which this demand is being met, particularly in the Eastern Health Board area, but a range of options must be made available to older people. A further source of concern is the different policies on long-stay care adopted by the health boards (Keogh and Roche 1996). While the North Western Health Board has the greatest number of community hospitals, along the lines of *The Years Ahead*, the Eastern Health Board has a higher reliance on nursing home beds. The provision of these different types of solutions to long-stay care must be addressed in a comprehensive and co-ordinated way at departmental level. Furthermore, there is also a need to ensure that public sector facilities meet the standards of care.

The move away from welfare homes has not been met by the provision of dedicated welfare places in alternative accommodation and this lack of dedicated places is placing a strain on other services. The issue needs to be addressed at Departmental and board level with a unified strategy for dealing with welfare cases. *Shaping a Healthier Future* emphasises the issue of health and social gain. The recognition of the inclusion of welfare as a health issue must be made by designating appropriate accommodation for welfare cases. This includes addressing the issue of the provision of sheltered housing and the recognition of this kind of housing as one viable solution for welfare accommodation.

CHAPTER TEN

The Care of the Elderly Mentally Ill and Infirm

10.1   Introduction

With an increasing older population, it has been envisaged that there will be greater demand on the health services including the mental health services (Ruddle and O'Connor 1993; Department of Health 1992, 1995c; Keogh and Roche 1996). The *Green Paper on Mental Health* (1992) noted that half of long-stay patients, that is those who had been in psychiatric hospitals for more than one year, were over the age of 65 (Department of Health 1992).

Planning for the Future (Department of Health 1984), marked a watershed in the psychiatric services and was also important for the provision of mental health services for older people. Its main recommendations formed the basis of the chapter on mental illness and infirmity among older people in *The Years Ahead*, principally in the establishment of district-level (called sector) psychiatric teams whose aim was the provision of a comprehensive and community-oriented psychiatric service. *Planning for the Future* emphasised out-patient treatment and day care so that patients could continue to live in their own homes. The integration of psychiatric services with general hospital care, community care, voluntary services and GP provision was also very important. This emphasis on integration and co-ordination of services was also found in *The Years Ahead*.

Key policy documents since *Planning for the Future* have emphasised the integration of mental health and primary health services and the provision of comprehensive specialist assessment and support services (Department of Health 1992, 1994b, 1995c) as has a recent report by the National Council for the Elderly (Keogh and Roche 1996). In practice this entails the integration of community and hospital-based psychiatric services with geriatric medicine to provide comprehensive and appropriate packages of care for older people.

This chapter examines current provision for older people who are mentally ill and is based upon responses received from the following: Consultants in Psychiatry of Old Age (4); Programme Managers of Special Hospital Care (all); Chief Nursing Officers, Psychiatry (17); GPs (7); Superintendent Public Health Nurses (26); Senior Public Health Nurses (8); Psychiatric Social Workers (representative group).

10.2   Current psychiatric services for older people

Following the publication of *Planning for the Future* in 1984, psychiatric services have been gradually re-organised in sectors catering for an average of 25,000-30,000 people. *The Years Ahead* recommended that other medical and social care services for older people be organised in a similar manner with the boundaries being coterminous as far as possible. Table 10.1 outlines the situation for all health boards. The Working Party recommended that:

- **(R3.12) services for the elderly be organised as far as possible in districts serving a population of approximately 25-30,000 people.**

Two health boards have health and social care districts coterminous with psychiatric sectors (Mid-Western and North Western boards), while a third (Eastern) has districts which are coterminous in most cases. The Midland Health Board has plans to re-organise its services for older people, while in the North Eastern Health Board, the districts were said not to vary too significantly from the sectors for psychiatric services.

Table 10.1: Services for older people correspondent with psychiatric sectors

Health board	Corresponding	Comments
Eastern	Mostly	Most districts correspond to sectors
Midland	No	Re-organisation plans are laid out in Board's Action Plan 1996-2011
Mid-Western	Yes	Ten districts coterminous with psychiatric sectors
North Eastern	No	Slight variations, but not significant
North Western	Yes	Two to three districts in each sector
Southern	No	Needs reviewing to make coterminous
South Eastern	No	Currently doing own review. May go back to county boundaries for community care areas. Some psychiatric services are not in own sectors at present, for example patients from Tipperary admitted to Waterford city
Western	No	Lack of necessary capital resources has meant sectors not co-terminous

Source: Interviews with Programme Managers of Special Hospital Care

10.3   Psychiatry of Old Age services
The Working Party recommended that:

- **(R10.29) psychiatrists with responsibility for the elderly be appointed in Dublin and Cork to provide a specialist service in their catchment areas, to develop a model service and to promote high standards in the care of the elderly mentally ill.**

At present there are four Consultants in the Psychiatry of Old Age, three in the Eastern Health Board and one in the Mid-Western Health Board. The three consultants in the former cover almost six out of the ten community care areas, while the latter is mainly confined to Limerick City and County. In the Mid-Western Health Board, furthermore, the lack of resources led to the closure of the day hospital in 1996, although this facility is vital to any Psychiatry of Old Age Service.

Catchment populations for those areas serviced by Psychiatry of Old Age consultants vary from 28,000 older people for community care areas 6 and 7 of the Eastern Health Board, to 19,000 in community care areas 3 and 4 of the Eastern Health Board (personal communication). The old age psychiatry service in these community care areas has a multi-disciplinary team comprising Registrars, Community Psychiatric Nurses, occupational therapists and psychologists. In community care areas 1 and 2, the service commenced in January 1996 and, at the time of interview, a multi-disciplinary team was at the planning stage. The Psychiatry of Old Age service in the Mid-West has psychiatrists and psychiatric nurses only. Ideally, a Psychiatry of Old Age service should consist of a range of provision including domiciliary assessment, day hospitals and acute in-patient treatment. As will be seen, however, development of the service has been slow, in the main, and there is a perception among Consultants in the Psychiatry of Old Age that more resources need to be deployed and more commitment made to the service in order to provide suitable care in appropriate settings for older people who are mentally ill.

10.4   Consultant psychiatrists with responsibility for older people with dementia
The Years Ahead recommended that:

- **(R10.31) one of the psychiatrists in the sectors which correspond to a community care area should have responsibility for the care of the elderly with severe dementia. Special training arrangements may be necessary to encourage psychiatrists to develop an interest in this field.**

Respondents from the Western, Midland and North Western Health Boards express the intention to appoint Consultants in the Psychiatry of Old Age but to date this has not happened. Respondents from both the North Eastern and South Eastern

Table10.2: Psychiatrists in each health board with responsibility for older people with dementia and associated behavioural problems[1]

Health Board	Psychiatrists with responsibility for care of older people with dementia	Training in psychiatry of old age	Provision of psychiatrists with responsibility for care of older people
Eastern	Yes (3)	Consultants in Psychiatry of Old Age	Third consultant appointed this year
Midland	No	No	At present informal arrangement exists, but older people with dementia are not admitted to psychiatric services unless present with concurrent psychiatric problem such as depression. Planned for Consultant in Psychiatry of Old Age to take responsibility in future
Mid-Western	Yes (1)	Consultant in Psychiatry of Old Age	Team headed up by consultant takes responsibility for Limerick City and County
North Eastern	Yes	No	General psychiatrists
North Western	Yes	One with some training in Psychiatry of Old Age	Recent appointment of psychiatrist with some training in Psychiatry of Old Age; general psychiatric services deal with older people at present and plans to expand
Southern	No	No	General psychiatric services
South Eastern	No	No	Scarcity of consultants until recently and difficulty in recruiting. Thinking about developing Psychiatry of Old Age
Western	Yes	No	Each psychiatrist deals with older people as required. This arrangement pending appointment of a psychiatrist with training in Psychiatry of Old Age and multi-disciplinary teams in each community care area

Source: Interviews with Department of Health, CEOs, Programme Managers of Special Hospital Care and Consultants in the Psychiatry of Old Age

Health Boards stated that they would like a Psychiatry of Old Age service, but in the former, the intention is to appoint psychiatrists with some expertise in the area, rather than a consultant. Currently, therefore, apart from the Eastern and Mid-Western Health Boards, responsibility for older people who are mentally ill falls

---

[1] In *The Years Ahead* reference was made to 'severe dementia', whereas, practitioners in the Psychiatry of Old Age prefer the term dementia with associated behavioural problems such as aggression. 'Severe dementia' appears to imply severity in cognitive decline rather than the association with behavioural problems.

between geriatric medicine and the general psychiatric services. The former deals with dementia in the absence of physical illness, whereas the latter deals with dementia and associated behavioural problems as well as older people with functional mental illness. Clearly, therefore, current provision for older people with mental illness and dementia is under-developed.

10.5   Availability of training in Psychiatry of Old Age

To develop a Psychiatry of Old Age service, or to put older people who are mentally ill on the agenda of the general psychiatric services, it is important that psychiatrists trained in the Psychiatry of Old Age are employed. Table 10.2 shows that only two boards have made such provision and that funding for these posts has generally not been made available. There is, however, some training available for Registrars in Psychiatry of Old Age. All trainee psychiatrists are recommended to undertake at least six months in the Psychiatry of Old Age, at which level they are employed as Registrars or Senior House Officers in the psychiatric service. On gaining membership of the Royal College of Psychiatrists, trainees compete for Senior Registrar posts which constitute higher training. This higher training lasts for up to four years and those wishing to specialise in the Psychiatry of Old Age spend half of that time in the Psychiatry of Old Age services while the rest of the time is spent in general psychiatry or in another speciality of relevance to the Psychiatry of Old Age. Once higher training has been completed, trainees can then apply for consultant posts in the Psychiatry of Old Age. The fact that few posts are currently available appears to be explained, therefore, by a lack of sufficient funds to appoint consultants or the lack of sufficient resources to redeploy psychiatrists to develop this service.

10.6   Liaison arrangements between the psychiatric and geriatric services

Where the general psychiatric services take responsibility for older people, very close liaison is required with geriatric medicine. Liaison arrangements in the community and in general hospitals are detailed in Table 10.3 below.

Most boards reported informal liaison arrangements and several Programme Managers expressed their belief that liaison would improve if more formal arrangements were in place. Chief Nursing Officers in psychiatry across all the health boards stated that they would prefer more formal liaison arrangements with protocols laid down.

10.7   Functional mental illness

10.7.1   Assessment and treatment

Functional mental illness affects more older people than does dementia (Keogh and Roche 1996). The prognosis for treatment of functional mental illness is good providing adequate and appropriate services are available and that the illness is

Table 10.3: Liaison arrangements

Health Board	Liaison in community	Comments	Liaison with General Hospital	Comments
Eastern	Consultant in Psychiatry of Old Age liases with geriatricians and ward teams. Planning meetings and case conferences	Fairly effective	Consultant in Psychiatry Old Age and geriatricians work 'hand in glove'. Formal Meetings, cross referrals and joint team meetings	Effective
Midland	Informal only	Fairly effective	Informal	Effective
Mid-Western	Consultant in Psychiatry of Old Age liaises with GPs; Psychiatric team liaises with community care personnel. Apart from Consultant in Psychiatry of Old Age, liaison is informal	Works well, but weakness in absence of protocol for liaison	Liaison operates between Psychiatrist of Old Age, geriatricians and physicians. Where no Consultant in Psychiatry of Old Age is in place, liaison on individual cases operates between community care team and geriatrician	Fairly effective but more staff required
North Eastern	Liaison between psychiatric teams and GP, PHN, CSE. Informal, ongoing, dependent on individual case	Effective	No geriatric departments in General Hospitals; Hospital consultant requests consultant psychiatrist to assess patient and report to GP	Effective
North Western	Involvement of District CSE with psychiatric team. Assessment, very regular visits and close liaison	Effective	Formal meetings between chief psychiatrist, geriatrician, Programme Manager for Special Hospitals and two psychiatrists	Effective
Southern	Informal liaison between individual Chief Nursing Officers, PHNs and GPs. Community Psychiatric Nurse follow-up	Ineffective	Problem with allocation of older patients between geriatric and psychiatric services. Referrals only from geriatrician	Fairly effective
South Eastern	Psychiatrist can attend meetings of district and assessment teams, and case conferences. Community Psychiatric Nurse liaises with GPs and PHNs	Effective	Geriatrician in Waterford City, so regular and more formal liaison	Effective and will improve when psychiatrist and geriatrician in post
Western	GP refers to geriatrician or psychiatric team as appropriate; informal	Effective	GP referral at both out-patient department and in-patient levels to psychiatric team	Fairly effective

Source: Interviews with Programme Managers of Special Hospital Care, Consultants in the Psychiatry of Old Age, CSEs, Chief Nursing Officers, District Liaison Nurses and Psychiatric Social Workers

managed the same way as in younger people (Department of Health 1992). The majority of older people with functional mental illness should be treated by their GPs with referral to specialist psychiatric services when necessary. Crucial, therefore, in the treatment of functional mental illness, as in other illnesses, is early assessment. This entails the appropriate use of GPs, PHNs and easy access to psychiatric services when necessary.

The Working Party on Services for the Elderly noted that the majority of older people with functional mental illness should be treated at home by a specialist psychiatric team. Central to this team is the Community Psychiatric Nurse who plays a role in domiciliary treatment and in liaison with the community. Table 10.4 gives details of the current situation across all health boards in this respect.

Table 10.4: Care at home provided for older people with functional mental illness

Health board	Adequate	Services available	What required
Eastern	Adequate	Domiciliary assessment, day hospitals, Community Psychiatric Nurse	Expansion of Community Psychiatric Nursing service, day hospitals
Midland	Inadequate	Community nursing services; assessment, day care, respite care	Home nursing, family education and training, screening and early diagnosis
Mid-Western	Fairly	Day care, outreach and home assessment, Psychiatry of Old Age and psychiatric sector teams	Capital and resource barriers; Psychiatry of Old Age still in infancy, and effectively only in Limerick area. Expansion and more staff required
North Eastern	Adequate	Day care, five days per week	Expansion of day care
North Western	Fairly	Out-Patient Department, day care, domiciliary mental health nursing services	Need to improve training of GPs in treating at home older people with functional mental illness. Community psychiatric teams need to be involved more with GPs.
Southern	—	Community Psychiatric Nurse, day care in some areas	More day care; transport; development of community-based services
South Eastern	Fairly	Community Psychiatric Nurse, Out-Patient Department, GP, day hospital and day care	More support — paramedical, home helps, day hospitals, day care and closer liaison. Policy to keep people at home as long as possible
Western	Adequate	Community Psychiatric Nurse	Needs review

Source: Interviews with Programme Managers of Special Hospital Care, Consultants in the Psychiatry of Old Age, Chief Nursing Officers and Psychiatric Social Workers

Services available for the care of older people with a functional mental illness include the Community Psychiatric Nurse, day hospitals and day care. Boards with Psychiatry of Old Age services provide domiciliary assessment as does the North Western Health Board. GPs and PHNs play an important role in the care of older people at home, and the North Western Health Board's respondent noted the importance of liaison and integration between community psychiatric teams and GPs. As can be seen, however, from the above table, greater development of psychiatric services is required across all health boards in order to improve the treatment of older people. The perception of the adequacy of the services currently provided indicates the need for improvement in this area. In the Mid-Western Health Board resource barriers have been experienced and the Psychiatry of Old Age Service has been limited to Limerick city and county. The need for more day hospital and day care places was emphasised in most boards, along with closer liaison and integration of services. Deficits were also noted in regular screening and early diagnosis. The value of early assessment and diagnosis of older patients with functional mental illness has not been recognised fully in Ireland (Keogh and Roche 1996) and in many cases, functional mental illness is still seen as understandable within the context of ageing. Consultants in the Psychiatry of Old Age stress the importance of early assessment and diagnosis with functional mental illness, as with other illnesses, in order to improve both physical and mental health.

10.7.2   Accommodation
The Years Ahead repeated the recommendation in *Planning for the Future* that:

- **(R10.4) 1.7 places per thousand population aged 65 or over with functional mental illness should be provided in high support hostels in the community. In the interests of the elderly high support hostels should be kept near to the minimum size recommended in Planning for the Future (15 places).**

Three health boards provide places above the norm recommended by *The Years Ahead* (Midland, Mid-Western and North Western) and the average size of high support hostels in one of these boards (the Midland Health Board) falls way below the size recommended. This is the only health board however where hostel places are dedicated to older people with mental illness. Problems with resources were cited as reasons for not reaching norms, or for not providing dedicated places but the lack of dedicated places means that many older people with functional illness reside in welfare, geriatric and nursing homes rather than in a psychiatric setting.

10.7.3   Attitudes in health boards towards norms
In the light of the failure of most boards to meet the norms on places for older people with functional mental illness, it is interesting to note the attitudes towards these norms in each health board. Table 10.6 shows that while availability of

Table 10.5: High support hostels for older people with functional mental illness

Health Board	Hostels	Places per 1,000 older people	Average size	Future plans and comments
Eastern	Yes	Not dedicated	12	Many older people with functional mental illness in nursing homes and in geriatric services. Great pressure on acute beds. No extra capital for more hostels; 11 places identified in plans
Midland	Yes (Longford/ Westmeath)	1.8	8	14 places being made available in Laois/Offaly community care area, some for older people if required
Mid-Western	Yes (Limerick and Clare community care areas)	2.18, but not dedicated	20	Never had resources to meet norms. Future depends on how de-institutionalisation works out
North Eastern	Yes	0.56, but not dedicated	15	48 places planned to raise level to 1 per 1,000 older people
North Western	Yes	3.5, but not dedicated	15	Three hostels planned with 50 beds (not all designated for functional mental illness)
Southern	None	N/A	N/A	N/A
South Eastern	Yes	0.95, but not dedicated	14 and 28	Future hostels will be dedicated
Western	Yes	0.6	10	Plans for development of psychiatric services

Source: Interviews with Programme Managers of Special Hospital Care and Consultants in the Psychiatry of Old Age

resources is highlighted as problematic, there is also a perception that the norms are not adequate or feasible.

10.8   Dementia

10.8.1   Assessment and screening

In *The Years Ahead* dementia was categorised into three types for planning purposes. These were (i) mild dementia with no physical disease; (ii) 'severe' dementia with no significant physical disease; and (iii) mild or 'severe' dementia with significant physical illness[2]. Care of the first group usually occurs at home or in the community under the supervision of the older person's GP. Day care

---

[2] See footnote 1

Table 10.6: Attitudes in health boards towards recommended norms for high support hostels

Health board	Adequacy	Feasibility	Cater for future
Eastern	Could not comment	N/A	N/A
Midland	Yes	Did not know	Yes
Mid-Western	Never had resources	N/A	N/A
North Eastern	Yes	Yes	Will need review over time
North Western	No	Yes	More staff needed and supporting services to work well
Southern	N/A	N/A	N/A
South Eastern	Could not comment, but said psychiatrists and geriatrician doubtful	N/A	N/A
Western	Yes	Yes	Yes

Source: Interviews with Programme Managers of Special Hospital Care

places are useful, too, in providing respite for carers and stimulation for older people. For the second category, more comprehensive care is required because of the behavioural problems associated with dementia. Assessment and continuing support are required, ideally within the community or residential accommodation specifically adapted to suit the needs of the older people with dementia who may wander. The third category of dementia requires treatment after assessment in a geriatric unit.

Accordingly, the Working Party recommended the development of a model for older patients with dementia along the lines of a model used in South Belfast which provides a range of services from domiciliary assessment through day centres and day hospitals to a long-stay unit at a mental hospital. Using this facility as a model of a continuum of care, the Working Party made a number of recommendations in relation to dementia. Firstly, it was recommended that:

- **(R10.21) general practitioners and public health nurses should be encouraged to screen elderly people at risk for early signs of dementia.**

Screening is not occurring in a uniform manner across the health boards and none of the health boards' Programme Managers, Consultants in the Psychiatry of Old Age or Chief Nursing Officers in psychiatry considered current arrangements to be adequate (Table 10.7). It was emphasised that GPs and PHNs are crucial in the early detection of dementia, in its treatment and in the provision of respite for patients, families and carers. As the table shows, GPs are involved to some extent, but screening is not uniformly carried out across all the health boards. Similarly, while the majority of PHNs stated that they were involved in screening for

Table 10.7: Screening of older people at risk for early signs of dementia

Health board	Screening	Adequate	What required
Eastern	Some GPs and some PHNs	No	GPs and PHNs essential for picking up early cases. Annual screening could take place. System required; professional education for GPs and PHNs and education for public about value
Midland	No	No	Early diagnosis and cognitive tests
Mid-Western	Yes, GPs, PHNs, backed up by Psychiatry of Old Age team and psychiatric teams	No	GP and PHN education and motivation. Availability of appropriately trained staff
North Eastern	Some GPs and PHNs	No	Informal screening at the moment with referral to general psychiatric services, perception that higher rate of referral if to Psychiatry of Old Age Service
North Western	Some GPs	No	Needs to happen more formally
Southern	No	No	Early screening to avoid development of problems
South Eastern	Some GPs	No	Needs to be more formal. GPs and PHNs stretched. Need to change priorities so that they have time and can refer to consultant geriatric services
Western	GPs and PHNs	No	Need for dementia beds to follow screening

Source: Interviews with Programme Managers of Special Hospital Care, Consultants in the Psychiatry of Old Age, GPs, Superintendent PHNs, Senior PHNs and Chief Nursing Officers

dementia, the situation differed depending on the health board concerned. In the Western and Mid-Western Health Boards, for example, Mental Test Scores are used as part of annual assessments carried out on those over the age of 75. In the North Eastern Health Board, Mental Test Scores are used on all older people looking for extending care. Mental Test Scores are used to some extent in both the Eastern and Southern Health Boards, but no screening is done by PHNs in the Midland, North Western and South Eastern Health Boards. Clearly, there is a need for screening to be carried out more formally and routinely. The National Council on Ageing and Older People has recommended that screening should form part of routine assessment and ongoing care of older people and that all GPs and PHNs should be trained in screening (Keogh and Roche 1996).

The need for a continuum of services was also noted as critical, as the treatment of dementia, like any other illness, cannot stop with screening and assessment but must be supported by adequate facilities. Not only, therefore, must screening be conducted on a formal basis, but this should mark the first stepping stone in a system designed to provide a range of appropriate psychiatric treatment. As will be seen, this system is not in place and such treatment is not occurring appropriately at the moment.

10.8.2   Availability of panel to care for older people with dementia

Table 10.8 gives details of the current situation with regard to the Working Party's recommendation that:

- **(R10.22) a panel of people who are willing and available to care for elderly people with dementia be available in each district under the supervision of the senior public health nurse to help the elderly person and her or his carers.**

Two health boards currently have panels available, one in the Eastern Health Board which has a Psychiatry of Old Age Service in six of its community care areas, and the other in the North Eastern Health Board. The Midland Health Board

Table 10.8: Panels for older people with dementia under the supervision of the Public Health Nurse

Health Board	Panels	Composition	Comments
Eastern	Yes	Community ward teams; Psychiatry of Old Age teams; Home Helps	N/A
Midland	No	N/A	Many nurses and home helps available. Covered in action plan
Mid-Western	No	N/A	Lack of resources has meant policy not implemented. Home support by qualified staff, and respite facilities required. Sitting service recommended
North Eastern	Yes	Nursing panel and home care assistance panel under supervision of PHN	Under Community Care Programme
North Western	No	N/A	Resources not available to introduce this except on limited basis and nursing service needs to be integrated from hospital to home without transferring responsibility to Community Care
Southern	No	N/A	N/A
South Eastern	No	N/A	Care attendants provided under supervision of PHN in Community Care Programme. Day places and home support required
Western	No	N/A	Lack of funding

Source: Interviews with Programme Managers of Community Care, Programme Managers of Special Hospital Care, Consultants in the Psychiatry of Old Age, District Liaison Nurses, Chief Nursing Officers, Psychiatric Social Workers, carers

refers to this issue in its current Action Plan, with GPs and PHNs forming the axis through which services will be sought and delivered. This plan had not been implemented at the time of writing.

Respondents from three health boards noted a lack of resources as the obstacle to their implementation of this recommendation. *The Years Ahead* recommended that £2m be provided immediately to create panels of general nurses to nurse dependent older people at home and to employ Care Assistants to help older people with dementia. The Department of Health indicates that a total of £7.2m (an average of only £800,000 per annum) has been allocated over the period 1989-1997 for the provision of panels of Registered General Nurses and Care Assistants but it is clear that the Care Assistants are not dedicated to the care at home of older people with dementia, as was envisaged by the Working Party. The evidence from this review suggests that more resources are needed.

10.8.3   *Day care facilities for older people with dementia*
Further components of a continuum of care for older people with dementia include day hospital, day care and home support. *The Years Ahead* recommended that:

- **(R10.22) day care facilities for the elderly with dementia be provided in each district and that it should be the responsibility of the Co-ordinator of Services for the Elderly to develop such a service, directly by health boards or by agreement with voluntary bodies**.

As already noted day care is valuable, not only because it provides a stimulating environment for the patient with dementia, but also because it provides respite for carers. Its role in respite care is important but research has shown that it does not fulfil this function to any significant degree because of low levels of provision (O'Connor and Ruddle 1988; Ruddle 1994).

As the Working Party noted and as is still the case, a lack of dedicated places tends to characterise the day centre situation for older people with dementia in Ireland. There are day care places available in each health board region, but these tend not to be dedicated unless provided by voluntary organisations such as the Alzheimer Society. Dedicated places are important because other day care attendants may be disturbed by the behaviour of older people with dementia. Several health boards for this reason have plans to provide dedicated day care facilities (North Western and Western Health Boards, for example). The above table shows the significant contribution made by the voluntary sector in the provision of day care places (Curry 1993). Feedback from Consultants in the Psychiatry of Old Age suggests that the contribution of day care centres is most notable in the social gain to both older people and their carers; an important objective of *Shaping a Healthier Future*. Day care centres provide rehabilitation facilities in a primary care setting, and in many cases come under the Community Care Programme. Voluntary

Table 10.9: Day care places for older people with dementia

Health board	Places	Availability	Voluntary involvement	Contribution	Comments
Eastern	Some	Not in every community care area	Significant	Respite, stimulation	Need one centre in each district in each area
Midland	Some	—	In 7 centres	Respite, socialisation	Community Care takes responsibility, liaison between Community Psychiatric Nurse and Community Care
Mid-Western	Approx 26 places	Adare and Limerick	Alzheimer Society has dedicated day centre. Religious orders also provide day care - 2 days dedicated	Respite, stimulation, keeps people longer at home	Day care not full-time dedicated to dementia
North Eastern	Not dedicated	Each community care area	Alzheimer Society	Respite	Target to provide 40 places per 100,000 for older people with mental illness
North Western	Not dedicated	Most community care areas	In many	Social support	Two projects at different stages of planning and will provide dedicated places
Southern	10 places for one day a week	One centre	Alzheimer Society	Respite	More planned, but funding is an issue
South Eastern	6-8 places, 3-day facility	Very few	Alzheimer Society and others	Secure place during day, family respite. Difficulties in day care with disturbances from dementia patients	Plans to establish in Dungarvan and Kilkenny
Western	50, but not dedicated	Some	Significant involvement	Fewer hospital admissions and shorter hospital stay Social gain	Dedicated day care facilities planned in Galway, Castlebar and Castlerea

Source: Interviews with Programme Managers of Community Care, Programme Managers of Special Hospital Care, Consultants in the Psychiatry of Old Age, CSEs, District Liaison Nurses, Chief Nursing Officers and carers

organisations play a significant role in this provision and are aided in the main by Section 65 grants from their respective health boards.

10.8.4   Day hospitals for older people with dementia
The Working Party recommended that:

- **(R10.23) health boards develop day hospitals for the elderly with dementia in the main urban centres, under the direction of psychiatrists with an interest in this field. A norm of two day hospital places per 1,000 elderly people should be used for planning purposes.**

Table 10.10: Day hospital places for confused older people

Health Board	Day hospital places	Responsibility	Contribution	Plans and comments
Eastern	Three day hospitals with provision for treating 100 people per week	Psychiatry of Old Age	Full range of treatment equivalent to hospital	N/A
Midland	None	—	—	Dedicated day hospital places proposed in Action Plan
Mid-Western	None	Psychiatry of Old Age	Maintains contact with home environment	Day hospital providing 10 places closed earlier this year
North Eastern	None dedicated	Community Care Programme	Tackle needs of older people without disadvantage of institutionalisation	Plans for future
North Western	None dedicated	Community Care (community hospitals)	Physical care and therapy	Two projects in progress
Southern	None	—	—	Long-stay unit (30 beds) available, but no day hospital
South Eastern	None	—	—	Problem with funding. Care of Elderly report will propose day hospitals for older people with mental illness
Western	None	—	—	50 places planned in short term (day care and day hospital)

Source: Interviews with Programme Managers of Special Hospital Care, Consultants in the Psychiatry of Old Age, Chief Nursing Officers and carers

The only health board with a dedicated day hospital service is the Eastern, where Psychiatry of Old Age services take responsibility (Table 10.10). In the Mid-Western Health Board, a day hospital providing ten places for older people with mental illness was closed during 1996. While this was only a limited resource, operating for two or three days per week, its important contribution was noted by the board's Programme Manager for Special Hospital Care. As in the Eastern Health Board the day hospital was split between dementia and functional mental illness, with different days dedicated to older people with these illnesses.

Three boards currently have plans for day hospitals for people with dementia (Midland, North Eastern and Western Health Boards). The latter, like the North Western, has plans for a mixture of day care and day hospital provision. It has been noted that the distinction between day care and day hospitals may be blurred especially when both services are provided from the same facility (Keogh and Roche 1996). According to the Consultants in the Psychiatry of Old Age, the accommodation of people with dementia is a poorly understood area. It was stressed that both dedicated day hospital and day centre places are required for dementia patients and that day care centres can back up and support day hospitals. However, a clear distinction between the different kinds of functions and treatment that each provides is necessary.

10.8.5   Accommodation
In addition to day care and day hospital places, the Working Party recommended:

- **(R10.24) a norm of six beds per 1,000 elderly for welfare accommodation and three beds per 1,000 elderly for high support hostels for planning purposes to ensure sufficient accommodation for the elderly with dementia**.

Appropriate accommodation for patients with dementia is a significant issue as they require nursing care and a secure environment where they may wander in safety (Department of Health 1984, 1995c) Both welfare and hostel accommodation are unsuitable, the former because it is not well equipped to provide high levels of medical or psychiatric care, and the latter because hostels can be problematic for those with mobility impairments. Most boards have not developed these options, providing care in hospitals or dementia units instead. For example, in the North Western Health Board, three places per 1,000 older people are dedicated in long-stay wards for older people with dementia rather than in high support hostels or in welfare accommodation. There is a need, however, for the provision of dedicated places, which most boards, as the above table makes clear, have not addressed.

The Department of Health indicated that the average annual capital allocation for welfare and high support hostel accommodation since 1988 has been very low and no exact figure could be provided. *The Years Ahead*, by contrast, had

Table 10.11: Welfare and high support hostel accommodation forolder people with dementia

Health Board	Welfare places (6 per 1,000 older people recommended)	High support hostel places (3 per 1,000 older people recommended)	Comments
Eastern	None	None	185 beds provided in units and hospitals as hostels not considered suitable for older people with dementia and associated behavioural problems
Midland	Not categorised this way	None	Not considered appropriate
Mid-Western	Would not support welfare for dementia sufferers	80 high support places in 1994; 2.18 per 1,000 older people but not dedicated	Belief that dementia patients should be relocated, as welfare accommodation is not suitable. Tried to get local authority involved, but difficult. Assessment and rehabilitation unit patients with dementia also available in elderly mentally ill unit in St Camillus Hospital
North Eastern	None	None	Belief that welfare unsuitable. Elderly mentally ill units being developed for older people with dementia and associated behavioural problems, for example, elderly mentally ill ward in Castleblayney. In Cavan former welfare home now an elderly mentally ill unit with 40 dedicated places
North Western	None dedicated	None	Considers norm adequate, feasible and catering for future
Southern	One per 1,000 elderly people	None	Doubled number of welfare beds in last three years; 60 beds available in hospitals (St Stephen's and voluntary)
South Eastern	None	None	Resource difficulties. Proposal to develop EMI units under General Hospital programme. Alzheimer Society also involved
Western	One per 1,000 elderly people	None	Places in long-stay geriatric services, norms considered adequate, feasible and catering for future

Source: Interviews with Programme Managers of Special Hospital Care

recommended:

- **(R12.15) as a priority £1.2m be made available each year over the next 20 years to provide welfare and high support hostel accommodation for the elderly with dementia.**

The Department of Health indicates that only £2m was spent on the development of this type of accomodation over the period 1989-1997, an average of only

(£222,000 per annum). Clearly the recommendation has not been implemented, but the accommodation needs of older people with dementia still need to be addressed. Nursing and geriatric homes can be suitable for older people with dementia as they provide safe environments, although older people who also have severe intractable behavioural problems require care in a psychiatric setting. Rather than the type of accommodation recommended in *The Years Ahead*, therefore, the norm of six per 1,000 older people would be better provided in a non-psychiatric nursing environment and the funding recommended used accordingly. This would then start to address the recommendation made by the Working Party that:

- **(R10.25) health boards provide residential accommodation adapted to the needs of the elderly with dementia as a matter of urgency.**

As already stated, most health boards provide places in hospitals or dementia units, but the need for dedicated long-stay places must be addressed (Keogh and Roche 1996).

10.8.6   Responsibility for accommodating older dementia patients
As has already been shown above, there are only four Consultants in the Psychiatry of Old Age in the country and only one other board (North Western Health Board) has a psychiatrist with some training in the Psychiatry of Old Age. Older patients with dementia and associated behavioural problems (referred to as 'severe dementia' by the Working Party) are usually seen by the general psychiatric services. Across the health boards, as Table 10.12 details, there are different arrangements in place with regard to older patients with dementia. In general, older people with dementia and associated behavioural problems are seen by the psychiatric services, while those without behavioural problems are the responsibility of the geriatric services. In some boards, however, the district teams for the elderly take responsibility for these patients, by seeking psychiatric advice or by including psychiatric personnel on their team.

10.9   Summary and conclusions
As already discussed early informal links tend to characterise liaison between the psychiatric and old age medicine services. This informality and division of responsibilities also occurs in relation to residential accommodation. *The Years Ahead* had recommended that a consultant psychiatrist with special responsibility for older people should take responsibility for high support hostels. Each community care area does not have such a consultant, so even if high support hostels were considered appropriate there would be further difficulties with where responsibility lies, with staffing levels and with the provision of a range of different kinds of accommodation for those with different problems associated with dementia.

Table 10.12: Responsibility for high support hostels and ensuring multi-disciplinary approach to care of older people with dementia

Health board	Responsible for high support hostels for older people with dementia	Responsible for ensuring multi-disciplinary approach to care of older people with dementia
Eastern	N/A	Psychiatric services and geriatric services liaise together
Midland	N/A	Psychiatric services see patients with dementia and behavioural problems and functional mental illness. Geriatric services see patients with dementia
Mid-Western	Psychiatric services	Psychiatry of Old Age in Limerick. Elsewhere psychiatric and/or geriatric services
North Eastern	N/A	Psychiatric services and geriatric services
North Western	N/A	CSE takes responsibility and psychiatric team aids in assessment
Southern	N/A	Ambiguous lines of responsibility between psychiatric and geriatric services
South Eastern	N/A	Psychiatric and geriatric services
Western	N/A	District team for elderly with advice for psychiatrist services

Source: Interviews with Programme Managers of Special Hospital Care and Consultants in the Psychiatry of Old Age

Psychiatry of Old Age services are poorly developed in Ireland with only four Consultants in the Psychiatry of Old Age currently in post. Furthermore, the Psychiatry of Old Age service in the Mid-Western Health Board is limited and was further reduced during the course of 1996 with the closure of a day hospital. More resources and greater commitment are needed to develop Psychiatry of Old Age services. Although training is available, consultant posts have been slow to develop. A planning norm of one consultant per 10,000 people aged over 65 was recently recommended (Keogh and Roche 1996), and is endorsed here. This would address the current geographical inequity which prevails with Psychiatry of Old Age services only available in certain parts of the country. Such services need to be developed to the same level in all health boards and each consultant should be provided with a multi-disciplinary team and facilities such as day hospitals, and acute and long-stay beds.

Early screening and assessment for mental disorders in old age are essential and need to be improved. Some screening for dementia is currently undertaken but needs to be standardised and consistently applied to all older people. Domiciliary assessment is currently provided in only six community care areas in the Eastern Health Board, and in one community care area in the Mid-Western Health Board.

Table 10.13: Summary of services for older people who are mentally ill

Recommendations	Current situation
Psychiatrists in each community care area with responsibility for older people with severe dementia	Psychiatry of Old Age in two boards. Recent appointment of a consultant with some training in Psychiatry of Old Age in one board. General psychiatry deals with dementia patients in most boards, but outside of Psychiatry of Old Age services expertise is poor.
Psychiatry of Old Age services to be developed in Dublin and Cork	Developed in Dublin and Limerick
1.7 places per 1,000 older people with functional mental illness in high support hostels	Provided (and above norm in three health boards) but not dedicated
Screening of older people at risk for early signs of dementia	Inadequate; some GPs and PHNs involved; not uniform across all boards
Panels for care of older people with dementia available in each district	Available in two boards
Day care facilities for older people with dementia in each district	Places in all boards, mostly inadequate provision and not dedicated
Two day hospital places per 1,000 older people in urban areas	In one board only
Six places per 1,000 older people in welfare accommodation for older dementia patients	None dedicated and very few provided as such accommodation is now deemed inappropriate for those with dementia
Three places per 1,000 older people in high support hostels for older dementia patients	None dedicated and very few provided as such accommodation is now deemed inappropriate for those with dementia

This needs to be expanded as it contributes to appropriate diagnosis and treatment, and helps reduce strain on both patients and their families. Recent recommendations made in relation to the training of all care professionals in the screening and assessment of mental health problems, therefore, are endorsed (Keogh and Roche 1996).

Liaison (between the geriatric and psychiatric services) was shown to be mostly informal. In the absence of a national Psychiatry of Old Age service, it is essential that this liaison is formalised to ensure better delivery of psychiatric services for older people. Dedicated day hospital and day care places are required for the treatment of older people with dementia and functional mental illness. Again, a Psychiatry of Old Age service, with day hospitals provided as part of the service, would ensure that this would occur. Chief Nursing Officers in psychiatry in both the South Eastern and North Eastern Health Boards also suggested the provision of night care places which would be useful for older people who wander at night causing extra stress for their carers. Again, recent recommendations in relation to respite for carers, including 24-hour, seven days-a-week community services, day hospital provision, flexible respite care and day sitting services are endorsed (Keogh and Roche 1996).

The recommended norms in relation to high support hostels for older people with functional mental illness have not been met by most health boards. The majority of older people with functional mental illness requiring residential care are accommodated in welfare, geriatric and nursing homes. For those with intractable conditions requiring close psychiatric supervision in a psychiatric setting, the dedication of places in high support hostels is needed. The recommendations made recently regarding increasing the supply and ensuring the quality of hostel accommodation of older people with a mental illness are supported here (Keogh and Roche 1996).

For older people with dementia, the norms laid down in *The Years Ahead* have not been met in either welfare or high support hostel accommodation. Thinking has changed in this area since 1988, and such accommodation is now considered unsuitable and inappropriate for those with dementia (Keogh and Roche 1996). Safe, secure accommodation, staffed at appropriate levels, is needed for dementia patients and the norms recommended in *The Years Ahead* could be re-designated as follows. For older people with dementia, but no associated behavioural problems, six dedicated places per 1,000 older people could be provided in a non-psychiatric nursing environment such as a nursing or geriatric home rather than in welfare accommodation. For older people with dementia and associated behavioural problems (referred to as 'severe dementia' in *The Years Ahead*), three places per 1,000 older people could be provided in a long-stay psychiatric unit or ward, rather than high support hostels. The £1.2m recommended annually up to the year 2008 by the Working Party has not been allocated, to any great degree, and there is a clear need to address this underfunding. If these resources were put into alternative suitable accommodation, this would help ensure that some of the needs of older people with dementia were met.

A continuum of care for older people is needed, but as this chapter has made clear, questions must be raised about service provision, particularly for older people with dementia. Each stage in the continuum is important, and there is a very real need for dedicated places for older people who are mentally ill in a range of accommodation.

Finally, social workers for older people can help in arranging for the provision of care at home, particularly for dementia sufferers and their carers. The emphasis placed on child care by the health boards has had repercussions for the care of older people. The inclusion of Psychiatric Social Workers on domiciliary assessment teams and on teams for the elderly would be beneficial, and one Consultant in the Psychiatry of Old Age, in recognition of this, is currently recruiting social workers in the Eastern Health Board.

CHAPTER ELEVEN

Partnership

11.1   Introduction

Partnership has been defined as a contract between people engaged in a common purpose or business. It assumes agreed objectives, joint planning and decision-making, frequent consultation and discussion, shared evaluation and agreement about the progress and continuation of any joint venture (Brenton 1985). Partnership is about much more than funding, it is concerned with styles of interaction and the sharing of power and responsibility. O'Sullivan (1994), in his review of the voluntary-statutory relationship in the health services in Ireland, identified three major components of such partnership. These were the clarification of objectives, tasks and roles, raising such issues as core services, contracting, funding and monitoring, the development of structures and systems to enable the voluntary and statutory sectors to work together and the planned development of voluntary services and the support of such development by statutory agencies.

In this chapter the focus is on partnership between statutory bodies, in particular health boards, and voluntary organisations engaged in the provision of services for older people and carers of older people in the home. Much of the material used in this chapter is derived from published studies of voluntary organisations or carers of older people, and from small-scale studies of voluntary organisations and carers undertaken in the course of this project; the latter were intended to supplement the available published material.

The sources of data for this chapter include a number of substantial recently published studies, extracts from interviews with Co-ordinators of Services for the Elderly and two small surveys of voluntary organisations and carers. A small random sample postal survey of voluntary organisations, focusing on their relationships with statutory authorities, was also undertaken. The sampling frame used consisted of lists of voluntary organisations supplied by the National Council for the Elderly and the health boards. Attention was focused on voluntary organisations engaged directly in the provision of services for older people, especially day care centres and Meals-on-Wheels. The following types of service providers and organisations were included in the sample: voluntary day centres, clubs/day centres organised by volunteers on a parish basis, Meals-on-Wheels organisations, voluntary transport, the Alzheimer Society, Society of St. Vincent de Paul, Friends of the Elderly, Alone, the Simon Community and the Salvation Army.

Initially 40 questionnaires were sent out and with the assistance of telephone reminders 25 replies were received. An additional 30 questionnaires were dispatched and this resulted in increasing the total number of replies to 34, and an overall response rate of 49 per cent. Though the sample size was small, it was intended that the distribution of the responses by health board area would be proportionate to the overall distribution of voluntary organisations. The Eastern Health Board area is over-represented with 13 responses while the Southern and Mid-Western Health Boards are under-represented, with two and one respectively, because of variations in the response rate. There were four responses from each of the Midland, North Eastern, South Eastern and Western Health Boards and two from the North Western Health Board.

Most of the respondent organisations are young. Fifteen were established since 1980, while 12 date from the 1970s. Their size, in terms of numbers of volunteer members, varies considerably: 15 have less than 20 members, 11 have between 20 and 99 members while only 5 have 100 or more members. As can be seen in Table 11.1 social and recreational activities, Meals-on-Wheels and day care centres were provided by a substantial proportion of the organisations. Twenty six organisations provided day care centres or Meals-on-Wheels or both; 12 provided both, eight provided Meals-on-Wheels only and six provided day care centres only.

A small random survey of carers was also undertaken. The carers were selected from lists provided by the Carers Association, and in the Eastern Health Board region, from information provided by other informed sources. Some of the carers were interviewed, others completed questionnaires. The biggest response was

Table 11.1: Services provided by voluntary organisations

Services provided	Number of organisations providing	Services provided	Number of organisations providing
Meals-on-Wheels	59%	Housing	18%
Day Centre	53%	Physiotherapy	18%
Transport	47%	Chiropody	44%
Home Help	18%	Social/recreation	79%

Source: Survey of voluntary organisations

from the Eastern Health Board region with eight responses followed by the Western Health Board with four responses. There was just one response from both the Midland and Western Health Boards.

11.2   Partnership in *The Years Ahead* report

The Years Ahead identified three partners in the care of dependent older people: families, members of voluntary agencies, and professionals working for statutory agencies.   It was pointed out that in terms of the numbers of older people receiving care, families made by far the greatest contribution but received little formal recognition and insufficient support from statutory agencies.   While voluntary organisations were perceived to make a very substantial contribution to the welfare of older people, especially those living alone, their relationship with health boards and local authorities was considered to be an uneasy one.   A comprehensive service for older people was seen to be dependent on each of these three partners playing their part and complementing the work of the others.

In regard to partnership between voluntary organisations and statutory agencies, *The Years Ahead* report hoped that health boards and local authorities would encourage by 'all possible means the involvement of voluntary organisations in caring for the elderly'.   In practical terms this would involve steps such as agreements on respective responsibilities in the delivery of services, the development of a mechanism to co-ordinate voluntary activity in each community care area and the establishment of a fund for the development of voluntary organisations.   At Government level, *The Years Ahead* report advocated a formal review of the relationship between the statutory and voluntary sectors with a view to establishing national guidelines for the development of a constructive relationship between the two sectors.

In regard to carers many of the recommendations made in other chapters of *The Years Ahead* report were designed to assist family carers.   Further recommendations included the right of carers to claim social assistance; the provision of relevant information and advice to carers; the encouragement of the formation of support groups for carers. The contribution that carers and voluntary bodies can make to the care of older people was restated in *Shaping a Healthier Future* where a key objective was 'to encourage and support the care of older people in their own community by family, neighbours, and voluntary bodies in every way possible' (Department of Health 1994b p. 67).

11.3   Voluntary-statutory partnership

It was recommended in *The Years Ahead* that:

- **(R11.17) health boards and local authorities should encourage by all possible means the involvement of voluntary organisations in caring for the elderly. Each board and local authority should agree with the**

voluntary organisations working with the elderly in their functional areas their respective responsibilities in the delivery of services ...this agreement (should) **be formalised as a contract between the voluntary organisation and the board or local authority for a period of 2 or 3 years.**

These recommendations refer to such matters as mechanisms for funding and consultation and engagement in policy making in the context of a voluntary-statutory partnership ethos.

11.3.1   Funding

The Years Ahead argued that funding arrangements for voluntary organisations should permit them to plan their services on a multi-annual basis. Faughnan and Kelleher (1993), in a study of 46 voluntary and community organisations (including a further 11 national umbrella organisations to which some of the 46 were attached) in the Eastern Health Board area, reported that the discretionary and *ad hoc* nature of the funding of voluntary organisations by statutory bodies created extreme difficulties for voluntary organisations, and militated against forward planning and good management practice. Faughnan and Kelleher observed 'There appeared to be no pattern or coherence to the health board's funding arrangements. Historical precedent, good access to key decision-makers, political expedience, and a measure of luck, appeared to provide the foundation on which the funding arrangements between individual organisations and health boards were initially established and subsequently maintained.' (pp. 19-20). Lundstrom and McKeown (1994) reported unexplained alterations and delays in the funding of the home help service and the necessity for Home Help Organisers in some cases to negotiate loans to keep the service viable.

Just under half (16 of 34) of the respondents to the voluntary organisation survey of the current review indicated that agreements had been made between their organisation and the health board in respect of the provision of services for older people. However, this could misrepresent the true position as half of those (10 of 18) reporting no such agreement would appear to have had at least an implicit agreement, insofar as they were in receipt of funding and/or material assistance from a health board.

11.3.2   Contractual arrangements

Faughnan and Kelleher (1993) reported that some voluntary organisations have serious reservations about contractual arrangements. Only 15 per cent of the organisations unequivocally stated that they would favour formalised or contractual relationships with state agencies, while nine per cent expressed total opposition to them. Forty-one per cent expressed major reservations with regard to the feasibility and desirability of introducing formal funding arrangements.

Their reservations centred around three themes. First, respondents were apprehensive about the capacity of state agencies to develop formalised funding arrangements which were compatible with the needs of their organisation and into which they could have an input. Experience of formalised funding arrangements were a source of concern for some organisations and there was considerable uncertainty regarding the State's commitment to a broad definition of contracting. Second, respondents who envisaged distinct advantages arising from the introduction of formalised funding arrangements feared the impact which such arrangements could have on the ethos and orientation of the organisation. In particular it was felt that contracts could limit severely the autonomy, dynamism and innovative thrust of the organisation. Third, organisations envisaged that the introduction of contracting would ultimately lead to tendering and to competition between organisations.

11.3.3   Consultative mechanisms

Few consultative mechanisms, within a context of transparent policy driven strategies, are available for voluntary organisations. Faughnan and Kelleher (1993) found that access to statutory agencies by such bodies was personalised and individualised, and even at the level of umbrella bodies formal consultative mechanisms were rare. Mulvihill (1993), in a study of nearly 900 voluntary organisations providing services for older people, reported that voluntary organisations had a limited involvement in policy and planning. Only eleven per cent of the organisations studied were involved with a statutory body in planning services for older people, 30 per cent had an input into interest groups who worked for older people and 14 per cent had a say in planning services for older people through other channels. Nonetheless, most voluntary organisations reported that their ongoing administration received adequate support from statutory bodies. Over two fifths were satisfied with their level of input in determining the amount of funding they received, and one fifth reported that assistance other than funding was received from statutory agencies. Just under a fifth reported that health boards had decision-making power in the running of their organisation and most of the voluntary organisations considered that this contribution from health boards was valuable for the running of their organisations (Mulvihill 1993). Lundstrom and McKeown (1994) concluded that partnership between the voluntary and statutory sectors was weak first because there were no written contracts between health boards and voluntary organisations for the delivery of services and second because arrangements were 'highly informal', and no mechanisms existed for the clarification and recognition of roles.

11.3.4   Advisory committees

Membership of advisory committees on the elderly was recommended in *The Years Ahead* as one of the ways whereby voluntary organisations could enter into a dialogue with health boards. However, as shown in Chapter Three of this report, only the North Eastern and Western Health Boards have established advisory committees. Most (23 of 34) respondents to the voluntary organisation survey did not know whether their health board had an advisory committee on the elderly. Three of them were represented on their health board's advisory committee on the elderly, and one knew of another voluntary organisation which was represented.

11.3.5   District teams for the elderly

Representation of voluntary organisations on district teams for the elderly was envisaged in *The Years Ahead* as another way in which voluntary organisations could engage in a dialogue with the health board. It was recommended in *The Years Ahead* that:

- **(R11.17) the district team for the elderly should be consulted in the preparation of a contract for services in its area**.

Chapter Three of this report shows that services for older people are organised in districts in the Mid-Western, North Eastern, North Western and Southern Health Boards only. In others they are organised on a community care area or county basis. Only five respondents to the voluntary organisation survey indicated that they were represented on a district team for the elderly.

11.3.6   Co-ordination mechanisms

It was recommended in *The Years Ahead* that:

- **(R11.18) the Co-ordinator of Services for the Elderly develop a mechanism to co-ordinate voluntary activity in each community care area**.

Table 11.2: Mechanisms developed to ensure co-ordination of voluntary effort

Health board	Mechanisms
Eastern	Voluntary organisations; representatives on Area 7 team; annual meeting in other area
Midland	Regular meetings between board's officers and voluntary organisations
Mid-Western	No formal mechanism
North Eastern	No formal mechanism; has been left to PHN service
North Western	Regular meetings between board's officers and voluntary organisations; district co-ordinators meet regularly with voluntary organisations
Southern	Community worker(s) liaise(s) with them
South Eastern	Voluntary organisations are represented on district teams
Western	CSE co-operates with social services and voluntary groups

Source: Interviews with CSEs

The mechanisms employed to ensure co-ordination of voluntary effort are shown in Table 11.2.

It was reported in the Mid-Western and North Eastern Health Boards that no formal mechanisms for co-ordinating voluntary effort were in place, though in the latter this role was undertaken to some extent by PHNs. In the Southern and Western Health Boards this function was exercised by community workers and the CSE respectively. In the Midland and North Western Health Boards co-ordination is addressed through meetings between the board's officers and voluntary organisations. In the South Eastern Health Board voluntary organisations are represented on district teams, and in the Eastern Health Board on two Area Care Teams.

Most (25 of 34) respondents to the voluntary organisation survey indicated that a health board liaised with their organisation on a regular basis. In 14 of these cases a particular member of the health board was thought to be responsible for this. Eleven of these identified the function of the person who liaised with them. Five identified the person as a provider of information, adviser or a co-ordinator of services; four described the person as a community care manager, administrative officer or area manager; one referred to the person as the project adviser while in one case the liaison was effected by community psychiatric care.

11.3.7   Development funds
It was recommended in *The Years Ahead* that:

- **(R11.18) each health board should establish a fund for the development of voluntary organisations**.

While it is not clear from *The Years Ahead* what precise purposes such funds were intended to serve, it would appear unlikely that they were intended to fund the delivery of services only. Most health boards seem to provide funds for ongoing service delivery rather than development work. CSEs in six health boards (Eastern, Mid-Western, North Eastern, Southern, South Eastern and Western) reported that such funds were operating. However, four of these referred to them explicitly in the context of Section 65 funding. Section 65 of the *1953 Health Act* empowered health authorities, the predecessors of health boards, to give financial and other forms of aid to a voluntary body providing a service similar or ancillary to a service which they themselves might provide.

Most (21 of 34) respondents to the voluntary organisation survey indicated that their organisation had not benefited from such a fund. Where funding was received, it seems as though most of the funded activities would be eligible for Section 65 funding. Six of the 12 respondents receiving funds indicated that grants had been received for Meals-on-Wheels or social/recreational activities. In two cases grants had been received for running day centres and in three cases they had been received for equipment/refurbishing. Only one respondent indicated a purpose which would appear consistent with organisational development rather than service development (participation in seminars organised by their health board).

11.3.8   Quality of relationships between voluntary organisations and statutory bodies

Faughnan and Kelleher (1993) reported that the working relationships between state agencies and voluntary organisations were perceived by over 60 per cent of the voluntary organisations studied by them as good or fairly good. In particular, a good understanding between voluntary organisational personnel and the officials with whom these organisations had day-to-day contact was reported. Mulvihill (1993) as indicated above, reported that most, or at least substantial minorities, of voluntary organisations providing services for older people were satisfied with aspects of their arrangements with statutory bodies. Most (22 of 34) respondents to the voluntary organisation survey also indicated that their relationship to the health board was good, while seven assessed it as fair. Of those, 14 referred to the quality of the relationship, in many cases with considerable enthusiasm, commenting that the health boards' staff were pleasant, helpful, fair, approachable, accessible, co-operative, supportive, and generally good.

Respondents to the voluntary organisation survey were also asked to indicate what they liked least about the way the health board related to them. Two organisations referred to communication problems indicating that no contact person with specific responsibility was available. Individual organisations referred to an insufficiency of social workers, procrastination, inability of the health board to make a commitment in advance of grants, the inadequacy of the contribution to Meals-on-Wheels, and the prohibition on people working as home helps for relatives. Two organisations that had assessed the relationship with the health board as bad suggested that the latter had no interest in the organisation and that the health board was not available.

11.3.9   Review of statutory-voluntary relationship
It was recommended in *The Years Ahead* that:

- **(R11.19) the Government undertake a formal review of the relationship of the statutory and voluntary sectors with a view to establishing national guidelines for the development of a more constructive relationship between the two sectors**.

The *Programme for Economic and Social Progress* contained a Government commitment to prepare a White Paper on Voluntary Activity. In May 1992 the Government approved the establishment of an Inter-Departmental Task Force and the setting up of an expert group in the voluntary sector to act as a resource to the task force (O'Sullivan 1994). The Minister for Social Welfare has given approval for the publication of a Green Paper on the role of the voluntary and community sector and its relationship with the statutory sector. The Green Paper will cover such issues as the principles underlying the relationship between the State and the voluntary sector; methods and sources of funding for national representative structures for the voluntary sector; criteria for funding by statutory agencies; issues relating to charitable status and taxation issues; effective consultative mechanisms already operating nationally and at EU level; and models of statutory/voluntary sector co-operation (Minister for Social Welfare 1996).

11.4   Partnership with carers

O'Connor *et al.* (1988a) estimated that about 66,300 older people living outside institutions in Ireland were at least partially dependent and received some level of family care. About 36 per cent of these were described as requiring a high level of care.

11.4.1   The stress of caring

There is much evidence in the literature that caring for dependent older people can be stressful and isolating. Strains reported by O'Connor and Ruddle (1988) included restrictions on leisure and social activities (59 per cent), adverse effects on relationships with children (23 per cent), strains arising with spouses (16 per cent) and family problems in general (24 per cent). Blackwell *et al.* (1992) observed that the findings reported by O'Connor and Ruddle (1988) indicated less carer strain than other studies, or a greater reluctance for the carers interviewed to report such strain. Stephens and Christianson (1985) found that 37 per cent of their sample reported a 'good deal' of emotional strain and 26 per cent reported a 'good deal' of physical strain. Blackwell *et al.* (1992) reported that 29.5 per cent of their sample of carers were at risk for psychiatric illness. The authors observed that this was well above the national average (16.2 per cent) considered to be at risk for psychiatric illness found by Whelan, Hannan and Creighton (1991) in a nationally representative sample. Moreover, whereas it is recognised that the people who are cared for can be abused, it should also be noted that carers can be subjected to physical or psychological abuse by those being cared for.

11.4.2   Services for supporting (cared for) older people in their homes

It was recommended in *The Years Ahead* that there should be an obligation on health boards to provide services to support dependent older people and their carers in the home. One factor contributing to the stress of caring is that care in the community is provided almost exclusively by the principal care giver. The use of statutory and voluntary services by cared-for older people is almost completely confined to GPs and PHNs. O'Connor and Ruddle (1988) found that while 80 per cent and 47 per cent respectively of dependent older people being cared for at home had availed of the services of their GP or PHN during the six months prior to interview, only small proportions had received any paramedical services, and domiciliary services such as the home help service or Meals-on-Wheels had been received by about three per cent of them. Blackwell *et al.* (1992) confirmed these findings.

Finucane *et al.* (1994), in their study of support services for carers of older people, found that the homecare services provided by statutory bodies of most relevance to carers were discretionary. In addition community-based and hospital-based services of greatest relevance to carers were overstretched. Home visits were rarely available and other services such as a sitting service and the provision of respite and hospital beds specifically for older people were found to be inadequate, as were the options for older people upon discharge from hospital. Most services required referral, and waiting lists of up to one year were sometimes found for essential services. Priorities for services were overwhelmingly medical and where a carer was taken into account, it was often only to reduce or withdraw the service if a carer was present.

Finucane *et al.* (1994) also found that GPs and PHNs were the main sources of medical support, information and advice. These services were found to be overstretched. PHNs in particular were limited by their case load and night, weekend and twilight nursing services were of limited availability. The home help service was found to be available on a very limited basis only and the absence of a carer and the poor health of the older person constituted conditions of eligibility. In general this service was seen as a substitute rather than complementary. Criteria of age and income in determining eligibility for the service were seen to exclude many who could benefit from it. It was also found that the provision of the meals service varied considerably. Again the older person's incapacity and the presence of a carer were taken into account when deciding its provision. Day centres, so vital to maintaining older people in the community, had been affected by financial cut-backs, and in rural areas by the unavailability of transport. Some had closed down while the services provided by others were being reduced. It was concluded that the transport provided by health boards did not meet existing needs and that this limited the efficiency of health board services.

11.4.3   Most important services for carers in their caring role
Nearly all (21 of 22) respondents to the carer's survey identified 'the most important services in caring for an older person at home'. Seven identified one service only and 14 identified more than one. The numbers citing each service are shown in Table 11.3. The services identified as most important by at least three carers in each case included: PHNs, Home Helps, respite care, advice/information and back-up (unspecified).

Table 11.3: Services identified by carers as most important in caring for an older person at home

Services	Number	Services	Number
Public Health Nurse	6	Contact/ companionship	2
Home Help	5	Doctor	1
Respite	4	Nursing care (regular)	1
Advice/information	3	Care Assistant	1
Back-up (unspecified)	3	Hospital	1
Family support	2	Day centre	1
Equipment	2	Irish Wheelchair Association	1
Training	2	Transport	1
Comfortable home	2	Relatives/friends/neighbours	1

Source: Carers' survey

Blackwell *et al.* (1995) reported that carers' priorities for support services, in terms of the percentage who agreed that more of the service would be helpful, were ordered as follows: direct payment, advice on health services or social welfare, day centres, short-term relief care away from home, more PHN support, support group for carers, chiropody, physiotherapy, alterations to home, GP support. They did however enter the *caveat* that it was not clear that carers were well informed about the potential range of statutory services available and the contribution which some services could make to their lives.

11.4.4   Services designed for the carer
Finucane *et al.* (1994) found there was very little provision of support services oriented directly to carers and catering specifically for their needs. Such services include information and advice, training, support groups, sitting services, relief and respite care.   Most of these services are provided by voluntary bodies, sometimes with funding from statutory bodies. Moreover, they found that carers had limited opportunity, if any, to influence any of the services available to them. They noted that the most notable feature of the planning and provision of community services was that carers were not a priority except in the public health nursing service. They also emphasised the importance of carer satisfaction and the desirability of including the carer in the planning of services.

11.4.5   Carer's Allowance
In *The Years Ahead* it was recommended that:

- **(R11.5) carers be entitled to claim social assistance in their own right and that such entitlement should replace the Prescribed Relatives allowance.**

In 1990 the Carers' Allowance was introduced for long-term full-time carers of very dependent older people. This allowance, classified as income support by the Department of Social Welfare, is strictly means tested. The maximum payment for a single person was £67.50 per week from June 1997 onwards. In 1997, 8,748 persons were in receipt of the allowance, which is only one quarter of the number of full-time carers. In addition, roughly one third of those receiving the allowance do not receive the full payment because of the means test. While this allowance is strictly means tested the means test is more favourable than for other categories of assistance. For example, the first £150.00 per week of a carer's spouse is disregarded in the assessment. Many carers find the allowance unsatisfactory and the means testing is especially resented.

Blackwell *et al.* (1995) noted that there were marked restrictions on the receipt of the Carers' Allowance and they proposed that there were grounds in equity for the relaxation of the restrictions as those who make sacrifices to care for older people are financially worse off than those who choose not to make such a commitment. Furthermore, they observed that a direct payment for caring would relieve financial strain and also confer status on carers as a valuable resource in the care of older people. Blackwell *et al.* (1995) also reported that the support most frequently sought by carers was direct payment for services. More than three quarters of carers agreed that direct payment would help their situation a considerably higher proportion preferred this to any other kind of support.

11.4.6   Information and advice
It was recommended in *The Years Ahead* that:

- **(R11.6) the Co-ordinator of Services for the Elderly should ensure that in each community care area, information and advice is available to carers on the ageing process, the medical aspects of caring, financial entitlements and services available locally**.

In Chapter Four of this report it was concluded that current health education services for carers, where available, are in general unstructured, uneven, uncoordinated, and opportunistic. Consistent with this, 12 of 22 respondents to the carers' survey reported that they had received no advice or information on any of the following issues: coping with problems of disability, coping with chronic illness, managing terminal care, coping with the death of the older person, coping with dementia or other medical disorders and the emotional and psychological effects on the older person of loss of function. Ten reported receiving advice on at least one issue. Most (15 of 22) respondents to the carers' survey indicated that they had received advice on at least one of the practical aspects of caring such as footcare, management of incontinence, dressing/undressing, lifting, toileting and bathing. Only three (of 22) respondents to the carers' survey indicated that they had received advice on social welfare entitlements.

11.4.7   Carer support groups
It was recommended in *The Years Ahead* that:

- **(R11.6) health boards should encourage and assist financially where necessary, the formation of support groups for the carers of elderly people**.

Finucane *et al.* (1994) noted that there is a small but increasing number of voluntary carer support groups, concentrated in Leinster and Munster. Lack of funding is a serious limitation on their activities and most groups report that they receive no funding from statutory bodies and meet their running costs by engaging in a wide variety of fund raising activities. Finucane *et al.* also found that most direct services for carers were provided by non-statutory bodies with a strong voluntary input.

11.5   Summary and conclusions
Funding arrangements for voluntary organisations, identified as an important issue in *The Years Ahead*, continue to create difficulties for voluntary organisations and have negative effects on their planning and management practices. Access to statutory agencies, even at the level of substantial umbrella organisations, is often personalised and individualised. Formal contracts underpinning funding, as recommended in *The Years Ahead*, are rare, and many voluntary organisations have serious reservations about entering into contracts with statutory bodies. Moreover, neither the scale, nor the legal status of many voluntary organisations would equip them for contractual relations.

There are no widespread formal procedures for consulting voluntary organisations and few voluntary organisations are involved with statutory bodies in planning services for older people to any significant degree. The mechanisms envisaged in *The Years Ahead* for providing structures to facilitate consultation of the voluntary sector (advisory committees on the elderly, co-ordination at area level and district teams for the elderly) have not been widely established. While most health boards indicated that they had a development fund for voluntary organisations, it was unclear how it was different from Section 65 funding, and whether it was structured as recommended in *The Years Ahead*.

While formal mechanisms are not widespread, most respondents to the voluntary organisation survey reported that a health board liaised with them on a regular basis, and most of them were funded by health boards. Some voluntary organisations providing services for older people are satisfied with the level of input they have in determining their funding, and receive assistance other than funding from statutory bodies. Despite the variations in, or in some cases the absence of, liaison/consultation, most voluntary organisations consider their relationships with statutory bodies to be good.

Table 11.4: Summary of the implementation of *The Years Ahead* recommendations

Recommendations	Current Situation
Health boards and local authorities should encourage by all possible means the involvement of voluntary organisations in caring for the elderly.	Few consultative mechanisms. Significant involvement of voluntary organisations in planning and policy-making is rare
Each board and local authority should agree with the voluntary organisations working with the elderly in their functional areas their respective responsibilities in the delivery of services. This agreement should be formalised as a contract between the voluntary organisation and the board or local authority for a period of 2 to 3 years	Only two health boards established advisory committees. Funding arrangements are incoherent. Funding remains discretionary and *ad hoc.* Voluntary organisations are distrustful of contractual relationships with health boards
District teams for the elderly should be consulted in the preparation of a contract for services in its area	Only four health boards have district teams
Co-ordinators of Services for the Elderly should develop a mechanism to co-ordinate voluntary activity in each community care area	Some mechanism is available in most health boards. Voluntary organisations are represented on committees in two health board areas only
Each health board should establish a fund for the development of voluntary organisations	No evidence of any such funds
The Government should undertake a formal review of the statutory and voluntary sectors with a view to establishing national guidelines for the development of a constructive relationship between the two sectors	*A Green Paper on the Community and Voluntary Sector and its Relationship with the State* was published in May 1997
Health boards should be obliged to provide services to support dependent older people and their carers in the home	Community-based and hospital-based services for older people are overstretched. Priorities for services are overwhelmingly medical. Services of most relevance to carers are discretionary. Some services are seen as substitutes rather than complementary. Serious deficiencies in transport provision
Carers should be entitled to claim assistance in their own right	Carers' Allowance was introduced in 1990. Only about one fifth of those providing a high level of care for older people receive some allowance. The means test is strongly resented
The Co-ordinator of Services for the Elderly should ensure that in each community care area, information and advice is available to carers on the ageing process, the medical aspects of caring, financial entitlements and services available locally	Health education services for carers, where available at all, are in general unstructured, uneven, uncoordinated and opportunistic
Health boards should encourage and assist, financially where necessary, the formation of support groups for the carers of older people	Most carer support groups receive no funding from statutory bodies

Despite the efforts of *The Years Ahead* to draw attention to the urgency of providing support to carers of older people, and detailing the supports required, several substantial studies have demonstrated clearly that little has been done. Support services for carers are largely unavailable, and where available, are often made difficult to access by a policy of reducing services where a carer is present. Little has been done to support carers themselves, most carers' groups receive no funding from statutory bodies, and guidance and education services for carers in respect of their caring role is widely acknowledged to be inadequate. Carers are rarely taken into account in the planning of services for the older person, and if they are it is often to curtail or refuse the service because the carer is present. The Carer's Allowance, the support service most valued by carers, is availed of by only a small proportion of those with onerous caring responsibilities. The value of the allowance is considered inadequate by some carers, and the means test controlling access to it has been condemned in a succession of significant studies of the caring process.

Some carers, because of their circumstances, resourcefulness, attachment to the person or persons they care for, and most importantly their freedom to choose, can take a positive view of their commitment. Others, less fortunate and without choice, sometimes with little, if any, support from family, community or community-based services, live lives of desperation, virtual hostages to a society failing to keep its promises of support. Clearly while often praised, sometimes in empty platitudes, carers are unfairly treated.

CHAPTER TWELVE

Needs and Priorities: Perceptions of Consumers and Service Providers

12.1   Introduction

The focus of this Chapter is on perceptions of the needs of older people and priorities for the development of care services. Needs and priorities are explored from two perspectives: consumers and service providers. As carers were discussed in the previous chapter, the consumer viewpoint is explored only in relation to older people themselves.

12.2   Data sources on needs and priorities

Consumer orientation is a recent phenomenon and it is only now that procedures are being developed to gauge consumers' needs and views. Consequently, a major difficulty in carrying out this review was the lack of structures for obtaining direct feedback from older people on the services they need, and the services they currently receive. In an attempt to provide some kind of consumer feedback, albeit indirect, submissions were sought from a number of organisations which, for present purposes, may be considered as representing the interests of older people in different ways. Replies were obtained from Age Action Ireland, Age Alliance, Age and Opportunity, Care Alliance, Dublin Port and Docks' Pensioners' Association, Irish Congress of Trade Unions, Retired Workers Committee, Irish Association of Older People, Society of St.Vincent de Paul and Soroptimist International Republic of Ireland. In addition previous studies, in which the views and experiences of older people were sampled, are reviewcd.

12.3   Different perspectives: consumers and service providers

The perspectives of consumers and service providers are often thought to be antagonistic but this is not necessarily the case. While the consumer's perspective is essential to needs assessment, sole reliance on the consumer to identify what is required can lead to gaps and lack of comprehensiveness. Consumers, for example, may not always be aware of, or able to clearly articulate, their needs, may feel reluctant or guilty about confessing to need or may never even have thought about their own needs or considered that they have a right to do so. Sole reliance on the perspective of the service provider also clearly leads to problems. Service providers' perceptions of needs and priorities may be determined by the actual availability of resources, and may be based on value judgements as to what would be best for the consumer or on perceptions of which consumers are 'most deserving'. Nonetheless, service providers have a valuable knowledge of resources and an understanding of service delivery, planning and the decision-making processes. Accordingly, a partnership between consumer and service provider can lead to a holistic, authentic, comprehensive and realistic assessment of needs and priorities.

12.4 Development of consumer orientation

12.4.1 Changing images of older people

Older people are a growing proportion of the population and this fact poses economic, social and policy challenges that are only beginning to be identified. The extent to which these challenges are addressed will be very much influenced by the degree to which older people themselves are involved. Up to recent times, older people have not been prominent in articulating their needs or in exercising influence over decisions that affect the services they receive. This may be due in part to the fact that, as a group, they participate less than others in public life and are frequently relatively poor. Societal attitudes, which see older people as a burden on services, rather than encouraging confidence and belief in their rights as consumers, are also a barrier to participation. There are, however, indications of a growing self-confidence among older people as consumers in their own right and a growing willingness to point out what has to be changed or initiated to address their needs. A new, more positive image of old age is discernible in the increasing use of concepts such as 'healthy ageing', 'age and opportunity' and 'inter-generational solidarity' in public discourse. Likewise, there is the use of terms such as 'third age' and 'fourth age' with the focus in the former on the potential for continuing social involvement and active participation. The traditional image of older people as infirm, ill, lonely, resigned and passive is giving way to the recognition that, at least to the end of their 70s, older people generally are active, healthy and socially involved, with a vitality and zest for life.

The establishment of Age and Opportunity and other bodies such as Age Action Ireland, Age Alliance, the Irish Association of Older People and the growth in Active Retirement Associations and Pensioner Associations across the country (see Chapter Four) are all indications of the new, more positive sense of old age which is now beginning to exist. The growing emphasis on older people as consumers is also evident in developments such as the Charter of Rights for Older People drawn up by the Irish Congress of Trade Unions and the Irish Senior Citizens National Parliament whose theme is 'making our voices heard'. The aim of the new parliament is to afford older people an opportunity to discuss the issues which affect the quality of their lives and to develop strategies to ensure their needs are taken into account in decision-making at local, national and European levels. Older people are developing into a group of consumers which can no longer be ignored.

12.4.2   Recent policy on consumer involvement

The new orientation towards older people is also evident among policy-makers. As discussed in Chapter One, *The Years Ahead* did not give much attention to the views of older people when identifying needs and recommending policy on service development. However, in recent years a number of national policy documents have emphasised the principle of consumer orientation. The National Economic and Social Forum (1995) has emphasised that the delivery of a quality social service depends on consultation and participation, information and advice, choice, access and redress. Similarly, the recent Strategic Management Initiative outlined five principles for quality services which include the consumer. First, the Initiative advocates consultation with, and participation by, customers on a structured basis. Second, quality information and advice should be provided to customers whenever possible. Third, services should provide reasonable choice for customers in relation to the methods of delivery. Fourth, a comprehensive system of measuring and assessing customer satisfaction should be developed and fifth, complaints and redress mechanisms which operate close to the point of delivery should be established.

In the area of health care, *Shaping a Healthier Future* also spells out a re-orientation of services towards the consumer. Plans for putting a consumer orientation into practice include quality initiatives such as Charters of Rights, clinical audits and consumer surveys. Plans are also outlined to ensure that detailed and accurate information is available on services, entitlements, eligibility criteria and assessment procedures. A third element in the consumer orientation of *Shaping a Healthier Future* is the establishment of measures to give individuals a better opportunity to have grievances redressed and to represent the views of users, as a group, in the decision-making process. These measures include the establishment of advisory groups in each health authority area to provide an input to the authority from the users of the various services; a requirement on all health authorities to put appropriate complaints procedures in place; and the introduction of a statutory function of the boards of the health authorities to act as a channel to the Minister of the views and concerns of their populations.

12.5   Perceptions of organisations representing older people

The responses on needs and priorities obtained from organisations representing older people vary considerably, reflecting their different agendas and areas of interest. Two main types of issue were identified: those concerned with the overall care system and those concerned with specific service deficits. With regard to the overall system, the most outstanding common theme in a varied picture is the perceived shortfall in community care services and the perceived failure to shift resources from institutional to community care services

Most of the specific service deficits also relate to community care. A frequently noted deficit in community care is the failure to provide counselling and guidance services for older people and for their families. Apart from counselling, a whole range of other deficits are identified including an inadequate chiropody service, inadequate provision of Home Helps, inadequate provision of PHNs and Care Assistants and inadequate day care provision. A further issue identified by many organisations is inequity in provision for older people. A number of factors are identified as giving rise to this perceived inequity. It is seen, for example, that children are given greater attention and more resources compared with older people in need. It is also perceived that because much service provision for older people is discretionary many are being left without essential services. A related issue is the perception of an over-dependence on voluntary organisations to provide essential services resulting, in many instances, in a 'patchy' service. Financial inequity was also mentioned. Those with financial means can avail of immediate medical and hospital treatment whereas those with low incomes have to go on waiting lists. This issue was also raised in the context of a perceived lack of nursing home placements for people with little money. Other complaints include a perception that urban areas have better access to services compared with rural areas and that service-provision is not standardised across health boards.

The inaccessibility of many services is also highlighted by a number of representative organisations. Two causal factors are identified: inaccessibility due to geographical location and lack of transport and inaccessibility due to failure of information services. The latter is one of the major deficits identified in the current care of older people. It is perceived that older people often do not know where to look for the help they need. This could be remedied by simple mechanisms that would signpost the client to the available services.

At the level of service planning, a key issue raised by the representative organisations is the lack of involvement by older people in the process. It is suggested that, as a consequence of this lack of involvement, policy-makers are often unaware of the needs of older people and service provision is based on the level of funding available rather than on needs. It is felt that current provision for older people is narrowly focused on 'care' needs and fails to take account of needs for continuing education, for creative fulfilment, intellectual challenge and contribution to the community. There is a call for a more holistic approach to needs and for increased attention to health promotion and the development of positive attitudes to ageing.

12.5.1   Charter of rights

Many of the concerns of the representative organisations are encapsulated in the following 'Charter of Rights for the Elderly' drawn up by the Irish Congress of Trade Unions and the National Federation of Pensioners' Associations:

- The right to live independent, active and full lives without discrimination on grounds of age;

- The right to an adequate income, substantial enough to provide a decent standard of living;

- The right to equity in taxation. Provisions in the income tax code relating to the elderly should be regularly revised;

- The right to adequate, secure and suitable living accommodation in the community. A range of housing options to be available to the elderly including sheltered housing, purpose-built flats, voluntary housing associations and controlled private rented accommodation. Subsidies and grants should be provided to encourage families to keep elderly relatives in the family environment;

- The right to a proper nursing homes service for the very frail and physically incapacitated. All nursing homes should be subject to statutory regulations to guarantee proper treatment of patients, including professional nursing care;

- The right to hospitalisation and medical services. These services to be provided through a comprehensive public health programme based on a positive commitment to the health of the elderly. Home nursing and public health nursing services should be expanded. Hospital and medical services impose a heavy financial burden on many elderly persons not entitled to medical cards. This situation should be remedied;

- The right to a properly funded home help service providing for the care of the elderly and organised in co-ordination with local community care services;

- The right to participate in formal and informal adult education;

- The right to proper pre-retirement facilities including paid time-off for retirement planning courses, flexible working hours, job-sharing and early retirement;

- The right to participate in and be represented on appropriate bodies dealing with matters concerning the elderly;

- The right to protection against violence. Local Community Alert Programmes which can be of assistance to the elderly, particularly those living alone, should be developed;

- The right to travel and recreational facilities providing opportunities for self-expression, personal development and fulfilment.

12.6   Experiences and perceptions of needs among older people

O'Connor *et al.* (1991) in a study of older people in the Mid-Western Health Board region found that a major deficit in the care system for older people identified by themselves was the provision of social contact. Where such contact exists it appears to contribute greatly to emotional well-being and, conversely, where it is absent the feelings of isolation and loneliness can be very distressing. Several studies carried out in the early 1980s identified loneliness and feelings of isolation as a significant problem among older people (Power 1980; Daly and O'Connor 1984; Carey and Carroll 1986). Silke (1994) found that although older people were often involved in active age/retirement groups and described themselves as busy and enjoying retirement, feelings of loneliness were common.

Transport is a second recurrent theme in studies where older people are asked about their needs. As a result of lack of transport, older people are often obliged to depend on friends, neighbours or relatives (O'Connor *et al.* 1991). Some even resort to hitching lifts. Under circumstances where no public transport is available older people point out that there is little value in having a free travel pass. In addition where transport is provided it is often of little value because of inconvenient time scheduling or inappropriate design. Silke (1994) also found that older people were affected by two major deficits in current transport services including problems with access to public transport in rural areas and the cost of maintaining a car for those on a basic pension.

When asked, older people are very clear that their preference is to stay put in their own homes for as long as possible (O'Connor *et al.* 1991). For some, the greatest problem in staying in their own homes is having to cope with isolation and loneliness. Others highlight an unmet need for adaptations to make their homes more suitable to their present levels of health and mobility (O'Connor *et al.* 1991). On the whole older people are quite happy with the area in which they live and report supportive relationships with their neighbours. There is a concern, however, about the costs of maintaining a house in old age (Silke 1994).

Older people in both the O'Connor *et al.* (1991) and Silke (1994) studies expressed concern about waiting-lists for hospital treatment. In the Silke study those interviewed were generally active and in good health and there was little use of Home Helps or Meals-on-Wheels. In the O'Connor *et al.* study, however, some felt that they needed home support services but were not getting them at all or only at an inadequate level. The general impression from the older people in the O'Connor *et al.* study is that they were unaware of any concept of 'active retirement' and tended to see themselves in a negative light as no longer having a useful purpose. By contrast, the older people in the Silke study were all involved in active age/retirement groups and the general feeling was that they were enjoying retirement.

12.7   Service provider perspective on needs and priorities

The service provider perspective on needs and priorities in the care of older people was explored through interviews with health board Programme Managers, Co-ordinators of Services for the Elderly and District Liaison Nurses. It should be noted that because the numbers in these posts are small it is not possible to identify definite patterns or to draw any definite conclusions. One of the most striking aspects of the feedback obtained from the different service providers is the large number of gaps identified in current provision for older people. There is wide variation in the perceptions of what is lacking both between different groups of service providers and within particular groups reflecting differences in both focus of interest and in circumstances across the health boards. There are also, however, some common themes across the different perspectives.

12.7.1   Perceptions of deficits: Programme Managers

From the point of view of Programme Managers of Community Care, the most frequently noted deficits are the inadequate development of community paramedical services and inadequate resourcing of the home help service. A whole range of other services are noted as being inadequately developed in their particular boards by individual Programme Managers including the public health nursing service, respite care, services for dementia sufferers, sheltered housing, social work services, transport and day care services. Apart from gaps in specific services, individual Programme Managers of Community Care also report inadequacies in current service-delivery such as lack of liaison in relation to discharge of older people from hospital, lack of co-ordination of the location and distribution of beds, lack of co-ordination of community support services and lack of co-ordination at local level. It is also noted that there is inadequate consultation with older people with regard to the services they require.

Programme Managers of Special Hospitals identify the lack of flexible support services for carers and the inadequate provision of day care services as problematic. Two Programme Managers reiterate the same concerns as the Programme Managers of Community Care, that is, inadequate development of paramedical and home help services. Again, individual Programme Managers identify different service gaps in their particular boards including lack of geriatric assessment units, lack of day hospitals, lack of specific services for older people with mental illness and lack of residential services. Some also point to gaps in community services such as inadequate development of boarding out schemes and the lack of a social work service for older people with mental disorders. With respect to service-delivery, two Programme Managers express concern, as did Programme Managers of Community Care, that there is a lack of co-ordination of services at local level.

From the perspective of Programme Managers of General Hospitals, the most commonly noted gaps are the lack of dedicated geriatric assessment beds and inadequate provision of day hospital beds. Also noted is the inadequacy of paramedical and home help services.

12.7.2   Perceptions of deficits: CSEs

Echoing the concerns of Programme Managers of Special Hospitals, the outstanding theme in feedback from CSEs is the inadequacy of support services for carers. Another frequently noted deficit is the inadequate provision of the home help service. Echoing the concerns of older people themselves and of their representative organisations, the CSEs also highlight the lack of transport facilities.

Other deficits within community care noted by more than one CSE include inadequate provision of paramedical services, lack of development of boarding out services, the insufficient number of day care places, and the insufficient number of Care Assistants. Compared with community care services, deficits in special hospital and general hospital services are less frequently noted by the CSEs but do include lack of respite beds, inadequate psychogeriatric services and insufficient long-stay places.

12.7.3   Perception of deficits: District Liaison Nurses

District Liaison Nurses reiterate all of the major concerns identified by the different Programme Managers and the CSEs. Many of the deficits identified come within the remit of community care but gaps are noted across the full continuum of care, from support of carers, to home support, to day care, to special housing, to hospital services.

12.7.4   Perceptions of service providers of recommendations with greatest impact

The recommendations from *The Years Ahead* identified as having the greatest impact vary according to the position of the service provider. From the perspective of Programme Managers, the greatest impact on care of older people has been observed with the appointment of geriatricians, the establishment of care teams (this applies mainly to the community ward teams established in the Eastern Health Board), the provision of day care services, the development of specialised assessment/rehabilitation services and the development of old age psychiatry services.

CSEs identify the establishment of care teams (where relevant) as having the greatest impact on the care of older people. The improvement in nursing home provision is another implemented recommendation which has had significant beneficial consequences. District Liaison Nurses have a somewhat different view of the services with the greatest impact. The emphasis is on community care services with the greatest benefits identified with the provision of day care centres, the appointment of Registered General Nursing panels and home care assistants, the development of respite care and the establishment of care teams.

It is of note that there is agreement among Programme Managers, District Liaison Nurses and organisations representing older people that the development of day care services is one of the recommendations of *The Years Ahead* which has had the most significant impact. Without objective evaluation, it is, however, impossible to assess to what extent such perceptions are accurate.

12.7.5   *Perceptions of priorities among service providers*

Programme Managers, CSEs and District Liaison Nurses believe that most of the major needs of older people were properly identified in *The Years Ahead*. There are, however, three need areas which are perceived as not having been fully recognised and addressed and which need to be taken into account in future policy and planning. The most frequently mentioned unmet need relates to the issue of abuse of older people, an issue of particular concern to the District Liaison Nurses. This abuse is not only about physical maltreatment but also includes problems such as financial exploitation of older people or denial of their entitlements. Little research has been carried out in this country in this area and no factual data on the extent and nature of abuse is available to inform decisions on the priority that should be assigned to this care need area. Echoing the views of some organisations representing older people, a second area of unmet need is the support needs of carers. Some point out that there may well be a connection between failure to address carers' needs and the abuse of dependent older people. A third need area which is seen to require greater attention relates to the needs of dementia sufferers.

Priorities for the future may be separated into those pertaining to increasing service-provision levels and those pertaining to establishing more effective delivery mechanisms. With regard to service provision, each health board has its own plan for the future reflecting the particular deficits it has identified and reflecting the particular needs and circumstances which apply in the area. However, some common themes across the boards are the need for an expansion of community paramedical services, home support and day care facilities in the community care area, further development of day hospitals in the hospital care area and the development of facilities for dementia sufferers in the special hospital programme.

With regard to service delivery, services in the future are to be organised according to 'care group' rather than on a programme basis as has been the case up to now. The most pervasive theme for the future of service delivery is the development of a 'seamless' service. The biggest issue in providing a seamless service is improvement of co-ordination and liaison mechanisms but it is not always clear how particular health boards plan to do this. The most usual proposals involve organising services at district level, located within a centre. At the centre of this plan is a key worker who is usually identified by service providers as a PHN but is sometimes a GP.

Most health boards specifically note a plan to develop personalised 'care plans' or 'care packages' which suit the particular needs of individual older people. There are different views on who should put together these care plans. PHNs, CSEs and special liaison nurses are all nominated. Another relatively frequent theme in plans for future service delivery is the development of effective partnership arrangements with voluntary organisations and with private and voluntary nursing homes. To a lesser extent, there is a focus for the future on evaluation of gain from the services provided and on involvement of the consumer in both evaluation and needs assessment.

12.8   Summary and conclusions

One of the most evident shortcomings of *The Years Ahead* is its failure to explore how older people themselves could be involved in the planning and delivery of the services intended for them. Up to recent times, little attention was given to the consumer viewpoint in any sphere of care and older people, in particular, were not vocal in making their needs heard. Older people, however, are not only a growing group of consumers in society but are also a group who are becoming more self-confident about speaking out on what they need. Age and Opportunity has been to the forefront in attempts to change the traditional image of older people as infirm, lonely and passive to a more positive view of them as capable of being active, vibrant and socially involved. Voluntary organisations such as Age Action Ireland, Age Alliance, the Irish Association of Older People and Active Retirement and Pensioners' Associations, are also making an important contribution in this regard. The growing recognition of older people as consumers is evident in developments such as the Charter of Rights for Older People (drawn up by the Irish Congress of Trade Unions and the National Federation of Pensioners' Associations) and the Irish Senior Citizens National Parliament (set up by the Retired Workers' Committee of the Irish Congress of Trade Unions) which aims to provide an opportunity for older people to discuss issues that affect the quality of their lives and to develop strategies to have their needs heard.

At Government level also, there is evidence of a growing awareness of the need for consumer involvement, expressed in policy documents such as the Strategic Management Initiative and *Shaping a Healthier Future*. In the latter document plans for consumer involvement include Charters of Rights, clinical audits, consumer surveys, the establishment of advisory groups and complaints procedures. The effectiveness of such measures in ensuring that the voice of the consumer is heard awaits evaluation. Consumer involvement requires that explicit strategies are put into action and that there are active efforts at training, support and encouragement so that older people and service providers are enabled to use whatever mechanisms for consumer involvement are put in place.

Organisations representing the interests of older people stress a number of policy issues which must inform the future care system. These include the inclusion of the consumer's voice, the recognition of diversity among older people and an accompanying recognition of their wider care needs. Health promotion must, therefore, be pro-active and greater time must be spent on education about older people and the creation of a more positive view of older life. There is a call for policy to take greater account of the role and contribution of carers and greater commitment to addressing their needs. With regard to delivery of services, there is a call for health care to be delivered on the basis of local areas, with a co-ordinated approach being taken, which would include voluntary organisations. In terms of levels of services, the major deficits identified relate to community care services, most particularly lack of community counselling services, inadequate chiropody provision, inadequate provision of Home Helps and Care Assistants and inadequate day care provision. Apart from community care, other deficits highlighted include inadequate provision for dementia sufferers and inadequate nursing home provision.

Reflecting the deficits noted, the priorities identified for the future include the provision of an adequate system of community care. But the foremost priority is seen to be the provision of adequate transport, the lack of which has seriously jeopardised the principles of equity and accessibility. From the perspective of the health boards, there is agreement that carers and dementia sufferers have not been adequately cared for. In their priorities for the future, the health boards indicate plans to address some of the deficits identified by the representative organisations including greater provision of home support and day care facilities.

The way ahead as identified by both health boards and organisations representing older people has several common strands. They are both interested in health promotion, local delivery of services, and more efficient transport. One of the greatest concerns among the health boards is the provision of a seamless service with effective liaison and co-ordination. The development of packages of care is being considered by several boards. Health boards, in general, however, have not made any obvious attempts to include the voice of consumers, or to put in place a system to ensure the accountability of their proposed structure as dictated by the needs of older people.

Too little is known about the needs of consumers from their perspective. This must be addressed so that older people are included in future policy and planning, in assessment of need and in evaluation of whatever initiatives are implemented.

CHAPTER THIRTEEN

Overview and Key Issues

13.1   Introduction

The preceding chapters of this review have examined the extent to which the recommendations of *The Years Ahead* have been implemented with regard to various aspects of the care of older people. Following the structure of *The Years Ahead,* the review has examined current provision of services related to health promotion, housing, care at home, care in the community, care in hospital and long-term care. In addition to recommendations on type and level of service provision, the review has also examined service delivery issues including co-ordination of services and partnership between the different agencies involved. Perceptions of current needs and priorities in the care of older people have been explored from the perspectives of organisations representing older people and service providers. The purpose of this final chapter is to draw together the main findings of the review, to highlight the policy issues arising from those findings and to assess the implications for the future development of an effective and appropriate care system for older people.

In making its recommendations for an effective and appropriate care system for older people, the Working Party was guided by the objectives of comprehensiveness, equity, accessibility, responsiveness, flexibility, co-ordination and cost-effectiveness. Judged against these objectives, the Working Party concluded that the care system operating in the 1980s left much to be desired. Now, almost 10 years on, it is timely to reassess the extent to which these objectives have been achieved.

13.2   Is the care provided comprehensive?

In its concern for the development of effective care for older people, the Working Party focused most of its recommendations on norms for comprehensive service provision. The Working Party interpreted a comprehensive service as ensuring that whatever help an older person needed to live in or return to the community would be provided through housing, medical and welfare services, acute hospitals and long-term facilities. The various services recommended in *The Years Ahead* may be placed along a continuum of care ranging from purely preventive care at one end to residential care at the other end:

| Preventative care | Anticipatory care | Care at home | Care Through housing | Care in the community | Acute hospital care | Long stay care |

A comprehensive system requires adequate provision of each care option along the continuum. This review reveals that while improvements in services have been made and new initiatives have been instigated, there are still significant gaps in the care options available to older people. Gaps at different points on the continuum of care mean that there is no real choice about the care option that should be selected when a care need arises, and implementation of the most appropriate care is seriously hampered. The gaps can also mean that older people find themselves either remaining at a stage too low down on the continuum and receiving an insufficient level of care or being moved to a care option too far up the continuum and being prematurely moved to institutional care.

13.2.1   Comprehensiveness of preventive care

As a result of *The Years Ahead*, when the National Council for the Elderly was established in 1990 as a successor to the National Council for the Aged, one of its new terms of reference was to advise the Minister for Health on measures to promote the health of the elderly. The publication of *Shaping a Healthier Future* in 1994 heralded a new emphasis on health promotion. This was followed in 1995 by the national *Health Promotion Strategy* which included a call for a Healthy Ageing Programme. One of the most significant steps in health promotion is the development of a Healthy Ageing Programme by the National Council on Ageing and Older People, which includes a healthy ageing strategy. The strategy will enable the health concerns specific to older life to be properly addressed and it will enable identification of the most appropriate channels and means of access for health promotion among older people.

The Working Party recognised the multi-faceted nature of health promotion and, accordingly, made a recommendation for inter-departmental co-operation through the Cabinet Sub-Committee on Health Promotion. Subsequent to *Shaping a Healthier Future*, a National Consultative Committee on Health Promotion was established which reports to the Cabinet Sub-Committee on Health Promotion. The effectiveness of this structure remains to be seen and there is as yet little evidence of inter-departmental co-operation in health promotion among older people. However, a potentially important development in relation to intersectoral co-operation is the Government's Strategic Management Initiative (SMI). One of the proposals in the Initiative is to develop Strategic Result Areas where teams would bring cross-departmental action, commitment and expertise to bear on the solution of problems. It is of note that the list of possible Strategic Result Areas suggested in the Second Report to Government on the Initiative includes child care along with other areas such as drugs, employment and local development, but not care of older people. Care of older people must be put forward as being of equal strategic importance to care of children and must be included as one of the areas demanding and deserving cross-departmental input and action.

At the level of the individual, an important aspect of health promotion is health education. In this regard, the Working Party had recommended provision by the health boards of specific health education services for both older people and their carers. It is clear from this review, however, that while there are attempts by the health boards at health education, much remains to be done to make services more focused, structured and widely available. Health boards must develop specific structures for the provision of a comprehensive, coherent health education service dedicated to the needs of older people. One of the key contributions of the healthy ageing strategy currently being developed will be to guide and inform the programmes provided at health board level.

13.2.2   Comprehensiveness of anticipatory care

The GP and the PHN are the central players in anticipatory care of older people. It is clear from the review that PHNs regard anticipatory care as a fundamental aspect of their work. At present, however, the PHN is frequently distracted from this work because of managerial duties and the demands for curative nursing care. If the PHN is to fulfil her proper role there must be an increase in the numbers dedicated to anticipatory care duties and an increase in back-up services such as RGN panels, Care Assistants and Home Helps. This would relieve the PHN of curative nursing duties and domestic and personal care tasks.

A related issue is the failure to modernise the method of identifying older people 'at risk'. The review shows widespread concern among PHNs about the current means of identifying risk. National guidelines must be developed for a formal, structured and standardised 'at risk' register which is uniform across all areas. Computerisation of the data on the register would facilitate easier access to, and retrieval of, the information collected and would make maintenance and updating less time-consuming. With regard to the role of the GP in anticipatory care, it emerges from this review that, at present, case finding by GPs is opportunistic rather than proactive. Contrary to the recommendation of the Working Party, there is little incentive in the current General Medical Service system to encourage anticipatory care and the infrastructure to support it is lacking. There are still major questions about the best ways of implementing and supporting anticipatory care, especially when dealing with vulnerable older people who do not wish to be treated.

13.2.3   Comprehensiveness of home and community-based care

The main aim of the care of older people is to enable them to remain at home for as long as possible. The implementation of this aim depends crucially on the provision of effective home-based and community-based supports. If these are not in place, the older person is likely to be moved unnecessarily to a more intensive form of care higher up the care continuum. While acknowledging the improvements that have been made in home-based and community-based services for older people since *The Years Ahead*, there are still a number of deficits to be remedied.

The public health nursing service faces three main problems: inadequate numbers employed; distraction from their proper function through pressure from other demands; and inadequate levels of back-up services. A review of the public health nursing service has been completed by the Department of Health which should spell out the appropriate functions of the PHN. The current review reveals that PHNs believe that the most effective use of their particular skills is in anticipatory care, health promotion and liaison. It emerges that the Registered General Nursing panels recommended by the Working Party play an important role in home-based curative nursing but there are problems in relation to low numbers and high turnover and a much greater level of resources must be given to the service if it is to fulfil its potential value.

The home help service is widely recognised as a key service in home care for older people. Despite the recommendation of the Working Party that there should be a legal obligation for its provision and calls from the National Council on Ageing and Older People to designate it as a core service, the service is still discretionary (Mulvihill 1993). This contributes to variations in levels of provision, eligibility for the service and the nature of the tasks carried out. While all the health boards have attained the norms for provision recommended in *The Years Ahead*, the level of the service still falls short of what is required. The scope of the service is also limited and it fulfils only to a limited extent the kind of out-of-hours and respite functions envisaged by the Working Party. A further issue to be addressed is the function of Home Helps compared to the care assistant service. The specific roles, functions and focus of each service need to be more clearly delineated so that decisions can be made about the most appropriate service to put in place in particular circumstances. The Department of Health is about to carry out a review of the home help service which should address these issues.

The Working Party had envisaged that a range of paramedical services would be available in the home to older people. One of the most evident deficits emerging from the review is the inadequate level of provision of paramedical services. Not only is domiciliary delivery of services extremely limited, but there is wide concern about the level and nature of community-based provision. As well as financial constraints there seems to be an ambivalence among health board managers about the necessity and feasibility of a domiciliary service. There is a suggestion from front-line service providers that the value of such services, particularly in the prevention of future health problems among older people, is not properly acknowledged.

A further gap in the care of older people identified in this review is the lack of a community social work service. Community social work services are focused almost totally on young families and children and are already overstretched in meeting the demands of these clients. There appears to be an attitudinal issue among managers whereby the full potential of a social work service for older people is not recognised. This view must be countered and, as in most other European countries, social workers must be involved in key areas of the care of older people such as needs assessment, case management, resolution of family conflict and advocacy. The development of a social work service was given little attention in *The Years Ahead* and requires exploration to allow the development of appropriate working models.

Finally, despite the recommendations of the Working Party, day care centres are still provided at the discretion of the health boards, with no legislative framework governing provision. In reflection of its discretionary status, this review found that current levels of day care are inadequate and there is unevenness in provision across different areas of the country, with some having no day care at all. Unfortunately there is a lack of precise information in the health boards on the current number of day care places provided and the estimated number of places needed to address future need. This may be because voluntary organisations have a significant input into the provision of day care services but do not have a system for providing precise information feedback to the health boards. The Working Party had recommended that the Department of Health draw up a model contract between the health boards and voluntary organisations for voluntary provision of day care centres but this recommendation has not been implemented and is now regarded as unnecessary by the Department. Failure to implement this recommendation makes it difficult to see how the health boards can ensure standards of provision and quality of service. Contracts of service should therefore be drawn up and funding procedures standardised across the country. There is a widespread perception among managers and service providers that day care facilities are one of the most valuable services for older people. Research is needed, however, to systematically evaluate the activities of day care centres, to assess their benefits from the point of view of the users and to determine principles of good practice.

13.2.4   *Comprehensiveness of housing options*
The contribution that sheltered housing can make to the welfare of older people is widely recognised. However, the availability of such housing is far too limited. There is a growing awareness of the benefits that versatility in housing design can confer on older people who have some form of disability or impairment. It is

important that such benefits are not lost because of insufficient planning of housing or insensitive management. Taking a longer-term view, more thought needs to be given to the concept of 'designing for life'. All housing design and all building and environmental design should be considered with the requirements of people over the entire life cycle in mind. Such an approach will require that more resources are allocated to housing research and planning to ensure a better fit between housing and people. More importantly, it must be clearly recognised that voluntary housing organisations, local authorities and health boards have a common interest in the housing of older people. This does not appear to be adequately reflected in current financing, planning and liaison arrangements. The development of partnership arrangements, reflecting the vital, actual and potential roles of each of these parties, is now urgent.

13.2.5   *Comprehensiveness of provision of acute hospital care*

While the number of geriatricians has increased substantially since 1988, in many instances these geriatricians are not dedicated full-time to older people and are also involved in general patient care. In smaller general hospitals, this can have a serious impact on the effective delivery of care to older people and needs to be addressed. In addition, geriatricians can act as lobbyists for older people, advocating for older people in the hospital service to ensure they receive the services they require. To ensure this occurs all acute general hospitals should have access to at least one geriatrician. In most cases this consultant should work full-time on medicine for older people but in the smallest hospitals this may not be possible. Where geriatricians must spend some time on general medicine there should be enough support to ensure that at least half their time is spent with older people.

None of the health boards has reached the recommended norm for assessment beds and only two have reached the recommended norm for rehabilitation beds. In addition, day hospital places are not dedicated and this, along with the number of part-time geriatricians, means that geriatric services are not as effective as they should be. Follow-up of older patients after discharge from hospitals needs to be addressed. Regular assessment in the context of a care package which includes a range of options, would ensure that the older patient does not get lost only to re-surface again with similar problems.

13.2.6   *Comprehensiveness of provision of long-stay care*

Community hospitals were envisaged by the Working Party as providing a local solution to long-stay care needs, but this review has shown that the development of the community hospital sector has been slow. Questions must be raised about whether community hospitals are catering sufficiently for long-stay needs and whether different options must now be sought. Dedicated beds are needed in a number of different areas, as most beds are generic in designation at present. This means that most beds can be counted as long-stay care beds if necessary and the review has shown that the number of long-stay beds currently provided is above the level recommended in *The Years Ahead*. The review also shows that the move away from welfare homes has not been matched by an increase in the provision of alternative welfare accommodation. The lack of dedicated welfare places must be addressed at Departmental and board level with a unified strategy for dealing with welfare cases.

The increase in the number of nursing home places is an indication of the way in which demand for beds is currently being met. Although the *Health (Nursing Homes) Act 1990* has improved relationships between health boards and nursing homes, nursing homes cannot be regarded as the panacea to cure all long-stay care problems. It may now be timely to re-evaluate the community hospital plan so that over-reliance on the nursing home sector does not occur. All long-stay options must meet standards of care and management and, in addition, have access to a comprehensive range of support services, so that older people are not disadvantaged as a result of their geographical location.

13.2.7   *Comprehensiveness of provision of psychiatric care*
Psychiatry of Old Age services are poorly developed with, at present, only four consultants in post. Although training is available, few consultants have been employed and a recent recommendation for a planning norm of one consultant per 10,000 people aged over 65 (Keogh and Roche 1996) is a long way from realisation. A developed Psychiatry of Old Age service would ensure essential early screening and assessment, which at present are in need of improvement. This would contribute towards the appropriate treatment and accommodation of older people with functional mental illness and dementia.

Dedicated day hospital and day care places are needed. The current lack of dedication raises questions about health boards' commitment to community care, particularly for older people with dementia. A reluctance by general psychiatric services to admit dementia patients, coupled with the lack of dedicated places, have meant that dementia patients are poorly catered for at present. While there is an indication from the Department of Health that increased resources are planned for dementia care services, a national Psychiatry of Old Age service would at the very least provide some help in ensuring better treatment and accommodation for dementia sufferers. Dedicated places are also required in high support hostels for those with functional mental illness, and in non-psychiatric nursing accommodation and long-stay psychiatric units for those with dementia, depending on their level of impairment and behavioural problems.

13.2.8   *Comprehensiveness of support for carers*
Comprehensiveness of care in the community depends on the willingness and availability of informal carers. Although the Working Party acknowledged the

role of informal carers, there is a perception among carers' organisations that carers' needs were not adequately covered in *The Years Ahead*. One of the policy issues which arises here is the extent to which there is 'choice' about being a carer. It appears from the accounts of carers that the decision about adopting the role is not often made in a considered fashion where different options are available and discussed (Ruddle *et al.* 1993). Assumption of the caregiving role is not always simply a matter of care and affection for the older person, but is also determined by factors such as the carer's availability, proximity to the older person, sense of obligation and the carer's gender, employment status and household composition. Policy-makers must not assume that family members will provide care. To operate on such an assumption denies choice both to those who receive the care and those who take on the job of giving care and makes it difficult to terminate the caregiving role should that become necessary for the carer's own well-being. It must also be recognised that the nature of the caring relationship is likely to be quite different for spouse carers and adult child carers, with the latter most likely having their own family and work responsibilities. The nature of the support services they need will also vary accordingly. In addition, the assumption that all families are happy and close-knit must be addressed; a dysfunctional family is not the best environment for the provision of care to an older person.

Research has shown that caregiving gives rise to many strains and can involve costs in different areas of the carer's life. A comprehensive care system implies that carers do not find themselves caregiving in isolation, as many currently do, but instead are part of an integrated system which involves public agencies, voluntary organisations, family members, neighbours and members of the local community. It is assumed in *The Years Ahead* that supportive neighbours and communities are readily available. This assumption needs to be tested.

This review corroborates the findings of previous research that major needs of carers, such as education and training, information and advice, adequate financial support, domiciliary support and respite, are not being adequately addressed and that carers require much greater public support than they are currently receiving. Among both health board management and service providers it is acknowledged that failure to provide adequate support services for carers is one of the major deficits in current care provision for older people. An indication of some progress in this regard is that *Shaping a Healthier Future* does promise to strengthen home support services for carers, while the national *Health Promotion Strategy* also plans a specific programme of health promotion for carers.

13.3   Is the care provided equitable and accessible?

Shaping a Healthier Future echoes *The Years Ahead* in putting forward equity as a key principle underpinning the health care system. (The principles of equity and accessibility are closely linked and are dealt with together in this section.) It emerges in this review that inequity is one of the issues in the current care system which still has to be addressed. Issues of inequity arise in relation to entitlement to services, obligation to provide core services, voluntary provision of core services, information on services and transport services. Each of these is discussed in the following sections.

13.3.1   Equity and entitlement to services

For the Working Party, the primary meaning of an equitable service was to ensure that older people who are disadvantaged by low income or disability are not deprived of care because they cannot afford it. This review shows that there is a view among organisations representing older people that certain services, such as nursing home care and prompt medical and hospital treatment, are inaccessible to those on low incomes. While the structure of eligibility for most of the major health services is clearly specified in legislation, there are a number of very important community services, such as paramedical services, home help and day care services, for which no eligibility criteria are set down in legislation. *Shaping a Healthier Future* promises that national guidelines on eligibility and charges, which will be applied in a uniform manner in all areas, will be introduced in respect of all services where legislative provisions are at present absent. *Shaping a Healthier Future* also acknowledges that existing legislation governing the needs of people in public long-term care is inadequate and promises new legislation which will provide for greater clarity and fairness.

13.3.2   Equity and obligation to provide core services

The Working Party identified certain services, such as home help and day care services, as so important that health boards should be obliged by law to provide them. Similarly, the National Council on Ageing and Older People considers Home Helps, Meals-on-Wheels, day care and sheltered housing as 'core services' that are so essential to the quality of life of older people that they require to be underpinned by legislation and appropriate statutory funding. To date, the recommendation on legislation has not been implemented. The Department of Health suggests that the health boards are already fulfiling their responsibility to provide such services and that it is unnecessary to impose a legal obligation.

This review shows, however, that while the level of provision of these core services has improved since 1988, their discretionary nature has led to a situation where older people in different areas of the country experience considerable variations in extent of provision, in scope and nature of provision and in eligibility criteria. It is clearly inequitable that an older person's access to an essential service should depend on the area in which she or he happens to live. The approach taken to the care of older people differs markedly from that adopted toward the care of children where the *Child Care Act 1991* imposes a clear statutory duty on the health boards to provide a range of child care and family support services. In the interests of equity, the same awareness of need and commitment of resources must be devoted to older people. It is acknowledged that more research is needed to determine exactly the constituents of a basic standard of care that should be obligatory in all health boards. Nevertheless, there is already sufficient evidence to indicate that the above services are essential to the care of older people.

13.3.3   *Equity and voluntary provision of core services*

Over-dependence on voluntary organisations to provide certain essential services is another factor which can lead to inequity of care. It emerges from the review, for example, that 50 per cent or more of day care places in some health boards are provided by voluntary organisations. Voluntary input is also important in the provision of transport facilities in all health board areas and in the provision of home help services in several boards. Dependence on voluntary organisations does not in itself necessarily lead to inequitable provision, but equity requires clear-cut partnership arrangements that allow for effective joint planning and that ensure standards are maintained and a quality service is provided in all areas. Formal contracts were seen by the Working Party as an element of partnership but the review shows that contracts of more than one year are rare and, moreover, many voluntary organisations appear resistant to such arrangements. The Governmental review of the relationship between the voluntary and statutory sectors, recommended in *The Years Ahead* and subsequently adopted in *The Programme for Economic and Social Progress*, has not yet been completed. *Shaping a Healthier Future* has promised the development of a legislative framework for working relationships between voluntary organisations and the new health authorities but, to date, this promise has not been fulfilled. *Shaping a Healthier Future* had also envisaged service contracts between the health authorities and at least the larger voluntary service providers but such contracts are still the exception rather than the rule.

13.3.4   *Equity and provision of information on services*

A further dimension to equity is knowledge of, and accessibility to services. In view of the major changes proposed by the Working Party, it is remarkable that the provision of information on services was not addressed in *The Years Ahead*. As a consequence, one of the deficits in the current care system identified by organisations representing older people, is lack of information. *Shaping a Healthier Future* promises that the Department of Health and the health authorities will ensure that people have ready access to information about their entitlements and how to avail of them. Assessment of the extent to which the proposed new structures will enable this to happen awaits research. There are also several voluntary organisations, such as Age Action Ireland, Age and Opportunity, the National Federation of Pensioners Associations, which are committed to the provision of information to older people. Inequity of access due to lack of information is a fundamental problem which must be eliminated. Pathways to care must be clearly signposted so that older people know the options available to them, the information they need to decide on the best option for their particular circumstances, and how to access that option.

13.3.5   Equity and transport services

For many years, researchers and service providers have been calling attention to the inequity experienced by older people, particularly in rural areas, because of the lack of adequate transport. This review reveals continuing widespread concern among both older people and managers and service providers about transport facilities. Unfortunately, no one Government Department appears to be taking clear responsibility for the problem. As a result none of the recommendations of the Working Party for action at Departmental level has been fully implemented. At health board level few attempts have been made to carry out the kind of review of transport resources recommended by the Working Party. This has hindered identification of options and possible solutions. Attempts at providing transport have been made in all health boards but not all see it as their responsibility. Instead, it is felt that the public transport authorities should be responsible. Indeed the most innovative and active proposals for addressing the problem have been put forward by voluntary organisations such as Forum and the Rural Transport Initiative which was due to start a pilot project on 'systems for advanced management of public transport' in the Summer of 1997.

13.4   Is the care provided responsive and flexible?

Effective assessment facilities are a key factor in ensuring that the care instituted is responsive to the particular needs of the person. The Working Party recommended that assessment should be provided in specialist geriatric departments in general hospitals and in assessment units in community hospitals. The review shows that not all health boards have developed community hospitals along the lines envisaged in *The Years Ahead* and that not all the community hospitals in existence have assessment facilities. Furthermore, there is a belief in some boards that the specialist geriatric departments in general hospitals are the most appropriate and suitable settings for assessment and these boards do not intend developing assessment facilities in their community units. The slow development of community hospitals coupled with failure to provide effective assessment facilities in all of them, is a deficit in the care system that needs to be acknowledged.

The role that geriatricians play in providing assessment must be recognised by the health boards. The review shows that geriatricians spend a limited amount of time providing assessment support in community facilities. This affects the appropriate and timely use of beds, as well as early and appropriate treatment. Given that geriatricians play such a critical role in the appropriate and effective care of older people, the fact that the posts created are not always dedicated to the intended client group raises questions about commitment to, and recognition of, the medical needs of older people. It also raises the issue of access based on geographical location and the matching of provision with local need.

Flexibility of care requires provision of a range of options along a continuum of care, with free movement up or down the continuum when necessary. However, as already discussed, there are still gaps in the range of care options available to older people and there are still issues of accessibility in regard to the options which do exist. A further influence on flexibility of care relates to effective structures for co-ordination and liaison between the different agencies involved in care. These issues are taken up in the next section.

13.5 Are the care services provided co-ordinated?

The Working Party made specific recommendations for a co-ordination structure at district, community care, regional and national levels. It emerges from the review that while attempts at co-ordination have occurred, the recommendations of *The Years Ahead* are still far from being realised. The review also raises questions about certain elements of the co-ordination structure proposed in *The Years Ahead*.

13.5.1 Co-ordination at district level

At local level, there are nurses who perform a co-ordination function. They cannot however operate in the manner envisaged in *The Years Ahead* because they are usually not dedicated to co-ordination and their time is not devoted solely to older people. It also emerges that few have the back-up needed to enable them to do their job effectively. For example, few have the support of district teams at local level and not all have the support of CSEs at community care area level. Although there are advantages to a district team dedicated to co-ordination, it may not be the most important focus for the future improvement of co-ordination. There appears to be some doubt about the feasibility and effectiveness of district teams and questions have been raised about the difficulty of keeping them going and maintaining commitment. Further research and evaluation are required to assess the effectiveness of teams and to determine principles of good practice for their operation. The absence of district teams and failure to institute an alternative raises questions about how the current system deals with certain co-ordination issues such as the representation of voluntary organisations in service planning and delivery.

13.5.2 Co-ordination at community care area level

At community care area level, most boards have made attempts to establish co-ordination structures. Co-ordinators of Services for the Elderly have been employed in most health boards but, in many cases, not to the level recommended in *The Years Ahead*. Again those performing the co-ordination function are not always dedicated to the task and often cater for groups other than older people. Like the District Liaison Nurses, the CSEs lack the support needed in carrying out their jobs effectively. Important issues in this regard is the slow implementation of new management structures, the continuing lack of effective linkages between care programmes and the lack of effective liaison between service-providers in many of the health boards. A further issue is the lack of clarity about the role of some CSEs.

In summary, while liaison does occur, it is for the most part *ad hoc* and informal. The Working Party was particularly concerned about liaison between GPs and PHNs, but the review shows that the situation remains much the same as in 1988 with no formal co-ordination arrangements between these professionals. Overall, the lack of formalised structures for liaison within health boards is a source of concern to GPs, PHNs, District Liaison Nurses, CSEs and other professional service providers in the health field and is an issue that must be addressed in any future policy for older people.

13.5.3   Co-ordination at health board level

Co-ordination of the different health board care programmes has long been a source of concern. In all the health boards there is an attempt at cross-programme co-ordination by having one person (usually a Programme Manager) take overall responsibility for the care of older people. Most health boards also have plans to move from the 'care programme' to the 'care group' approach. The review highlights the need in the present system for more formal liaison arrangements between hospitals and community services. The absence of dedicated liaison personnel in general hospitals is a significant deficit. The hospital-community barrier needs to be lowered further with effective discharge procedures. Unless effective liaison structures are in place there is a danger that older patients will be 'lost' once they are discharged from hospital and that inappropriate re-admissions will occur as a consequence.

13.5.4   Inter-agency co-ordination

At the level of inter-agency co-ordination, *The Years Ahead* identified the lack of formal co-ordination links between the health boards and local authorities as one of the major problems to be addressed. It appears from the review that little has been done to remedy the problem. District Liaison Nurses and CSEs, for example, have very little contact with housing officers even though appropriate housing is a part of the care continuum. This is a continuing source of dissatisfaction for District Liaison Nurses, CSEs and PHNs. The lack of inter-agency liaison at local level is in part due to a lack of liaison at Departmental level. A clearer lead on co-ordination must be taken by the Departments of Health and the Environment to ensure that co-ordination of health and housing services begins to happen at regional and district levels. While there is evidence of inter-departmental links with regard to some aspects of the care of older people, such as their security needs, nevertheless most existing linkages are informal and *ad hoc*. A potentially important development in this regard is the Strategic Management Initiative which focuses on inter-departmental co-operation and sets out structures for its implementation.

13.5.5 *Challenges involved in co-ordination*

Since the publication of *The Years Ahead*, pilot projects on co-ordination at local level, established by the National Council for the Elderly, have highlighted the challenges involved. Co-ordination is a difficult goal to achieve and the specification of administrative structures, as in *The Years Ahead*, while necessary, is not in itself sufficient to ensure that co-ordination will happen. Certain elements of the structure proposed in *The Years Ahead*, may need to be re-evaluated and support is required for effective structures that are currently in place. An ethos of co-ordination needs to be created which permeates the entire care system, starting at the national level and filtering down to regional and local levels. Accordingly, this review calls for the development of a national policy on co-ordination. Support, education and training are needed to enable different service providers to work together, and to enable the development of a common mission across agencies with disparate goals and responsibilities. This is particularly relevant at a time when resources are scarce and the setting of priorities is essential. Co-ordination also requires that issues of responsibility and accountability are acknowledged and addressed. This kind of support for co-ordination requires a much greater commitment of personnel and financial resources than is currently evident. Resolution of these issues is vital as lack of co-ordination seriously hampers the provision of appropriate, flexible and effective care.

13.6 Obstacles to implementation of recommendations of *The Years Ahead*

The focus of this chapter has been on highlighting how the different agencies involved — government departments, health boards, local authorities, voluntary organisations, local service providers — fall short of achieving the objectives of *The Years Ahead*. Throughout the review an attempt has been made to identify the obstacles involved in those cases where a recommendation has not been implemented. It has to be acknowledged that in some instances lack of implementation reflects not so much failure on the part of the implementing agency but a shortcoming within *The Years Ahead* report itself. The main thrust of *The Years Ahead* was the establishment of norms for different services and it allowed little scope for individual health boards to explore the fit between such norms and their own particular needs and circumstances. Variations in service provision across the health boards can sometimes represent innovative attempts to adapt to local needs, but some services should be available to a certain standard for all older people wherever they live. Where such core services are not provided it is imperative to discover why this is so.

In some instances failure to implement a recommendation may be traced to ambivalence at management level about its value or effectiveness. This is evident, for example, in regard to services such as community social work, domiciliary paramedical services, boarding out and Care Assistants. There is also some ambivalence evident in regard to delivery mechanisms such as district teams and advisory committees. Ambivalence also arises at Government Department level. This is evident in failure to implement recommendations requiring inter-departmental liaison and collaboration, failure to provide national guidelines for services such as 'at risk' registers, day care facilities and boarding out and failure to produce a model contract for partnership between voluntary and statutory agencies.

A basic obstacle to implementation which emerged in several instances in this review was lack of information about the recommendation. This lack of information applied not just to specific recommendations but also to *The Years Ahead* document itself. For example, some agencies outside the health boards, such as local authorities and the Health and Safety Authority, were not aware that any recommendations had been made concerning their area of responsibility.

Perhaps the most important obstacle to implementation is the legal status of recommendations. *The Years Ahead* report had no statutory basis and the recommendations made by the Working Party for the legal underpinning of certain services and of co-ordination structures have not been implemented. At Government Department level it appears that encouragement and support are preferred to legal obligation as a means of ensuring services are provided for older people. However, developments in the field of child care indicate that legislation is considered to be essential to ensure standards of care for other groups. While acknowledging the danger of rigidity in legislating for all aspects of care, the absence of a legislative framework for a certain standard of care, with obligatory provision of core services, is an issue which has to be addressed.

Each of the factors identified above has contributed to shortcomings in achieving the objectives of *The Years Ahead*, but the most frequently mentioned obstacle in feedback from managers and service providers is failure to provide the funding required. Table 13.1 below summarises the capital and revenue recommendations made by the Working Party and the amount of finance actually allocated to implement the report.

It can be seen from Table 13.1 that some services — Departments of Geriatric Medicine and community hospitals — without taking inflation into account, have

Table 13.1: Summary of capital and revenue allocations of *The Years Ahead* report

CAPITAL FUNDING RECOMMENDED	FUNDING ALLOCATED
Day care: £0.5m in each of five years from 1989	£0.2m per annum 1989-1995. £0.4m 1996. £0.7m 1997
Departments of Geriatric Medicine: £0.1m in each of next five years from 1989	£0.1m per year
Day hospital places: £0.5m annually from 1989	£0.2m annually up to 1996. £0.4m in 1997
Community hospitals: £2m in each of next five years from 1989	£1m 1989-1994 (in total). £2m each in 1995 and 1996. £4m in 1997
Facilities for dementia: £1.2m in each of next 20 years from 1989	£2m in total up to 1997
Alarm systems: £0.2m in each of the five years from 1989	£50,000 annually
REVENUE FUNDING RECOMMENDED	**FUNDING ALLOCATED**
Panels of Registered General Nurses and Home Care Assistants: £2m to be given immediately in 1989	Average of £800,000 annually 1989-1997 inclusive. Total £7.2m
Home Helps: additional £6m to be made available to a total of £13.65m annually	Total in 1995 was £16.4m and £17.6m in 1996. Extra 10m in total
Physiotherapy: additional £0.5m annually	Total of £0.5m since 1989
Joint replacement and cataract surgery: additional £0.25m per annum	£1.65m approx. allocated 1995, joint replacement and cataract surgery not categorised separately
Medical aids and appliances: £0.5m	£100,000 annually
Dental, chiropody and speech therapy services: £0.75m	Dental: running at £9.8m per annum since 1994 (£6m to older people annually since 1994)
	Chiropody: £300,000 in total since 1989
	Speech therapy: £200,000 in total since 1989
Boarding out: initial £0.5m	£250,000

Sources: Department of Health and The Years Ahead report

received approximately the level of capital funding recommended. In the case of community hospitals, however, it was only in the period 1995-1997 that substantial funding (£8m) was given which compensated for the significant underfunding in 1989-1994. It should be noted in respect of these services that the recommendations applied to the years 1989-1993 only, and it is assumed here that the same level of funding would apply after 1994.

With regard to dental services, under the Dental Treatment Services Scheme 1994, £9.8m was made available annually from that year, £6m of which has been spent on older people. The provision for Home Helps increased substantially in recent years and is now estimated to be running at £17.6m for 1996. Day care, day hospital places, alarm systems and especially facilities for the mentally infirm have been underfunded. It is unclear whether revenue funding for joint replacement and cataract surgery, chiropody and speech services, or panels of Registered General Nurses and Care Assistants, received the amounts recommended. It is clear, however, that the funding for physiotherapy and boarding-out schemes was much less than recommended.

The Working Party acknowledged the constraints in finance operating in the 1980s but had assumed that a decline in births would present an opportunity to redeploy resources towards older people. This redeployment has not happened. Rather there is now a greater focus on children as a client group, a greater acknowledgement of the care needs of children and a new identification of certain needs among this group. The enactment of the *Child Care Act* in 1991 led to a major programme of investment in child care and family support services, including an additional £10m in each of the years 1993-1996 for new service developments. No such major programme of investment has occurred with regard to the care of older people.

The transfer of resources to community care has also not occurred in line with the principles espoused by *The Years Ahead* report. As a proportion of the aggregate health budget, community care has remained at approximately one quarter since 1988. Similarly, community psychiatric services have not increased their proportion of the overall psychiatric budget, which itself has decreased as a proportion of the aggregate health budget. This contrasts with significant increases in spending on the subvention of private nursing home care in the wake of the 1990 *Health (Nursing Homes) Act*. Department of Health figures show that more than £65 million has been spent on implementing the Act over the period 1993-1997 inclusive. This raises serious questions about the financial commitment to maintaining and supporting older people in the community.

13.7 *The Years Ahead*: still an appropriate blueprint?

Almost 10 years since its publication, *The Years Ahead* remains a highly significant influence on the care of older people in this country. The question now arises as to the relevance of *The Years Ahead* blueprint as we approach the twenty-first century. *The Years Ahead* was normative in approach and allowed little scope for innovation to match changing and varied circumstances within the individual health boards. It is clear that there are elements in the care system proposed by the Working Party which need to be re-evaluated, new orientations which need to be included, and certain assumptions which should be further tested and evaluated. Key issues for the future care of older people relate to the need for a vision of ageing, the need for a holistic approach to needs in older life, the need for adoption of a consumer orientation and the need for research and evaluation. Each of these is discussed in turn below.

13.7.1   A vision of ageing

One of the first issues in developing a vision of ageing is the terms and definitions employed. The term most commonly employed to describe those over 65 years of age is 'the elderly'. This term suggests a group distinct from other groups in society and it was overwhelmingly rejected in the Eurobarometer Study on Age and Attitudes. The latter study found that the term favoured in this country was 'senior citizens' which has connotations of being active and socially engaged and does not marginalise people of older years as a separate group distinct from others in society. The preferences of older people about how they wish to be described need to be acknowledged and respected.

The age of 65 is the accepted dividing line between middle-age and old age. In the present care system those over the dividing line are often treated as if they formed a homogeneous group characterised by infirmity, ill health and inactivity. This arbitrary dividing line has remained despite advances in health care which have led to longer life expectancy and better health in old age. A vision of ageing needs to acknowledge that people over the age of 65 years are as diverse as those in young adulthood or middle-age and finer distinctions are needed which reflect the different experiences, life circumstances and needs of persons in their sixties and those in their seventies and eighties. In *The Years Ahead*, the needs of all older people often appears to be synonymous with the needs of vulnerable and dependent older people. The resulting approach to care is narrowly focused on a particular set of needs.

In the period since *The Years Ahead* was published there has been a significant move away from the image of the older person as dependent, infirm, useless and passive, to a more positive view of old age as a time of opportunity and potential for active contribution to society. The foremost contributors to the development of this new image of old age are Age and Opportunity and voluntary organisations such as Age Action Ireland. This new attitude is visible also in the 1995 national *Health Promotion Strategy* which promises action to promote self-respect, dignity and a positive role for older people in society. Policy on care for older people in the future needs to be informed by this wider, positive view of old age and definite plans need to be developed for putting the positive view into action.

13.7.2   A holistic approach to needs in older life

The 'policy for the elderly' outlined in *The Years Ahead* deals primarily with the needs of older people who require physical care. *Shaping a Healthier Future*, published six years after *The Years Ahead*, also displays a narrow view of older people with its focus on the 'ill and dependent elderly'. Physical health is only one element of the well-being of older people and, in a modern vision of ageing, social, emotional, intellectual and spiritual care needs must also be taken into account. In the area of social care, *The Years Ahead* recognised the importance of creating a social, cultural and economic milieu in which older people can participate and contribute effectively and two recommendations were made by the Working Party to enable this to happen. The implementation of one of these recommendations led to the formation of Age and Opportunity and has facilitated a broadening of approach to the later years of life and an acknowledgement of needs other than physical care. Recommendations on planning for retirement have been implemented by ICTU through initiatives such as the Retired Workers' Committees, the production of *Guidelines on Retirement Planning* and the development of a *Charter of Rights for Older People*. There are still however important issues to be addressed in relation to the employment prospects of people approaching old age and age discrimination in current training and employment schemes.

There is also a need for attention to the intellectual, emotional and spiritual care needs of older people. It is a matter of concern that, at present, older people are largely absent from the formal education system. In recent years the concept of 'lifelong learning' has gained more prominence, and the Department of Education has indicated that provision for this will be included in the forthcoming *Education Act*. The Age and Opportunity agency also works with Adult Education Organisers in efforts to address continuing education needs.

Failure in *The Years Ahead* to give due consideration to needs other than physical care is a deficit that must be addressed in future policy on the care of older people. The over-emphasis in *The Years Ahead* on physical health probably reflects the fact that the Working Party was set up by the Department of Health. A holistic approach to older life demands that policy and action in relation to older people does not remain the responsibility of one Department. The well-being of older people must also be a matter for the Departments of Education, Social Welfare, the Environment, Transport, Energy and Communications, Justice and Equality and Law Reform. Designation of the care of older people as a Strategic Result Area as is proposed for the care of children, could facilitate the development of realistic and effective structures for a holistic approach to older life at governmental level. Consideration of needs in a piecemeal and fragmented manner is clearly at odds with people's lived experience where needs are interconnected.

13.7.3   A consumer orientation
One of the more conspicuous gaps in *The Years Ahead* report was the failure to allow for consumer participation in the health care system. The current system for planning services allows little scope for the representation of consumers' interests, hampering its ability to be responsive. Since the publication of *The Years Ahead*,

there has been an increasing focus on the consumer. Several non-governmental organisations attempting to represent the interests of older people have been active in seeking a consumer voice. One practical example of this is the establishment of the Irish Senior Citizens National Parliament. The Government has also begun to recognise the need for consumer participation, and this is evident in recent public policy documents such as the *Strategic Management Initiative*. *Shaping a Healthier Future* also declares a deliberate re-orientation of delivery structures towards the service user and specific measures are planned to enable service user participation. It remains to be seen how effectively the rhetoric of consumer involvement works out in practice.

In order to meet the needs of older people, it is essential that they are involved in the decisions which affect them. This kind of approach requires structures to enable the consumer to have input into needs assessment, planning of services and evaluation of outcomes. These are of little value, however, unless measures are also initiated to enable and support the consumers to use them. In the case of frail or vulnerable older people, it may be necessary to have advocates to ensure their voice is heard. As admitted in *Shaping a Healthier Future*, putting the consumer orientation into practice poses a big challenge for a system which in the past gave insufficient attention to the service user.

13.7.4   Research

A recurrent problem for this review was the lack of reliable data in many areas of the care of older people. A base of data to underpin policy and practice must be established through research on assessment of needs, exploratory research on possible services and solutions to address needs and problems and evaluation research on the services provided. In an earlier section the necessity of thorough assessment was discussed in the context of providing a responsive service in the case where an older person needs some kind of physical or medical care. Here the focus would be on a wider, holistic assessment of need among all older people in the community. As discussed in an earlier section, the involvement of older people themselves is of critical importance in any kind of meaningful needs assessment. Possibilities for consumer-led needs assessment include community workshops and community surveys. As a complement to consumer input, feedback from service providers from a variety of professional backgrounds must be brought to bear on needs assessment. This kind of approach requires the development of networks and information systems which allow for ready access to findings from both experience and research. For example, in the area of medical care, medical professionals and researchers could provide reliable and up-to-date data on the health status and problems of older people in the country or in the case of social care, social workers could provide data on the extent and nature of abuse or the factors facilitating continued social engagement.

Innovative ways of resolving problems and unmet needs must also be explored. Examples of areas where such research is critical include transport services, the meaning of 'risk', implementation of anticipatory care, consumer involvement, implementation of an integrated approach to service provision and case management. Here again, effective networks for exchange of information and research findings among people from different professional backgrounds and an openness to a cross-professional team approach, will influence the usefulness of the research work carried out.

Finally, research on the effectiveness of current service provision is also required. At the time *The Years Ahead* was drafted the major focus in the health care system was on the *level* of provision of services. Accordingly, *The Years Ahead* emphasises inputs into the care system, such as staff and bed numbers, and it makes little reference to outcomes and how those outcomes should be assessed. With the publication of *Shaping a Healthier Future* in 1994, the focus has been shifted from level of provision to provision of a positive outcome and health services must now have a demonstrable benefit in terms of health and social gain. Outcome assessment requires systematic and comprehensive data, firstly, on pre-care conditions to provide a benchmark against which gain may be judged, and secondly, on the conditions prevailing after an intervention. Participation by older people at both stages of data collection is of vital importance. It is only now that outcome measures are being developed to assess the health and social gain achieved by the implementation of particular care services. Throughout this review, a recurrent problem was the lack of objective evaluation of the outcomes achieved through implementation of the various recommendations of *The Years Ahead*, and a consequent reliance on qualitative experiences and perceptions to judge the significance of much of what has been achieved. For example, there is widespread belief in the value of day care facilities but little data available to prove this. Similarly, there is no evaluation data to inform decisions on boarding out services, on domiciliary delivery of paramedical services or on the value of Care Assistants. It must be acknowledged, however, that certain kinds of outcome, related for example, to quality of life, do not lend themselves to measurement as readily as others, such as cure of a physical illness or an increase in mobility. Evaluation of outcomes does not just apply to healthcare, but must also become an integral part of any initiatives that are instituted to meet any area of need.

13.8   Future strategy for care of older people

If we are to build on the achievements of *The Years Ahead* to find the best way forward, the main dimensions which have to be addressed are the development of a more positive view of older people and old age, the broadening of the view of older life to encompass more than health care needs and the broadening of the view of responsiveness to needs to encompass more than just norms of service provision. A possible framework for a future strategy for older people is outlined in the figure below.

Figure 13.1 Framework for strategy on care of older people

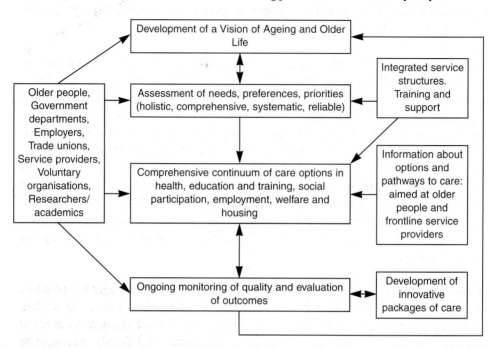

Moving on from *The Years Ahead*, the proposed future strategy for older people is grounded in and informed by a positive vision of ageing and older life. *The Years Ahead* did recognise the importance of independence in older life — mainly through its emphasis on the 'staying put' policy — but its major focus was on older people as recipients of care. A vision of ageing must, in addition to independence, also include the dimensions of social interaction; active participation and contribution; lifelong learning; self-development and self-fulfilment. A positive vision of ageing would not only ensure quality of life in old age but would also ensure that the potential of older people is released and their knowledge and resources are used for the benefit of all age groups. In this way, older people engage in reciprocal and mutually beneficial relationships with people in other age groups rather than being seen solely as 'receivers of care' from others who are more resourceful and able. A variety of perspectives must be brought to bear on the development of a vision of ageing and older life but, most importantly, the perspective of older people themselves must be taken into account.

The proposed strategy moves on from *The Years Ahead* by emphasising that health care is not the only significant need area that has to be addressed in older life and by giving due recognition to other significant needs including: social participation and contribution, education and training, employment, social welfare and income security, housing and family relationships. In the strategy, holistic, comprehensive and reliable assessment of need provides the framework to guide the options and services that must be provided in the different need areas. In the assessment of need, as with the development of a vision of ageing, the proposed strategy assigns a critical role to older people themselves.

In the case of older people requiring health care, the strategy incorporates the provision of a continuum of care options ranging from anticipatory care to long-stay institutional care. It is in this area that *The Years Ahead* provides the most significant lessons. This review of *The Years Ahead* has identified the significant gaps that currently exist in the continuum of health care and the obstacles that have given rise to these gaps. Through the experience of attempts to implement *The Years Ahead* there is now some feedback available on which health care services are essential, which services are effective, which services are difficult to implement. Building on this knowledge acquired from *The Years Ahead* but providing an advancement on it, the proposed strategy incorporates rigorous procedures for monitoring the quality of all services provided and evaluating the outcomes achieved.

Implementation of a strategy based on a wide-ranging vision of older life requires the input of many different agencies. Traditionally, the main actors in the welfare of older people are the Department of Health at national level, the health boards at regional level and voluntary organisations, neighbours and family members at local level. The proposed strategy requires partnership among a much wider range of agencies than these traditional actors. At national level, quality of life in old age should be designated as a Strategic Result Area requiring national partnership between government, national voluntary organisations and other non-traditional actors in the field including business, employers, trade unions and researchers and academics. Only in this way can the policy implications of a positive vision of ageing be taken into account in the areas of health, social welfare, training and education and employment. Within the Department of Health may take the lead role within Government, other departments must also assume clear-cut responsibility for the effective implementation of the strategy.

At regional and local levels partnership is required between, for example, health boards, local authorities, education authorities, social welfare agencies and voluntary organisations. At every level, older people themselves must be given a place as an equal partner. This implies support for a national body representative of the interests of older people, and regional and local structures to ensure the voice of older people is heard throughout the country.

The proposed strategy respects the heterogeneity within the population of older people while acknowledging that there are certain groups whose frailty or vulnerability requires particular attention. *The Years Ahead* has served to bring greater awareness and knowledge of the needs of ill and dependent older people and the services that are valuable in addressing these needs. The major challenge for strategy in the future is an increased quality of life for all groups within the older population and the full social integration of older people as members with continuing needs not only for physical health but also for fulfilment, contribution, choice and dignity

References

Age and Opportunity, 1997. *Lifelong Learning: A Guide to Educational Opportunities for Older People in Ireland.* Dublin: Age and Opportunity.

Blackwell, J., Moane, G., Murray, P. and O'Shea, E., 1992. *Care Provision and Cost Measurement: Dependent Elderly People at Home and in Geriatric Hospitals.* Dublin: The Economic and Social Research Institute.

Blackwell, J., Moane, G., Murray, P. and O'Shea, E., 1995. Care Provision for the Dependent Elderly: Implications of Recent Research for Policy Development, in F. J. Convery and A. McCashin (eds). *Reason and Reform — Studies in Social Policy.* Dublin: Institute of Public Administration.

Boarding Out Regulations 1993, 1993. Statutory Instrument S.1. No. 225 of 1993. Dublin: Stationery Office.

Brenton, M., 1985. *The Voluntary Sector in British Social Services.* London: University of Essex.

Carey, S., and Carroll, B., 1986. *Patch Work. Establishing the Needs of the Elderly at the Local Level.* Dublin: The Glendale Press.

Central Statistics Office, 1988. *Population and Labour Force Projections 1991-2021.* Dublin: Central Statistics Office.

Charles, R., Mulligan, S. and O'Neill, D., 1997. *The Identification and Assessment of Under-Nutrition in Patients Admitted to the Age Related Healthcare Unit of an Acute Dublin General Hospital.* (In Press).

Clayton, S., 1984. 'Social Need Revisited', *Journal of Social Policy*, Vol. 12: 215-234.

Commission of the European Communities, 1993a. *Age and Attitudes: Main Results from a Eurobarometer Survey.* Brussels: European Commission.

Commission of the European Communities, 1993b. *European Social Policy: Options for the Union.* Green Paper. Brussels: Commission of the European Communities.

Commission on Health Funding, 1989. Report. Dublin: Stationery Office.

Convery, J., 1987. *Choices in Community Care: Day Centres for the Elderly in the Eastern Health Board.* National Council for the Aged, Report Number 17. Dublin: National Council for the Aged.

Co-Ordinating Group of Secretaries, 1996. *Strategic Management Initiative. Delivering a Better Government.* Second Report to Government.

Curry, J., 1993. *Irish Social Services.* Dublin: Institute of Public Administration.

Daly, M and O'Connor, J., 1984. *The World of the Elderly. The Rural Experience.* National Council for the Aged. Report Number 6. Dublin: National Council for the Aged.

Department of the Environment, 1988. *1988 Housing Act.* Dublin: Stationery Office.

Department of the Environment, 1991. *The Assessment of the Scale of Homelessness as at 31st March 1991.* Circular 3-91, Department of the Environment.

Department of the Environment, 1991. *A Plan for Social Housing.* Dublin: Department of the Environment.

Department of the Environment, 1995. *Social Housing — The Way Ahead.* Dublin: Department of the Environment.

Department of the Environment, 1996a. *Annual Housing Statistics.* Dublin: Department of the Environment.

Department of the Environment, 1996b. Memorandum.

Department of the Environment, 1997. Memorandum.

Department of Health, 1953. *Health Act 1953.* Dublin: Stationery Office.

Department of Health, 1975. *Report on the Workload of Public Health Nurses.* Dublin: Stationery Office.

Department of Health, 1984. *Planning for the Future.* Dublin: Stationery Office.

Department of Health, 1986. *Health — The Wider Dimensions — A Consultative Statement on Health Policy.* Dublin: Stationery Office.

Department of Health, 1990. *Health (Nursing Homes) Act 1990.* Dublin: Stationery Office.

Department of Health, 1992. *Green Paper on Mental Health*. Dublin: Stationery Office.

Department of Health, 1994a. *Dental Health Action Plan*. Dublin: Department of Health.

Department of Health, 1994b. *Shaping a Healthier Future. A Strategy for Effective Healthcare in the 1990s*. Dublin: Stationery Office.

Department of Health, 1995a. *A Health Promotion Strategy*. Dublin: Department of Health.

Department of Health, 1995b. *Survey of Long-Stay Units 1994*. Dublin: Department of Health.

Department of Health, 1995c. *White Paper: A New Mental Health Act*. Dublin: Stationery Office.

Department of Health, 1995d. *The Code of Practice for Nursing Homes*. Dublin: Stationery Office.

Fahey, T. and Murray, P., 1994. *Health and Autonomy among the Over-65s in Ireland*. National Council for the Elderly. Report Number 39. Dublin: National Council for the Elderly.

Fahey, T., 1995. *Health and Social Care Implications of Population Ageing in Ireland, 1991 - 2011*. National Council for the Elderly. Report Number 42. Dublin: National Council for the Elderly.

Fahey, T. and Watson, D., 1995. *An Analysis of Housing Need*. General Research Series Paper Number 168. Dublin: The Economic and Social Research Institute.

Faughnan, P. and Kelleher P., 1993. *The Voluntary Sector and the State*. Dublin: Conference of Major Religious Superiors.

Finucane, P., Tiernan, J. and Moane, G., 1994. *Support Services for Carers of Elderly People Living at Home*. National Council for the Elderly. Report Number 40. Dublin: National Council for the Elderly.

Focus Point, 1992. *Patterns of Hostel Use in Dublin*. Dublin: Focus Point Project Limited.

Frazer, H. and O'Neill, C., 1992. *Telling It Like It Is*. Dublin: Combat Poverty Agency.

Harvey, B., 1995. 'The use of legislation to address a social problem: The example of the Housing Act, 1988'. *Administration*, Vol. 43: 76-85. Dublin: Institute of Public Administration.

Health Services Development Unit, 1995. *Health Fact Sheet 8/95*. Dublin: Institute of Public Administration.

Hospital In-Patient Enquiry, 1997. Personal Communication.

Inter-Departmental Committee on The Care of the Aged Report, 1968. Dublin: Stationery Office.

Irish Council for Social Housing, 1993. *Advice Note — Formation Series 1/93 F.* Dublin: Irish Council for Social Housing.

Irish Council for Social Housing, 1996. Memo. Dublin: Irish Council for Social Housing.

Irish Medical Times, 1996: *Almost 1,650 Patients Awaiting Cataract Ops*, 15 November.

Kelleher, C., 1993. *Health and Autonomy for Older People: Directions for Future Policy*. Paper presented at Conference on Measures to Promote Health and Autonomy of Older People in Ireland, Publication Number 32. Dublin: National Council for the Elderly.

Keogh, F. and Roche, A., 1996: *Mental Disorders in Older Irish People: Incidence, Prevalence and Treatment*. Dublin: National Council for the Elderly.

Leiss, W., 1976. *The Limits to Satisfaction: An essay on the problems of needs and commodities*. Toronto: University of Toronto Press.

Lundström, F. and McKeown, K., 1994. *Home Help Services for Elderly People in Ireland*. National Council for the Elderly. Report Number 36. Dublin: National Council for the Elderly.

Midland Health Board, 1996. *Statistical Data in Support of the Action Plan for the Care of the Elderly in the Midland Health Board*, unpublished.

Minister for Social Welfare, 1996. Information Note from the Minister for Social Welfare.

Mulvihill, R., 1993. *Voluntary Statutory Partnership in Community Care of the Elderly*. National Council for the Elderly. Report Number 25. Dublin: National Council for the Elderly.

National Council for the Aged, 1983. *Community Services for the Elderly.* Report Number 4. Dublin: National Council for the Aged.

National Council for the Aged, 1985a. *Institutional Care of the Elderly in Ireland.* Report Number 11. Dublin: National Council for the Aged.

National Council for the Aged, 1985b. *Housing of the Elderly in Ireland.* Report Number 10. Dublin: National Council for the Aged.

National Council for the Aged, 1989. *Sheltered Housing in Ireland: Its Role and Contribution in the Care of the Elderly.* Report Number 20. Dublin: National Council for the Aged.

National Council for the Elderly, 1992. *Co-Ordinating Services for the Elderly at Local Level: Swimming against the Tide. A Report on Two Pilot Projects.* Report Number 23a. Dublin: National Council for the Elderly.

National Council for the Elderly, 1994a. *Home Help Services for Elderly People in Ireland. Proceedings of Conference.* Report Number 41. Dublin: National Council for the Elderly.

National Council for the Elderly, 1994b. *Older People in Ireland: Social Problem or Human Resource. A Submission to the National Economic and Social Forum.* Report Number 37. Dublin: National Council for the Elderly.

National Council for the Elderly, 1995. *Planning Health and Social Care Services for the Elderly: Implications of the Projected Increase in our Elderly Population (1991-2011). Proceedings of Conference.* Report Number 43. Dublin: National Council for the Elderly.

National Council for the Elderly, 1996. *Submission to the Task Force on Security for the Elderly.* Dublin: National Council for the Elderly.

National Economic and Social Council, 1987. *Community Care Services: An Overview.* Dublin: National Economic and Social Council.

National Economic and Social Council, 1988. *A Review of Housing Policy.* Dublin: National Economic and Social Council.

National Economic and Social Forum, 1995. *Quality Delivery of Social Services.* Dublin: National Economic and Social Forum.

National Pensions Board, 1993. *Developing the National Pensions System. Final Report of the National Pensions Board.* Dublin: Stationery Office.

North West Connemara Community Transport Study, 1995. Forum.

O'Connor, J. and Ruddle, H., 1988. *Caring for the Elderly Part II: The Caring Process: A Study of Carers in the Home*. National Council for the Aged. Report Number 19. Dublin: National Council for the Aged.

O'Connor, J., Smyth, E. and Whelan, B., 1988. *Caring for the Elderly. Part 1: A Study of Carers at Home and in the Community*. National Council for the Aged. Report Number 18. Dublin: National Council for the Aged.

O'Connor, J., O'Gallagher, M. and Ruddle, H., 1989. *Sheltered Housing In Ireland: Its Role and Contribution To The Care Of The Elderly*. National Council for the Aged. Report Number 20. Dublin: National Council For The Aged.

O'Connor, J., Ruddle, H. and Craig, S., 1991. *Speaking Out. A Study of Unmet Welfare Needs in the Mid-West Region*. Limerick: Mid-Western Health Board.

O'Donovan, O., 1993. *Education and Training for Social Care Networks*. Galway: Centre for Health Promotion Studies, University College Galway.

O'Mahony, A., 1985. *The Elderly in the Community: Transport and Access to Services in Rural Areas*. National Council for the Aged. Report Number 15. Dublin: National Council for the Aged.

O'Shea, E., Donnison, D. and Larragy, J., 1991. *The Role and Future Development of Nursing Homes in Ireland*. Dublin: National Council for the Elderly.

O'Shea, E. and Larragy, J., 1993. *Social Integration of Older People in Ireland*. Irish Report to the European Observatory on Ageing.

O'Shea, S. and Larragy, J.,1995. *The Social Integration of Old People in Ireland*, University College Galway, Department of Economics, Working Paper No. 3. Galway: University College Galway.

O'Sullivan, T., 1994. 'The voluntary-statutory relationship in the health services'. *Administration*, Vol. 42: 3-24.

Partnership 2000 for Inclusion, Employment and Competitiveness, 1996. Dublin: Stationery Office.

Power, B., 1980. *Old and Alone in Ireland*. Dublin: Society of St.Vincent de Paul.

Programme for Competitiveness and Work, 1994. Dublin: Stationery Office.

Programme for Economic and Social Progress, 1991. Dublin: Stationery Office.

Promoting Health through Public Policy, 1987. Report of group established by the Health Education Bureau, 1987. Dublin: Stationery Office.

Ronayne, T. and Duggan, C., 1993. *Too Old at 45? An Investigation of Labour Market marginalisation among the Long-Term Unemployed*. Dublin: Work Research Centre.

Ruddle, H., 1994. *Caring for the Carers*. Dublin: Soroptimist International.

Ruddle, H. and O'Connor, J., 1993. *Caring without Limits: Sufferers of Dementia/Alzheimer's Disease*. Dublin: The Alzheimer Society of Ireland.

Silke, D., 1996. 'Older People's Attitudes to their Accommodation'. *Administration*, Vol. 44: 87-106.

Stephens, S. and Christianson, S., 1985. *Informal Care of the Elderly, III*. Lexington Books.

Task Force on Security for the Elderly, 1996. Report to the Minister for Social Welfare.

Walker, A., 1993. *Age and Attitudes*. Brussels: Commission of the European Communities.

Walker, A., 1995. 'Social Care in the European Union - Constructing Dependency or Interdependency', in Convery and McCashin, *Reason and Reform — Studies in Social Policy*. Dublin: Institute of Public Administration.

Whelan, C.T., Hannan, D. and Creighton, S. Unemployment, Poverty and Psychological Distress. Dublin: Economic and Social Research Institute. 1991.

Working Party on Services for the Elderly, 1988. *The Years Ahead: A Policy for the Elderly*. Dublin: Stationery Office.

World Health Organisation, 1985. *Targets for Health for All — Targets in Support of the European Regional Strategy for Health for All*. Copenhagen: World Health Organisation Regional Office for Europe.

World Health Organisation, 1989. *Health, Lifestyles and Services for the Elderly*. Copenhagen: World Health Organisation Regional Office for Europe.

The Years Ahead REPORT:
A REVIEW OF THE IMPLEMENTATION OF
ITS RECOMMENDATIONS